Zapped!

Irradiation and the Death of Food

Praise for *Zapped!*

"Food irradiation has been able to skate by without serious public scrutiny for decades. Finally, someone has sorted the facts from the fiction about these small but deadly nuclear facilities that are littering our world. Hauter and Worth perform a valuable public service."

— **Mark Ritchie**, President,
Institute for Agriculture and Trade Policy

"Government bureaucrats and food industry executives want you to think that irradiation can work miracles. What they don't say is that irradiation can't rid meat of feces. Sterile or not, I do not want to eat feces, thank you very much. *Zapped!* might turn your stomach, but it will open your mind."

— **Gary Dahl**, President, Local 925,
National Joint Council of Food Inspection Locals

"Food irradiation is one of a growing number of dangerous megatechnologies being promoted to improve our quality of life. In reality, irradiation is being promoted to boost the financial bottom lines of multinational conglomerates driven only by profits, and by government agencies that are avoiding comprehensive food-safety reforms. *Zapped!* enlightens these truths like no book has ever done."

— **Andrew Kimbrell**, Executive Director,
Center for Food Safety and International Center for Technology Assessment

"Buyer beware! As irradiation quietly seeps into our food supply, *Zapped!* explodes the scandalous ways government and industry have colluded to approve this potentially deadly technology. Like those who ingest irradiated food products, readers may never fully recover from the fallout of *Zapped!* Expect *Zapped!* to have an exceedingly long half-life!"

— **Gail A. Eisnitz**, author, *Slaughterhouse*;
recipient, 2004 Albert Schweitzer Award

Zapped!

Irradiation and the Death of Food

Wenonah Hauter and
Mark Worth

Food & Water Watch Press
Washington, DC

Published in Washington, DC, by Food & Water Watch Press,
a division of Food & Water Watch
www.foodandwaterwatch.org

ISBN 978-0-9801157-0-3

Food & Water Watch Press
Washington, DC
First Edition
2008

Contents

Preface

The U.S. is rushing toward food irradiation as a panacea for preventing food poisoning. Recent outbreaks of *E. coli* bacteria in lettuce, spinach, and onions have reinvigorated interest in irradiation as a way to prevent foodborne illness. At the same time, as this book goes to press, the Food and Drug Administration (FDA) is considering a new rule that would weaken labeling of irradiated food and prevent consumers from knowing that their food has been exposed to large doses of radiation.

The goal of this book is to create a public awareness about irradiation—particularly its many hazards and drawbacks—and to provide grassroots activists another tool in their struggle for a more thoughtful and sustainable system to producing safe and nutritious food.

Food & Water Watch believes that food irradiation is a shortsighted solution that does little or nothing to address the fundamental problems that plague the food production system—from "farm to fork," as it is known. Food irradiation is ineffective, impractical, and expensive.

Irradiation does not kill all of the bacteria on a food item. In 2003, Consumer Reports tested 500 samples of irradiated meat from 60 cities and found that irradiated beef and chicken still have bacteria. Irradiated meat can easily be reinfected, when it comes into contact with a dirty cutting board or other contaminated foods or cooking surfaces.

Currently, there are only two irradiation plants in the U.S. that are solely dedicated to food irradiation. Eighty more plants would have to be built just to irradiate the eight billion pounds of hamburger consumed yearly in the U.S.

Not only is it not feasible to build large numbers of new irradiation plants, irradiation makes food more expensive. When the United States Department of Agriculture (USDA) put a bid out for irradiated hamburger to serve to school children as part of the school lunch program, the cost for irradiation was between 38 and 74 cents per pound of meat. Grocery stores that sell irradiated hamburger charge up to a dollar more for it.

There has to be a better way.

Instead of merely "zapping" meat and other foods potentially contaminated with harmful microorganisms at the end of inhumane, lightning-fast slaughter lines, hygienic conditions in today's increasingly industrialized livestock feed-lots, slaughterhouses, and processing plants must be dramatically improved. The same is true of the large industrialized and centralized agribusiness operations that produce fruits and vegetables. The outbreak of foodborne disease from *E. coli* contaminated spinach that sickened 200 and killed three in August of 2006 demonstrated the tragic consequences of the way our food is produced.

Beyond looking at production in the U.S., we need to re-examine the consequences of moving food production to the developing world, and determine how this trend impacts the lives of family farmers and consumers here and abroad.

Do the benefits really outweigh the costs? These issues raise alarm bells, and top-to-bottom reforms are needed both at the political and corporate levels.

While the public is being sold on irradiation as a solution to the growing crisis of foodborne illness, this technology is used to satisfy the food industry's ever-growing craving to cut costs and increase profits. The fact is that irradiation can save money for the food industry because producing safe food is expensive and time consuming. However, irradiation does virtually nothing to actually improve food quality.

Most people think of meat when they hear irradiation, but its proposed use extends far deeper into the foods we eat. Because it not only kills bacteria but also increases shelf life and renders insects incapable of reproduction, irradiation is slated for fruits and vegetables, too.

Proponents are seizing upon the deadly 2006 *E. coli* outbreak linked to California spinach as a pretext to expand the irradiation of vegetables, particularly packaged, pre-cut greens. Industry advocates busily stated their case in the national media, despite the fact that irradiation is highly impractical for spinach, lettuce, and other vegetables. Among many problems, their fragile cellular structure cannot withstand the brunt of irradiation, which wilts lettuce, depletes vitamins, and ruins flavor and color. Beyond that, very little research has been conducted on the potential health effects of eating irradiated vegetables.

Aside from safety, irradiation has profound economic consequences: producers can grow their products in distant countries where labor is cheaper and regulations are scant, further threatening U.S. farms. For industrial food production, this trinity—killing bacteria, increasing shelf life, and rendering insects incapable of reproduction—represents a silver bullet for improving the bottom line of corporate agribusiness, which usually comes at the expense of jobs and food quality.

These issues led the consumer advocacy organization, Public Citizen, to organize a multi-year educational campaign about the dangers of irradiation. In November 2005, because the food and water work at Public Citizen had grown so extensive, a new organization, Food & Water Watch, was spun off. The food and water staff at Public Citizen, including myself, are now carrying on and expanding the work at Food & Water Watch.

Public Citizen has been engaged in a wide range of activities related to food irradiation over the past 20 years. In the mid-1980s, when the FDA began its recent push to legalize food irradiation, there was little interest in commercializing the technology, and the organization's interventions were mainly in the regulatory realm.

By 1999, however, it became evident that the nuclear industry, agribusiness, and their allies in government had formed a juggernaut determined to force food irradiation onto an unknowing public. In response, Public Citizen began an active grassroots campaign to prevent irradiation from becoming adopted without the public's knowledge and consent. We initiated an enormous outreach effort focused first on educating food activists about the new threat, and second, on raising public visibility of the debate around irradiation.

At the same time, we began organizing to maintain and strengthen labeling because it was clear that consumers would not widely accept irradiated foods if they were labeled as such. This included a campaign focused on the FDA, which was attempting to eliminate the already weak labeling regulations for irradiated food. Once informed about the issue, thousands of people told the FDA that they had a right to know if their food was irradiated. As the industry and its government cheerleaders attempted to squelch all public debate on irradiation, we partnered with national, regional, and local food safety, consumer, farm, and environmental groups to create a broad-based grassroots campaign about irradiation. Those efforts served to educate a broad range of policymakers, and raise awareness through participation in numerous conferences, local initiatives, and media events throughout the U.S.

We also found that the industry was using its political muscle to force irradiation on countries around the world, and so forming an international campaign to stop the industry's momentum became one of our primary goals. As a result of the new awareness about irradiation, our allies in the European Union (EU) achieved a stunning victory when the European Parliament voted not to expand the small list of foods that could be irradiated and sold in the EU until scientific research proves that irradiation is safe. Activists in the Philippines initiated a campaign to stop an irradiation facility from being built in their country. Activists in Australia spent seven months occupying a site for a new irradiation facility, and in Brazil a consumer awareness campaign was launched.

Meanwhile, in the U.S. we engaged in a long and nasty battle with Sure-Beam, the most vociferous and dishonest promoter of irradiation. They hired public relations firms, attempted to smear us publicly, and even tried to discredit us by hiring private investigators to look into our staff's personal lives. The company, originally a spin-off from the defense contractor Titan, declared bankruptcy following a series of problems, including a federal investigation into questionable accounting practices and lawsuits filed by disgruntled stockholders.

The fact is that people don't want to eat irradiated food and that there was no market for it. Public Citizen wears as a badge of honor its role in keeping irradiation from being profitable by reducing the public's acceptance of irradiated food, and making irradiation plants a bad investment. The staff is especially proud of exposing suppressed research about the toxicity of some of the chemicals that are formed through irradiation.

As food irradiation cannot be adequately critiqued in isolation, at Food & Water Watch we are expanding our agenda to challenge the economic and political forces that are promoting industrialized food production and the commodification of the oceans and fresh water sources.

We are a consumer advocacy group that forms opinions and seeks reforms. This book, however, is not chiefly a polemic. It is a chronicle of a technology that dates back more than 100 years, and that if not challenged will have a greater role in food production. Consumers—and political and corporate leaders, for that matter—need to know the whole story of food irradiation, beyond the facile claims promoted by the industry and accepted at face value by the media.

As Thomas Jefferson said, "Information is the currency of democracy." This book is written in that spirit.

Wenonah Hauter
Executive Director, Food & Water Watch
www.foodandwaterwatch.org
October 2007

Foreword

Getting Down to It

by Jim Hightower, former Texas Agriculture Commissioner and author of several best-selling books, including Thieves in High Places

Ask somebody what he or she knows about food irradiation, and you're likely to get a puzzled look or a joke about glow-in-the-dark Frankenfood.

Not many food-related issues are less understood than irradiation. Despite a history that can be traced back 100 years, despite desperate tactics by the food and nuclear industries and powerful government agencies to popularize it, and despite fiery debates between advocates and skeptics, consumers know disturbingly little about a technology that is affecting us all.

While consumers, the media, and most public interest groups are fixated on obesity and self-help fads like low-carb diets, industry executives and their allies in government have been given almost complete freedom to propagandize irradiation. Enjoying this lack of serious public critique or government oversight, irradiation has emerged as a solution, with industry claiming it's necessary to battle foodborne illness, particularly casualties caused by dirty meat.

People are dying and falling ill from bacteria-infested beef, deli meats, and other foods in record numbers; 5,200 in 2004 alone. The entire meat production chain is out of control—from gigantic feed-lots where immune-deficient cattle are crammed in hopelessly grotesque and inhumane conditions, to "disassembly lines" where ever-mutating bacteria run rampant in wretched slops of body parts, fluids, and excrement.

Radical solutions are needed. Unchecked "progress" by the food industry—industrialization, consolidation, and globalization—has the government conceding it's already too late to stop this revolution. But behind the cheery

PR about technology revolutions lies a devolution of the food industry as profit continues to trump health and safety. Absent an epiphany by regulators or a quantum leap in public protest, the food industry will continue to hurtle toward one of the most frightening public health disasters facing our new century.

Rather than cleaning up the food industry's act, such voices as the Food and Drug Administration, U.S. Department of Agriculture, World Health Organization, and American Medical Association are hawking the techno-quick-fix of irradiation, instead.

Yes, irradiation can kill bacteria. Contrary to claims by industry and the government, these radiation doses are incomprehensibly high. It's the equivalent of up to one *billion* chest X-rays all in one shot. Machines originally designed for the "Star Wars" missile-defense program are sometimes used. Under the brunt of enough radiation to kill a person 5,000 times over, food can lose nutrients, taste and smell lousy, or just plain fall apart. And irradiation does nothing to remove the feces, urine, pus, and vomit where microorganisms live, so you could still be eating filth, though bacteria-free.

And, contrary to suggestions by the food industry, irradiation is helpless against mad cow disease, bird flu, foot-and-mouth disease, Norwalk virus, and other pathogens that cannot be destroyed by the doses of radiation that are used on food.

Further, irradiated foods can contain dangerous chemicals. One class of chemicals, in fact, has never been detected in *any* normal food, and has been linked to colon cancer. The FDA has known about this poison for 20 years but has done nothing to protect Americans from consuming it. As though in the Twilight Zone, the FDA hasn't even publicly acknowledged the existence of these chemicals, called cyclobutanones, or 2-ACBs.

Stepping even deeper into the fog, the FDA recently increased radiation doses to the point that food can actually become radioactive, as discussed in Chapter 1.

Thanks to pathetic labeling laws, you almost certainly have no idea whether you've eaten irradiated foods. Only single-ingredient foods in grocery stores, like apples, lettuce, or pork chops, have to be labeled. How? With a green flower that looks like a happy thing, and the phrase "Treated by Irradiation," deploying one of the industry's favorite buzzwords. As meek as it is, this warning is still enough to alarm today's label-savvy consumers.

But if the garlic powder in your spaghetti sauce, the carrots in your baby's food, or the seasonings in your chicken soup have been irradiated, federal rules allow corporations to conceal this from you, and from the government itself. There's simply no way of knowing. Corporations also don't have to tell people in hospitals, nursing homes, or day-care centers whether they're eating zapped foods of any kind.

And here's the real mind-blower: schools don't have to tell parents if their kids are eating the stuff.

This program of deception is already underway. In 2003 the USDA lifted its ban on irradiated foods in its subsidized meal programs that serve millions of economically disadvantaged children. Companies that couldn't sell irradiated foods in stores badgered the USDA to allow their zapped beef into schools, and the agency caved. Experts are calling it one of the largest uncontrolled food-safety experiments in history, and a particularly offensive one given the test subjects. Untold hundreds or thousands of schools could one day participate, though as of this writing no public schools are known to have served any irradiated burgers.

Meanwhile, corporations, industry groups, and government agencies are perpetuating a 50-year-old public relations scam, telling Americans that irradiation is a miracle that can fundamentally change how food is grown, processed, and sold. Like the nuclear-powered car that would need 50 tons of lead shielding to keep passengers from being zapped to death (seriously!), irradiation is an unrealistic science-fiction gizmo dreamed up back in the Atomic Age. It's hard to find a more zealous bunch than the nuclear industry, which often turns deaf and blind to evidence threatening its naïve, dogmatic belief in the omnipotence of radioactivity.

As much as any other technology, irradiation has been pursued for all the wrong reasons. It is a supreme innovation of the post-Industrial Age. The Reagan administration wanted to use irradiation as a front to dispose of deadly radioactive waste left over from making nuclear bombs. The FDA, which once believed irradiated foods were unsafe, buckled under the political pressure and legalized irradiated fruit, vegetables, beef, poultry, pork, eggs, shellfish, and spices. This happened with scant input from consumers, or for that matter from the food industry itself. As a result, lingering health and safety questions remain today.

With the nuclear industry's image tarred by Three Mile Island, Chernobyl, Hanford, Rocky Flats, and other health and environmental nightmares, irradiation has become a way to resurrect the industry by associating it with something we all want: safe food.

The food industry was barely interested in irradiation until 1993, when *E. coli*-tainted hamburgers from Jack-in-the-Box restaurants killed four children and sickened hundreds of people in the Western U.S. For decades, irradiation had been a marginalized play-thing for scientists fishing for research dollars to look for alleged solutions to alleged problems.

But with the public outraged by killer hamburgers, the food industry "discovered" irradiation and, with the FDA's complicity, gave the technology a clean slate. The FDA has become the latest agency to declare that irradiated foods are just around the corner. Irradiation has a new future, and new players suddenly became believers.

With foodborne deaths and illnesses on the rise, and with trade prospects brighter than ever imagined, the food industry has embraced irradiation as its best hope to avoid food poisoning lawsuits while expanding its global reach. Nowadays, food preservation isn't just about preserving food, it's about preserving profits.

Agribusiness globalizers are particularly eager. Here is a technology that not only kills bacteria but also extends shelf life. Animals can be raised in Brazil, where the Amazon is being mowed down to make way for cattle grazing, and then slaughtered under the eye of company employees rather than government meat inspectors. Meat can then be zapped to destroy bacteria and extend shelf life, and sent to the United States. Translation: more lost jobs.

Because irradiation also kills fruit flies and other invasive pests, corporations like Del Monte and Dole can increase their profits at the expense of American jobs by moving fruit and vegetable production to the developing world where labor is cheap, and environmental and agricultural chemical regulations are lax. They can grow strawberries in Mexico or apples in Brazil instead of the U.S., where production costs are higher. Once fruit is zapped, its shelf life increases dramatically and any insects that could invade new parts of the world are killed or sterilized. This is a scheme crafted by accountants who, instead of the people who actually produce food, now make the decisions about the food we eat.

It's as though the many past failures of irradiation have been erased. Irradiation is associated with puzzling deaths and illnesses of lab animals fed irradiated foods, as explored in Chapter 1. The construction of irradiation plants is fought vehemently in many communities, as described in Chapter 7. There have been accidents and criminal cover-ups at irradiation facilities as described in Chapter 9. On many levels, the fact that irradiation is continuing to be promoted defies logic. For its backers, though, failure is not an option; they soldier on.

The irradiation movement is still exploiting the public's real alarm about food safety to do something unreal: launch a disinformation campaign to get you and me to accept the zapping of our food supply. No trick is too low. Compare irradiation to microwave ovens, television sets, and sunshine. Call irradiated foods "cold pasteurized." Warp scientific research. Put the smiling little kids on hamburger boxes. Whatever works.

Besides the health effects of irradiation detailed in Chapter 1, irradiation could have a major impact on agriculture. Because it increases shelf life, it extends the reach of agribusiness, making it feasible to grow crops that can be stored for long periods. The transnational agribusiness companies believe in the philosophy of competitive advantage—growing crops on a mega-scale, usually in the southern hemisphere, where land and labor are cheap, and environmental regulations are minimal. By increasing shelf life and rendering insects sterile, irradiation bolsters exportation of fruits and vegetables by large corporations.

Many questions should be asked about the sustainability of producing food thousands of miles from the market where it will be sold. Further, what happens to peasant farmers who produce food for their families and community when giant corporations move in and either force them off the land into city slums, or compel them to grow export crops? Is the risk of this technology really worth the opportunity for consumers to eat hard, tasteless strawberries in January?

Food industry executives and government officials aren't asking these important questions.

It's time to drag irradiation out of its lead-lined closet. The irradiation phenomenon is a story filled with drama—citizens from Pennsylvania to Australia fighting nuclear-fueled irradiators, a lone food scientist from India standing up to the establishment, backroom dealings between Congress members and corporate executives, fuzzy science at the World Health Organization, wretched slaughterhouses, and much more.

Zapped exposes the truths that nuclear and food corporations, U.S. government agencies, and shady health and atomic research organizations have withheld for decades. Many mysteries have been solved, such as the cynical and stubborn motivations behind a largely failed technology that has cost taxpayers tens of millions of dollars while detracting from more sensible solutions.

Other important questions—such as precisely what foods are being irradiated, who is doing it, and where these foods are being sold—lack complete answers. Just like the nuclear industry, also beset by technological and public relations flops, many irradiation and food companies are concealing these facts from the public; and with good reason. They don't have to tell the government what they're doing, either. In particular, very little is known about the 95 million pounds of spices reportedly irradiated in the U.S. each year.

As recently as five years ago, grocery store chains, meatpackers, and other food processors proudly announced their irradiated food sales to consumers. Not anymore. Companies now keep their mouths shut, fearing critical press, consumer backlash—even boycotts and protests. This information blackout is perplexing to consumers and watchdog groups that demand to know whether food has been "treated" with astronomically high doses of radiation, including Food & Water Watch, Public Citizen, the Government Accountability Project, and the Center for Food Safety.

In this book, Wenonah Hauter and Mark Worth tell us a story that has never been told. The book has many goals, the most urgent being to overcome the massive misinformation campaign designed to generate confusion among consumers, and to help you decide whether you should eat irradiated foods and serve them to your family.

There's a broader mission: to stimulate an honest public debate about reforming a food production and marketing system that is broken, though not beyond repair. The problems are too urgent and important to leave to government bureaucrats and corporate executives to fix. Solutions that work depend on a vibrant, functional democracy—and the heart of our democracy is you.

Jim Hightower
September 2006

Chapter 1

Pick Your Poison: Why Irradiated Food Isn't Safe

Vijayalaxmi Chinta was raised on a cotton and peanut farm in Velmakur, a village of 3,000 people in the southern state of Andhra Pradesh, about 500 miles southeast of Mumbai, India. The land was dry, and local farmers prayed for rain because droughts were not uncommon. Neither were food shortages. Velmakur didn't get electricity until Vijayalaxmi turned 12. Prior to that, she studied by the light of kerosene lamps.

Vijayalaxmi (pronounced "vee-jay-ah-LASH-mee") thought her fate would be the same as nearly every other girl in her village in the 1950s. She assumed she would enter an arranged marriage, quite possibly with a distant family member. She would live the way nearly all young Indian women lived at the time: consigned to raising children, cooking, and cleaning.

But there was something different about Vijayalaxmi, and something different about her grandmother. "She encouraged me to go to college. Given the era, she was very progressive. Women didn't go to college. My father and mother of course wanted me to start a family.

"I was not interested in marriage," she says, "I was rebelling against societal norms." To the amazement of family and friends, Vijayalaxmi went off to college at age 14, becoming the only young woman in her town at the time to leave home for school. Her grandmother helped pay the tuition. But there was a catch. "My parents said that if I failed in any year, they would marry me off and send me away. I had that fear in my mind," she says. "College was something that I dreamed about. I was determined to succeed."

It was at a women's college far from her hometown where Vijayalaxmi met a biology instructor who inspired her to enter the medical field. She went on to earn a Ph.D. in animal physiology and do post-doctoral work in the emerging area of genetic toxicology in Scotland and the Netherlands, under a fellowship from the World Health Organization. The educational course she charted as a teenager ultimately placed her at the center of the high-profile international debate over food irradiation.

She seemed destined for notoriety. Her parents called her "Vijay," the Indian word for victory, and "Laxmi," the deity of wealth. "I was born during a huge bumper crop, and my father believed that this goddess had come into the family."

The name Vijayalaxmi—or Dr. Vijay as she is better known—is well known within health organizations, research centers, and government agencies throughout the world, including her former patron, the WHO. She has been a thorn in the sides of bureaucrats and scientists who do not want to hear that irradiated foods might not be safe for human consumption.

In scientific and medical journals, her byline appears only as Vijayalaxmi. According to Hindu tradition, people are encouraged to make a pilgrimage to the River Ganges, among India's holiest places, and sacrifice something they greatly value in the hopes of reaching eternity. At age 24, Vijayalaxmi rode a boat down the Ganges and sacrificed her family name. Her independence continued to grow.

Dr. Vijay first got involved with food irradiation in the early 1970s, while working for India's National Institute of Nutrition. Then-Prime Minister Indira Ghandi was searching for answers to solve the country's dreadful malnutrition problems, particularly the difficulty of storing wheat, which is used to make the staple bread, chapati. Like many other countries, India was exploring "peaceful" uses of radiation. Food irradiation was at the top of the priority list.

An expert in genetics, Dr. Vijay began researching whether poor nutrition can lead to genetic damage, which can be a precursor to cancer, birth defects, and other serious health problems. A study on humans had only been performed twice before—by the U.S. Army and a researcher in Sweden. In 1975, the Institute fed irradiated food to people; in this case, the Indian wheat bread chapati was fed to children by two colleagues of Dr. Vijay.

Malnourished children were chosen because three-fourths of India's population was nutritionally deprived, and children were especially bad off—to the point that the seriously malnourished had to be replenished in hospitals. Plus, health problems develop more readily and are more easily detectable in young people.

"We knew that we had to look into this problem," says Dr. Vijay. "But we did not know what to expect."

Five children entered a hospital for six weeks, were fed irradiated chapati, and had their blood drawn every two weeks. Bad news arrived quickly. Genetic abnormalities were detected in the children's white blood cells. The number of chromosomes in each cell had doubled, and in some cases the chromosomes were so damaged that they could not be counted at all. The children had developed a genetic disorder called polyploidy, which has been associated with leukemia.

Polyploidy is one of the most common symptoms in people who have been *directly* exposed to radiation. On March 1, 1954, the U.S. detonated an atomic bomb code-named "Bravo" on Bikini Atoll in the Marshall Islands. Winds carried radioactive fallout to the Japanese tuna boat *Lucky Dragon* 85 miles away. Tests found that polyploidy levels in the fisherman were four times higher than normal.[1]

"The children's chromosomes did not look normal," Dr. Vijay says. "And the number was so high that we got worried." Feeding of the irradiated chapati promptly stopped. It took four to five months for the children's chromosomes to return to normal.[2] The results were and remain some of the most alarming ever to come to light in the 50-plus-year history of food irradiation experiments.

For ethical reasons, further experiments on people were not conducted, though Dr. Vijay went on to lead a series of tests on animals.

In other tests involving irradiated wheat, Dr. Vijay found chromosome damage in monkeys,[3] mutations in rats,[4] polyploidy in rats (in two separate studies),[5,6] and mutations, polyploidy, and low sperm counts in mice. This last study was perhaps the most distressing. Female rats that mated with males fed irradiated food had twice as many dead embryos in their uteri than female rats mated with males that ate non-irradiated wheat. The deaths were attributed to birth defects caused by damaged sperm cells produced by the males fed irradiated wheat.[7]

Dr. Vijay's research on irradiation was done between 1973 and 1978. Speaking about it, she says, "There had been very few studies on the genetic effects of irradiated foods...When we found these problems in children and in animals, we thought we were really onto something."

The findings came at an inopportune time for agencies advocating the expansion of food irradiation, mainly the U.S. Food and Drug Administration and two groups affiliated with the United Nations—the World Health Organization (WHO) and the International Atomic Energy Commission (IAEA). The FDA began a series of approvals in 1983, and the WHO and IAEA jointly endorsed irradiation for all foods in 1980, just two years after Dr. Vijay's final study was published.

The FDA, WHO, and IAEA strenuously attacked Dr. Vijay's findings, arguing that no other researchers had ever arrived at the same conclusions. She was also challenged by irradiation company owner Martin Welt, who served eight months in prison for lying to the U.S. Nuclear Regulatory Commission about accidents at his New Jersey facility. The agencies, and Welt, were wrong. Embryo death, mutations, and chromosome damage in fact had been observed in animals fed irradiated foods by researchers in England,[8] Belgium,[9] Sweden,[10] and Germany.[11,12]

The controversy ignited an international furor, the ripples of which can still be felt today. The "Indian studies," as they are known, are still hotly debated by irradiation advocates and critics throughout the world. To Dr. Vijay, the level and intensity of the attacks by officialdom reveal a deeper truth.

"The FDA has its own interests. The WHO has its own interests," says Dr. Vijay. "And the IAEA has its own interests. The IAEA wants to use food irradiation to promote atomic energy."

She eventually noticed a disturbing pattern: "It is difficult to escape from the feeling that all findings which are in favor of wholesomeness of irradiated foods are readily accepted, while observations which question this stand are either viewed with suspicion, covertly or overtly, or outright rejected."[13]

Dr. Vijay suggests her research has been rejected because she is from India, and not a Western country. "Sometimes you really have to wonder, because of the way that your research is treated. It is dismissed. But you have to stick with what you find. You have to be honest."

The Indian study on children is one of four experiments known to have been conducted on people. In China during the 1980s, 35 men and women aged 18-23 were fed a variety of irradiated foods for three months, comprising two-thirds of their diet, including beef, rice, apples, oranges, potatoes, mushrooms, and sausage. Another 35 people were fed non-irradiated foods. Like the Indian study, an increase in polyploidy was observed in those fed irradiated foods.

A significant increase was also observed in blood urea nitrogen. High levels of this substance, a waste product formed when the body digests protein, can be a symptom of a variety of health problems, including kidney malfunction and dehydration. The scientists who conducted the study, at the Shanghai Medical University and Shanghai Institute of Nuclear Research, offered no explanation for the irregularities.[14]

In another experiment conducted on people in 1967, seven adults in Sweden were fed irradiated potatoes for ten days. Their red blood cell counts were significantly higher during this period than before, and the levels remained high even after the feeding stopped.[15] Elevated hemoglobin levels can be a symptom of several problems, including a malfunction of the chemical that manufactures red blood cells, which is produced by the kidneys. Over time, this condition can increase the risk of stroke and blood clots.

The U.S. Army conducted a series of experiments on people during the 1950s; no apparent health problems were reported.[16,17,18]

These are the only experiments known to have been conducted on humans. Researchers have cited ethical quandaries as the main reason more tests have not been performed.

Several experiments have been conducted on human blood cells, by culturing them in irradiated substances such as sugar. In one experiment, the irradiated material was shown to be "extremely toxic" to white blood cells, and chromosomes were "shattered or pulverized."[19] In another study, chromosomes were damaged and polyploidy developed.[20] These disturbing results raise serious questions about the harm that irradiated foods could pose to humans.

Tests on animals, however, number in the hundreds and date to the 1950s. The results have been conflicting, with health effects ranging from benign to fatal. In an attempt to settle the matter, Dr. Joseph Barna of the Hungarian Academy of Sciences reviewed 1,223 studies on the wholesomeness of irradiated foods. He identified only 185 beneficial effects, while finding 1,414 harmful effects on animals that ate irradiated foods, and on the foods themselves.[21]

The harmful effects should give pause to anyone in the position to assess the safety and wholesomeness of irradiated foods: premature death, fatal internal bleeding, mutations and other genetic abnormalities, fetal death and other reproductive problems, immune system disorders, organ damage, tumors, stunted growth, and nutritional deficiencies.[22]

Among the more gruesome experiments, rats fed irradiated beef died from internal bleeding caused by, in some cases, ruptured hearts.[23,24]

In another experiment in which rats were fed irradiated beef, the animals had such a severe shortage of vitamin E that they became incapacitated. The researchers observed "general incoordination, spastic hopping gait and sometimes complete loss of movement. Those [young offspring] most severely affected often became completely prostrated a short time before death."[25]

Among numerous reproductive problems that have been observed, mice fetuses and embryos died from mutations after their mothers were fed irradiated foods,[26,27] deaths of rat and mice offspring increased,[28,29,30] and mice sperm were damaged.[31]

Chromosome abnormalities have been observed in numerous experiments, including those conducted on monkeys, rats, mice, and hamsters.[32,33,34,35,36,37]

In one of the most puzzling findings ever published, "considerable amounts" of radioactivity were detected in the liver, kidney, gastrointestinal tract, blood, urine, and feces of rats fed irradiated sugar. The study was conducted at an atomic research lab in Bombay, India, and published in 1969 in the respected journal, *Radiation Research*, which has published dozens of food irradiation studies. (To the authors' knowledge, this is the only study in which researchers measured for radioactivity.) The researchers dismissed their own findings, explaining that the irradiated sugar did not harm "the whole animal."[38]

This finding is particularly chilling in light of the FDA's December 2004 decision to increase by 50 percent the maximum dose of X-rays that can legally be used to irradiate food. Remarkably, the agency admits that food treated with these higher doses could actually become radioactive, but dismisses any possible radioactivity as "trivially low" and any health hazards as "inconsequential."[39]

The decision, quietly announced two days before Christmas, is shocking on many levels. In particular, the FDA and the food industry are essentially surrendering the key argument they and numerous health organizations have used for 50 years to support the safety of irradiated foods: that food cannot become radioactive. And, the FDA and the industry will no longer be able to say truthfully that irradiated foods pose no cancer risks.

In typical FDA fashion, the ruling is gravely flawed.

The agency reached its decision without the benefit of any government or other official standards vouching for the safety of foods irradiated with X-rays packing 7.5 million electron-volts. This is equal to the amount of energy released by nuclear fission in a reactor. Instead, the decision was based largely on an unpublished opinion from the Oak Ridge National Laboratory. The lab said "it makes little sense" to calculate the health risks of eating radioactive food.[40]

Oak Ridge scientists should be the last people consulted to assess the safety of food. The facility, located near Knoxville, is best known for refueling nuclear weapons and incinerating radioactive waste. Many workers there have been stricken with cancer, and the lab has released tons of radioactive and toxic waste into the environment since the 1940s.

The FDA also dismissed a report by a prominent irradiation researcher who calculated the number of people who could get cancer by eating foods irradiated with the higher X-ray doses—0.008 per million.[41] Though arguably a small number, *any* number is too high for citizens who oppose the conscious introduction of carcinogens into the environment. It also marks the first time in the 50-year history of irradiation research that a cancer calculation has ever been made public. Accordingly, the FDA's decision could run afoul of a federal law that bans carcinogenic food additives.

And the cancer estimate is probably a conservative one: it was made by Ari Brynjolfsson, who has worked for numerous institutions strongly supportive of irradiation, including the IAEA, World Health Organization, and the U.S. Army. As of this writing, no independent analysis of Brynjolfsson's findings has been published.

Further, the FDA dismissed a recent International Atomic Energy Commission report stating that 21 types of molecules exposed to the higher X-ray doses could spew neutrons, which can easily make substances radioactive. The report says 33 types of molecules can become radioactive when pummeled with neutrons.[42]

And, one of the key documents the FDA used to support its decision actually suggests that X-ray doses should be *lowered*, in order to reduce the number of neutrons that could be produced.[43] This raises the prospect that food irradiated under the *previous* X-ray standard could cause health problems.

No company has announced plans to irradiate food with the higher X-ray doses. Federal law does not require public disclosure and, given the growing opposition to irradiated foods, it is highly doubtful that any company would make such an announcement voluntarily.

If anyone eating food irradiated with the higher X-ray doses is exposed to radioactivity, genetic mutations might be among the first symptoms to manifest.

In one of the most telling lines of research into the safety of irradiated foods, mutations have been observed on many occasions in fruit flies, which are often used as a bellwether to determine whether a substance could cause mutations and other genetic damage in people.[44,45,46,47,48,49,50] In one experiment, fruit flies were born with extra wings, half of an upper body, and other radical disfigurations.[51]

For more than 30 years, Robert Rinehart researched and taught genetics at Indiana University, San Diego State University, the Atomic Energy Commission, and the Netherlands' Leiden University. At Indiana he worked with biology pioneer Hermann Muller, who won the Nobel Prize in Medicine in 1946 for discovering that radiation can cause mutations.

During the 1960s, Rinehart conducted numerous studies on hundreds of thousands of fruit flies. They were raised from birth to adulthood in vials containing irradiated food to determine whether the food would cause mutations. Rinehart's results were alarming. "My God—we had a doubling and tripling of mutations. There was no other way to explain this except to say it was due to the irradiated food," he says. "Essentially what that tells me is that there would also be a danger to any other biological organism that eats irradiated food."

Rinehart found that the mutations were passed on to subsequent generations of fruit flies. Therein lies veiled dangers. "Mutational changes are much more subtle than poisons," he says. "If you take a poison, like cyanide, you die immediately. But if something affects your genetic material, you pass it on to your offspring and it would be years before you could tell the results."

Rinehart, now retired and living in California, says he discovered enough about irradiated foods to steer clear of them: "Would I eat irradiated food? No."

Genetic damage has also been observed in bacteria and other microorganisms exposed to irradiated foods, providing more reasons for concern.[52,53,54,55,56,57,58,59]

Disturbingly, genetic damage is one of the most common and most serious health problems resulting from *direct* radiation exposure. The appearance of genetic damage in people, animals, human cells, and microorganisms has fueled the theory that consuming irradiated foods might be, in some way, the equivalent of being exposed to radiation. One researcher concluded that mutations and genetic damage he observed in animals were "qualitatively similar to the direct effect of ionizing radiation."[60] Another stated his findings and those of other researchers "definitely establish the production of mutants by indirect radiation."[61]

Lower white blood cells counts were observed in several other experiments. Similar to genetic damage, this condition is common among people exposed to radiation, again leading several researchers to suspect that irradiated foods could carry the same risks as radiation itself. In one study, a substantial decrease in white blood cells was detected in rats fed a mixed diet of irradiated foods. The researcher wrote: "The effect of irradiated food on blood bears a resemblance to the consequence of total body irradiation of the animals."[62] This potential linkage has not been fully explored.

In a rare acknowledgement that the FDA has never publicly repeated, the agency admitted in 1968 that health problems have been observed in lab animals exposed to irradiated food. The agency stated in an obscure official report that rats fed irradiated bacon and fruit died younger and contracted cancer more frequently, dogs and rats fed zapped pork had fewer live offspring, and mice fed irradiated bacon gained less weight than animals fed regular food. "Experimental work with irradiated foods," the FDA concluded, "has shown that there are still significant questions concerning safety."[63]

These questions have been nagging Dr. Donald Louria for 20 years. Louria was worried in 1987 when he testified before a Congressional committee that was considering a ban on further FDA approvals. "I do not believe that irradiated foods have been shown to be safe for general consumption," he told the panel. "I believe the prudent action to take is to prohibit the irradiation of food until the basic issues are sorted out. To do less would be irresponsible."[64]

And he's still worried today. "Nothing has changed for me. The scientific data we have can't be dismissed."

Louria is a professor at the University of Medicine & Dentistry of New Jersey in Newark. He chaired the school's Department of Preventive Medicine and Community Health for 30 years. He is the author of five books and more than 300 articles in peer-reviewed medical journals, and the recipient of numerous academic awards. He has worked at the National Institutes of Health and founded a chapter of Physicians for Social Responsibility.

Louria points out that chromosome irregularities were observed in the only two human studies ever conducted on the genetic effects of irradiated foods. He contends more research is needed. "If chromosome abnormalities do occur with short-term feeding of irradiated foods, what might the risk of genetic damage be if people are given irradiated foods for years or decades?"

Louria says the FDA should handle irradiated foods the same way it handles pharmaceutical drugs. "Think of food irradiation as the equivalent of a new drug. Would any new drug be accepted for general use in the United States without doing our own studies, if the only two relevant studies, both conducted in other countries, suggested the possibility of potentially dangerous adverse effects?"

For years, Louria has been saying publicly that the food irradiation industry should commission additional genetic research. "They're going to make a lot of money selling irradiated foods—they can afford to pay for research. But they don't want to do the studies. They are afraid of getting an answer. I think it is unconscionable.

"If they want me off their backs," he says, "they should do the research."

Louria has long advocated for studies involving children, young adults, and elderly people from different ethnic and socioeconomic groups. Similar to Dr. Vijay, Louria believes that malnourished people could be especially vulnerable to side effects, particularly because irradiation destroys vitamins and other nutrients.

"What about the 36 million people who live in poverty in the United States?" he says. "They have enough trouble getting adequate nutrition without being fed foods with deliberately reduced vitamin content. The industry's glib defense is that we have a nutrient excess in the food supply. This is not true for the elderly and people with low incomes."

He has an even deeper concern: "For fruits and vegetables, we do not know which of the hundreds of substances they contain are responsible for offering protection against some cancers, heart disease, and stroke. If we cannot yet identify the beneficial components of fruits and vegetables, how can we tell whether irradiation will damage these health-promoting components?"

George Tritsch also testified before the Congressional committee that considered a food irradiation moratorium in 1987. Like Louria, Tritsch has profound concerns about the long-term effects of eating irradiated foods.

A retired cancer researcher with the New York State Department of Health and the State University of New York at Buffalo, Tritsch compares the dangers of eating irradiated foods with the hazards of smoking cigarettes.

"Even if all smoking ceased today, there are enough past smokers in the pipeline to keep lung cancer at the top of human cancer incidence. Likewise, with food irradiation. It will take four to six decades to demonstrate a statistically significant increase in cancer. It will take years to convince the public and combat denials from a well-entrenched irradiation industry. When food irradiation is finally prohibited, several decades' worth of people with increased cancer incidence will be in the pipeline. This will therefore be an experiment of a century's duration. Is this worth the benefits that irradiation will provide for the food industry?"

"The long-term consequences of irradiation," Tritsch wrote recently, "will be far worse than any disease against which it may be directed."[65]

As Drs. Vijay, Louria, and Tritsch suggest, it is the unknown long-term effects of eating irradiated foods that are most bothersome. Part of the mystery surrounding irradiated foods has to do with substances that cannot be seen, tasted, or smelled.

Like everything else, food is made up of chemical compounds—untold thousands of them, in fact. When food is irradiated—whether with powerful electron beams, X-rays, or gamma rays—many of these chemicals are blown apart. From here, it's Chemistry 101: electrons are ripped from their orbits and cobble together to form new chemicals.

These new chemicals have baffled scientists since the 1950s. They know the chemicals are there—well over 100 by the latest count—but they don't know precisely how they are formed. Neither can they predict what chemicals will be formed when certain foods are irradiated. This should come as no surprise. Though modern physics dates back 100 years, the subatomic world remains a black box that defies explanation and logic.

Among the chemicals found in irradiated foods are several known or suspected to cause cancer or birth defects, or both. Some of these chemicals are quite well known to government regulators, scientists, and even laypeople who have done a bit of reading about environmental toxins.

These chemicals include some of the most notorious substances ever produced:

- Benzene is a common ingredient in solvents, paint, plastics, pesticides, and other industrial products, as well as motor vehicle exhaust and tobacco smoke;

- Toluene, which is distilled from crude oil, is used in paint, sealants, lacquer, paint thinner, glue, and cleaning agents. It's what makes glue sniffers high; and

- Methyl ethyl ketone is an ingredient in protective coatings, printing inks, paint removers, solvents, and cements. People who have seen methyl ethyl ketone in its pure form on the shelf at hardware stores should not be fooled: this is dangerous stuff.

Dozens of other chemicals associated with lesser though still serious health problems, including organ and neurological damage, have been detected in irradiated foods, particularly irradiated beef. In one irradiated beef study commissioned by the U.S. Army, 55 of the 65 chemicals detected in the beef either do not occur naturally in any food, do not occur naturally in beef, or grew in quantity as a result of irradiation.[66]

The good news is that the U.S. government and researchers throughout academia have known about the presence of these chemicals for 50 years. The bad news is that they have never figured out whether there are enough of these chemicals in irradiated foods to cause cancer, genetic abnormalities, central nervous system damage, or other health problems. By its inaction, the FDA has abandoned its statutory responsibility to determine "safe" levels of food additives.

The most alarming chemicals ever to be detected in irradiated foods are 2-ACBs. (For those not intimidated by lengthy chemistry terms, the full name is 2-alkylcyclobutanones.) Two University of Massachusetts food scientists discovered 2-ACBs in irradiated beef in 1971.[67] They have never been found to occur naturally in any food—or, for that matter, in any other substance anywhere on Earth.

These chemicals were not studied for potential health hazards, however, until the late 1990s. The first four studies all came back positive, linking 2-ACBs to colon cancer promotion and genetic damage in rats, and genetic damage in human cells.[68,69,70,71]

Public Citizen and the Center for Food Safety investigated what the FDA knew about 2-ACBs and when they knew it, and presented the findings in the 2001 report, *Hidden Harm: How the FDA is Ignoring the Potential Dangers of Unique Chemicals in Irradiated Food.*

In a startling example of regulatory negligence, the FDA legalized irradiated eggs in July 2000, four months after several agency officials attended a conference at which the toxic properties of 2-ACBs were discussed. By this point, several scientific articles confirming the presence of 2-ACBs in irradiated eggs had been published.[72]

These chemicals are formed when fat is exposed to radiation. Since fat is found in many foods, including meat, fish, shellfish, grains, dairy products, and some fruits and vegetables, 2-ACBs can be expected to be formed in these foods when irradiated. They have been definitively identified in many foods, including beef, chicken, pork, lamb, eggs, peanuts, salmon, mangoes, and papayas.[73] Even though the FDA has legalized irradiation for most of these foods, the agency has never studied the potential health hazards of 2-ACBs. The agency has not so much as publicly acknowledged that 2-ACBs exist.

The FDA has done the opposite, in fact. Though it first learned about 2-ACBs in 1984, the agency has publicly stated on several occasions that irradiated foods are chemically the same as regular food.

French and German scientists who studied 2-ACBs under a European Union grant have issued stern warnings about ingesting these chemicals: "Since our results point to toxic and even tumor-promoting activity of 2-ACBs, we consider it necessary that further research be conducted to permit an assessment of the possible risks." Among many issues, the scientists don't know how the body metabolizes 2-ACBs, whether they're broken down into other potentially poisonous chemicals, and whether they could cause organ damage.[74]

Research on 2-ACBs is still in its infancy, and irradiated foods have only recently begun to enter the marketplace. Before all is said and done, 2-ACBs could become household names like DDT and PCBs.

Dr. William Au is trying to prevent just this from happening.

Au is an expert in genetic toxicology—the study of how chemicals can damage chromosomes and lead to cancer, birth defects, and other health problems. He is a professor and researcher at the University of Texas Medical Branch in Galveston. He is the editor of the *International Journal of Hygiene and Environmental Health*. And he is on the advisory board of the U.S. government's Agency for Toxic Substances and Disease Registry, which has elected him to its Hall of Fame. Au travels the world lecturing and advising universities and government agencies about the health effects of environmental toxins.

Au can hardly believe that the FDA would legalize and the World Health Organization would endorse food irradiation without an in-depth study of the potential hazards of 2-ACBs. "It's really amazing," he says. "They're supposed to be proactive in protecting public health. But they have been hostile to people who are concerned about the safety of irradiated foods."

Au says the discovery that 2-ACBs can be toxic raises a variety of weighty questions. Colon cancer is already a major health problem, attributed, in part, to the consumption of low-fiber, high-fat foods, as well as foods containing carcinogens, such as smoked meat. Ingesting 2-ACBs present in irradiated foods, he says, could lead to more cases of colon cancer. He is also worried about whether these chemicals could damage other organs and systems in the body.

"More tests on animals are needed," Au says. "And depending on the outcome of these experiments, tests involving people might be called for." Human tests, he says, could consist of monitoring the health of at least 50 people eating irradiated foods. In particular, researchers should be on the lookout for irregularities at the genetic level and problems with the immune system.

Genetic toxicology, which Au has been researching for more than 20 years, is still a relatively new field that has grown in sophistication only since the Love Canal scandal of the 1970s, when 20,000 tons of toxic waste were discovered buried under a residential neighborhood in Niagara Falls, New York. Among many lines of research, Au has studied the connection between benzene and leukemia, trying to determine a "safe" level to which people can be exposed without getting sick.

He says the same approach should be taken with irradiated foods. "As more irradiated foods are eaten, the risk to the consumer will increase. I hope that the FDA does not move ahead with any more approvals until we know more about 2-ACBs."

Meanwhile, some U.S. consumers have likely already ingested 2-ACBs. In 2003, the presence of these chemicals in ground beef sold directly to the public was confirmed by laboratory tests commissioned by two consumer and food-safety organizations, Public Citizen and the Center for Food Safety, both based in Washington, DC. The findings are detailed in the report, *What's in the Beef?: Scientists Question the Safety of Irradiated Ground Beef*. The irradiated ground beef was purchased at four locations:

- Fresh ground beef from a Safeway store in Washington, DC. Based in Pleasanton, California, Safeway has more than 7,000 stores in the United States and Canada. At the time of the tests, irradiated ground beef was reportedly for sale in about 135 stores in Delaware, Maryland, Virginia, and Washington, DC.

- Fresh ground beef from a D'Agostino's store in New York City. Based in Larchmont, New York, D'Agostino's has about 25 stores in the New York City area. At the time of the tests, irradiated ground beef was reportedly for sale in all stores.

- Frozen ground beef patties from a Publix store in Hollywood, Florida. Based in Lakeland, Florida, Publix has more than 700 stores in Alabama, Florida, Georgia, South Carolina, and Tennessee. At the time of the tests, irradiated ground beef patties were reportedly for sale in all stores.

- Cooked hamburgers from a Dairy Queen restaurant in Minneapolis. Based in Edina, Minnesota, Dairy Queen has about 6,000 restaurants in the United States, Canada, and 20 other countries. At the time of the tests, irradiated hamburgers were reportedly for sale in Minnesota, South Dakota, and certain parts of the Northeast and Southwest.

The beef from Safeway, D'Agostino's, and Dairy Queen was irradiated by SureBeam, the now-defunct San Diego company that zapped food with linear accelerators. A linear accelerator, like X-ray machines, uses electricity to produce ionizing radiation. Whether ionizing radiation comes from radioactive materials or linear accelerators, its effect on food is the same; the only difference is how the radiation was produced.

The beef from Publix was irradiated by Food Technology Service, a company based in Mulberry, Florida, that irradiates food with gamma rays emitted from radioactive cobalt-60.

The results: 2-ACBs, which have been associated with the promotion of colon tumors in rats, and with cellular and genetic damage human cells, were detected in all four irradiated ground beef products. Cooking generally but not always reduced the amount of 2-ACBs. No 2-ACBs were detected in the non-irradiated ground beef, which was purchased at a Safeway store in Washington, DC. The absence of 2-ACBs in the regular beef confirms the findings of numerous previous studies.[75]

Based on these findings and a long list of well-documented safety concerns, the Center for Food Safety, led by attorney/policy analyst Peter Jenkins, and Public Citizen filed a formal petition with the FDA requesting that the agency rescind its 1997 approval of irradiated beef. Though the FDA was presented with the beef tests, the agency has offered no public response.

FDA negligence extends far beyond overlooking 2-ACBs.

In 2000, Public Citizen, the Cancer Prevention Coalition, and the Global Resource Action Center for the Environment released an in-depth study of the FDA's record of regulating irradiated foods, *A Broken Record: How the FDA Legalized—and Continues to Legalize—Food Irradiation without Testing it for Safety.*[76] The findings are alarming and numerous.

From 1986 to 2000, the FDA legalized irradiated fruit, vegetables, poultry, red meat, and eggs. In the course of issuing these approvals, the FDA on more than 100 occasions relied on scientific studies that the agency's own staff criticized as being substandard. In the most notorious instance, the FDA legalized irradiated red meat in 1997 while relying on 46 studies that agency scientists said were deficient. Among them was a study that FDA staffers said was "flawed by experimental design and cannot be used to support" the safety of irradiated meat.[77]

More bizarrely, the FDA relied on five studies that agency staffers said suggested irradiated foods are *un*safe. In one study, rats fed irradiated beef were significantly more likely to die by the age of 18 months than those fed non-irradiated food. In another, rats died from pneumonia and had low sperm counts, abnormal metabolisms, and atrophied testicles.[78]

In the FDA's most significant approval, for fruit and vegetables in 1986, the agency relied on five ostensibly irrefutable studies intended to assess whether irradiated foods are toxic in general, or could cause cancer or birth defects. None of the studies, however, met the FDA's own standards for how animal feeding studies should be designed and conducted. In several studies, a vast majority of required tissue and other examinations were not done. And, in two birth defect studies, the fetuses were not examined.[79]

As flawed as it was, the 1986 "Omnibus Rule" formed the foundation of every subsequent FDA approval over the next 14 years—poultry, red meat, eggs, and sprouting seeds. This rule legalized the irradiation of fruits and vegetables, and tripled the maximum irradiation dose for spices.

Meanwhile, the FDA dismissed 32 studies that yielded health problems in lab animals that ate irradiated foods, including fatal internal bleeding, premature death, decreased fertility, organ damage, stunted growth, and blood disorders. Incredibly, one of these studies was used to underpin the 1986 Omnibus Rule.[80]

The FDA has not publicly explained why it has accepted studies showing no adverse health effects, but has ignored research indicating health problems.

The agency has stayed perfectly on message for the past 25 years, holding unreservedly that irradiated foods are safe for human consumption. "There is no factual evidence for risk,"[81] said George Pauli, who has worked on food irradiation policy at the FDA for more than 20 years. "We have never seen an adverse effect."[82]

The U.S. Department of Agriculture, which began researching irradiated foods in 1980 and currently has a hand in regulating irradiated meat, could not agree more. According to Donald Thayer, recently retired as the USDA's lead irradiation researcher and an international figure for decades, "I don't see anywhere that the public has anything to be concerned about."[83]

Yet another problem the FDA has systematically ignored is the well-documented fact that irradiation destroys vitamins and other nutrients. This could aggravate a crisis that already finds children, the elderly, and people with low incomes seriously undernourished.

Irradiation kills up to 91 percent of Vitamin E;[84] 90 percent of Vitamin C;[85,86] 50 percent of Vitamin A (beta-carotene);[87,88,89] and 95 percent of Vitamin B$_1$ (thiamine).[90,91,92] Studies at higher levels of irradiation have also demonstrated the destruction of vitamins A and K.[93,94] Cooking can exacerbate the problem of vitamin loss, in some cases accelerating vitamin destruction in irradiated food when compared to non-irradiated food.[95]

Given that irradiation can form toxic chemicals and destroy nutrients, it should come as no surprise that the process can also ruin flavor, odor, and texture. Food scientists have known about these problems since the early 1950s, yet they have largely failed to come up with ways to avoid them.

Some of the changes can be downright disgusting. In numerous experiments, the taste and odor of various irradiated foods have been compared to "a wet dog," "burned feathers," "burned oil," and "barbecued corn." Irradiated meat can taste "metallic," "bloody," and "burnt."[96] Pork, chicken, and turkey can turn pink when irradiated, and beef and other types of red meat can turn brown, gray, or greenish-brown.[97]

How and why this happens remains a mystery, though researchers suspect the changes to be associated with the breakdown of protein and fat. Some of the chemical byproducts linked to nasty flavor and odor have toxic qualities.[98]

Two of these experiments were conducted by Dennis Olson, the renowned food irradiation expert who left Iowa State University to become a vice president at the irradiation company SureBeam.[99,100] Olson changed his tune after SureBeam hired him, stating repeatedly that irradiation does no harm to food.

Dennis Olson is not alone in turning a blind eye to the facts. Despite the body of evidence that points to the risks of eating irradiated food, the industry and its allies in government continue to insist that irradiated foods are nutritious, wholesome, and taste just like regular food.

They are ignoring a large body of research that raises major concerns about safety. As Dr. Vijay says, "God knows what might happen if you eat it your whole life."

Chapter 2

The Long and Winding Road: Wishing for the Big Time

Food irradiation is good for food because it's so dangerous for everything that is living.
 – Ari Brynjolfsson, Massachusetts Institute of Technology

In 1954, after one hundred years of colonial rule, the French were defeated in Vietnam and American cold warriors were plotting to prevent the country from becoming the next "domino" in their war against communism. Few knew it at the time, but President Dwight Eisenhower was sending military support to a place that most Americans couldn't find on a map. While Eisenhower's military advisors were secretly recommending a series of nuclear attacks on Vietnam, the president's Atoms for Peace initiative was launched.

The Dawn of Food Irradiation

In Ann Arbor, at the University of Michigan's Fission Products Laboratory, Phyllis Judge became a human face of Atoms for Peace—a domesticated Rosie the Riveter. A Detroit newspaper pictured Judge eating a piece of irradiated cake with a smiling colleague, pencil and clipboard in hand, recording her impressions.

Yes, it was a victory for Eisenhower's public relations operation. But shaping public opinion wasn't in Judge's job description.

Then a refrigeration expert with Kelvinator, Judge was chosen by UM and the U.S. Army to become one of the nation's first publicly funded irradiation researchers. With conflict in Southeast Asia sure to deepen, the military urgently needed better ways to preserve field rations shipped halfway around the world.

"We had one goal—helping the troops," says Judge, now retired and living in Florida. "And we were definitely in a hurry."

Judge created recipes for meals that could be eaten on the battlefield, and calculated radiation doses at which the meals would still be edible. She invited her mother, Genevieve, to join the testing panel.

Tomato beef swirls and pennywise city chicken, two trendy dishes of the era, held up well when blasted with the equivalent of tens of millions of chest X-rays. (Chicken was scarce in urban areas at the time and became a pricey gourmet item, so people made do with pork-and-veal kabobs shaped like a chicken leg.) Also performing well were pastry shells made with "Fluffo," a Crisco-esque shortening invented by Procter & Gamble and pitched by radio announcers, Mike Wallace and Red Barber.

Foods fared poorly under the treatment. Beef stew had to be masked with rosemary to cover up the "radiation flavor." Brussels sprouts developed a strong acrid taste, pineapples had an "extreme off-flavor, sharp and bitter," and broccoli disintegrated.

Letdowns at the dawn of any experiment are inevitable. But Judge looks back with satisfaction. "These would have been good dinners for the Army. We developed something very important, and we were among the first to do it."

Judge worked for pioneering UM physicist Lloyd Brownell, who in 1963 won the second irradiation approval ever handed down by the U.S. Food and Drug Administration for wheat and wheat flour.

Judge and Brownell irradiated food with cobalt-60, which was stored in a 16-foot well of water. Judge acknowledges not knowing much about radiation at the time, but she had no fear. "They assured me it was safe." Still, she had to wear a "badge" that measured the amount of radiation to which she was exposed. She did not get radiation sickness. Nor did she suffer any long-term effects.

How the irradiated food tasted, not whether it could make you sick, was Judge's first and only priority. Though animal tests in other labs were turning up reproductive problems and various diseases, the Army continued its research for another 25 years before giving up.

Thirty-five miles east of Tampa, Florida, where strawberry farms once thrived before the North American Free Trade Agreement (NAFTA) made them "noncompetitive," is a place called Mulberry. Here, 50 years later, scientists at a facility similar to Judge's in Ann Arbor are trying to put irradiated foods on the dinner table.

The facility in Mulberry wouldn't exist if Johnnie B. Smith didn't believe in prayer. The Mulberry City Council member opposed the irradiator but needed validation from a higher authority. A local Methodist pastor and former Navy medic told Smith about the importance of sterilizing medical equipment, which the facility's owners wanted to do. "It was confirmation of the prayer I asked of the Lord." Smith changed his mind and the irradiator was approved in 1990. [101,102]

Irradiation Opposition

Smith's heavenly plea is only a single footnote in the battle between proponents of food irradiation and activists determined to prevent the technology from being commercialized. In 1986, Wally Burnstein, a charismatic osteopath from New Jersey, founded an organization called Food and Water in the basement of his home to battle the irradiation industry. A year later, Michael Colby helped open the group's Manhattan office, and eventually moved it to Vermont where he writes and farms today.

During the late 1980s through most of the 1990s, Food and Water waged war on the irradiation industry, especially focusing its efforts on stopping the technology in the marketplace by organizing campaigns, boycotts, and protests. After Burnstein's death in 1996, the organization changed its tactics. According to Michael Colby's blog, *Broadsides*, "the organization has morphed over the years from a full-fledged activist organization to a tart-tongued publishing brigade."[103]

But in the early 1990s Food and Water was a vocal activist organization engaged in a bitter and strangely personal battle with Vindicator, an irradiation company founded by the acerbic Sam Whitney.

Food and Water ran ads on 57 Florida radio stations, sent a thousand letters to Gov. Bob Martinez and staged protests. "We've stopped them all except for Vindicator, and we'll get them, too," Wally Burnstein told supporters.[104] Michael Colby rented an apartment across the street from the irradiator. He was quoted as saying, "We're watching."[105,106]

The cranky Whitney, a former phosphate hauler, could have stepped out of a Tennessee Williams play. "They're liars and they're sleazy. Who cares about what they say anyway?" he scowled to *The Washington Post*.[107] "They're all a bunch of kooks and quacks," he groused to the *Miami Herald*.[108]

Whitney's sour grapes came during an otherwise happy time for him—Vindicator's irradiation debuted in January 1992, when a half-ton of strawberries were zapped with blue-glowing, radioactive cobalt-60. Whitney hoped irradiation would replace ozone-depleting methyl bromide as a pesticide for insects that plague strawberries, citrus fruit, and other Florida produce. Insect-infested produce from Florida cannot be sold in states like California unless the pests are destroyed, because introduction of an "invasive species" could cause potential harm to crops and native plants. Irradiation solves this problem by rendering insects incapable of reproducing.

The facility has 1.7 million curies of cobalt-60, about two-thirds the radiation released at Three Mile Island and 1.5 percent of Chernobyl. Food and Water did not stop the facility from being built, but it was extremely successful in impeding the commercialization of irradiation. As a result, Vindicator, since renamed Food Technology Service, never became a successful operation.

Whitney died around the time that Food Technology Service hired Oklahoma native Richard Hunter, a nationally known advocate of food irradiation who was the Florida Health Department's second-in-command. Unlike many of his contemporaries, Hunter does not come across as a zealot. Instead he comes across as an articulate and measured public health advocate; he has been a very valuable spokesperson for the industry.

Food Tech was happy to help Hunter transition into the private sector; it hired him as CEO in 2001. Hunter is clear about his mission, saying "We're in business to make money for stockholders."

Hunter has helped the company stop losing money. After just a year on the job, he landed a deal to irradiate frozen hamburgers for the Southeastern grocery store chain, Publix. Food Tech also irradiates hamburger for mail-order service Omaha Steaks. The company has reported modest profits of about $135,000 since Hunter took over, after losing $9 million the previous 15 years.[109] The company also irradiates fruit and vegetables, and medical supplies such as hand wipes and saline solution. And Food Tech zaps food for Space Shuttle crew members and experiments with the military on field rations, like Judge did back in the 1950s.

To some extent, Food Tech's fortune lives and dies on rumors and misunderstanding. Its stock price soars upon reports of bacterial outbreaks, food recalls, and anthrax scares, which the company claims it has the technical ability to prevent. It also spikes when news breaks about mad cow disease, Norwalk virus, and Avian Flu, against which irradiation is useless. The stock price jumped 40 percent in one day upon speculation the company could somehow capitalize on the Asian Tsunami, according to Food Tech Vice President Jim Jones. Relief agencies never called.[110]

Hunter politely doused a question about the company's motives. "I don't want to be accused of trying to do something with the stock. We don't target people who have had a tragedy. We don't write letters to companies that have had a foodborne illness. We don't seek to profit from that."

Rumors can benefit a company like Food Tech. The *Tampa Tribune* speculated somewhat heartlessly, "Every dark cloud has a silver lining, and Food Technology got a glimpse of silver after the Jack-in-the-Box restaurant poisonings in 1993."[111]

Hunter comes by his interest in irradiation honestly. He became interested in food irradiation when his secretary's daughter became severely ill from *E. coli* poisoning. "Irradiation is something I strongly believe in," he says. "Eventually, science will win out."

Separated by a half-century, Judge and Hunter are pioneers of a technology linked to the days of Einstein, Ford, and the Wright brothers. Fame, though, has eluded food irradiation and its progenitors. The technology has clung to life not because of commercial success, which it has yet to and may never achieve, but on the efforts of its effusive supporters and government subsidies.

What Irradiation Is and Isn't

Over the decades, the effects of irradiation have been compared dismissively to sunlight and glibly to atomic bombs—and many images in between. Few grasp it completely, one of many reasons for its obscurity. Though the issue is kaleidoscopic, one needn't be an expert in physics or food science to gain a basic understanding.

Knowing what irradiation *isn't* is just as important as knowing what it is, if not more so. Irradiated foods don't glow in the dark. It doesn't make food measurably radioactive, though a mind-boggling FDA ruling could change this by dramatically increasing the maximum allowable radiation dose. And you won't sprout a sixth finger if you eat the stuff.

Now for what irradiation *is*. It uses astronomically powerful blasts of X-rays, electron beams, and gamma rays to kill bacteria, to extend the shelf life of food by delaying ripening and spoiling, and to eradicate fruit flies and other invasive pests.

Here's where a little chemistry and physics come in. This radiation is *ionizing*, meaning it has enough energy to blow apart molecules and eject electrons that then bounce around crazily to form new bits of matter. On the opposite end of the spectrum, *non*-ionizing radiation such as microwaves, infrared, and visible light can't smash molecules. The industry commonly exploits this misunderstood subtlety to confuse the public by inferring that irradiation is just like microwaving.

No matter what type of facility you're talking about, food is exposed to ionizing radiation. The ionizing radiation can be from gamma rays produced by radioactive materials like cobalt-60. Or the ionizing radiation can be generated by using electricity to produce X-rays or electron beams. Electron beams are produced by linear accelerators. Because of its high energy level, ionizing radiation can knock electrons out of molecular orbits, which then slam into other molecules, dislodge more electrons, form new molecules, dislodge more electrons, and so on.

Gamma radiation is often preferred by food irradiators because it can penetrate deeply, and using a radioactive material to irradiate is cheaper. Electron beams penetrate food to a depth of only one-and-a-half inches, which means that linear accelerators are only useful for irradiating thin foods like hamburgers. X-rays can also penetrate deeply, but this technology is much more expensive to use because of the large amounts of electricity that are necessary.

Other forms of ionizing radiation include cosmic rays and higher-frequency ultraviolet rays. Because they are emitted from the nuclei of radioactive isotopes, gamma rays, the type of radiation created by radioactive materials like cobalt-60, have the added ability to make other things radioactive.

Non-ionizing radiation includes visible light, infrared (heat), microwaves, and radio waves. This type of energy does not have sufficient energy to dislodge electrons.

The best example of how ionizing and non-ionizing radiation have vastly different effects is the human body. Ionizing radiation damages chromosomes by blowing apart DNA molecules, which can lead to leukemia and other cancers. In the case of chromosomes of sperm and egg cells, this can cause birth defects. Children of women exposed to ionizing radiation during pregnancy can be born with brain and eye abnormalities, skeleton defects, an abnormal number of fingers and toes, and failure to thrive.

Non-ionizing radiation, because of its lower energy level, can merely cause molecules to vibrate and heat up—again like microwaving leftovers. Electrons are not ripped out of their orbits. Chromosomes and DNA are not damaged.

No, the ionizing radiation used to "treat" food does not get passed on to people who eat irradiated foods (though there is some debate about this, as was discussed in Chapter 1).

However, irradiation does create changes in food, and is regulated as a food additive. The FDA is required by federal law to establish at least a 100-fold safety factor for humans. This is achieved by determining the highest level at which laboratory animals are unharmed by a proposed additive—the "highest no-adverse effect level"—and then dividing that level by 100.[112]

But, in violation of its own safety protocols, including the 100-fold safety factor, the FDA has approved many foods for irradiation. Scientists have observed serious health problems in lab animals fed irradiated foods. Those include premature death, cancer, tumors, stillbirths, mutations, organ damage, immune system failure, and stunted growth. (See Chapter 1.)

However, it's what irradiation does to bacteria that's found in food—obliterating its DNA so it cannot reproduce—not the safety issues that has created interest among meat industry executives and their allies in government. Foodborne illness, largely the result of industrialized food production, has sown panic both here and abroad. Once-harmless bacteria are mutating into deadly strains that medicine can't keep up with. For instance, *E. coli*, a common bacteria in feces mutated into a the deadly 0157:H7 strain, which has killed hundreds of people. Yet very few industry and government leaders are interested in fundamental, long-overdue reforms of the food safety and inspection system that would address this issue.

USDA Reduces Inspections, Filth Increases

Quite the opposite. Starting with the Clinton administration, the federal government has been lobbied by the meat industry to sharply reduce the authority of U.S. Department of Agriculture (USDA) inspectors and handed more power to meat companies to "inspect" themselves. This was done at the same time that the technology to speed up slaughter lines became available—200 birds per minute, 1,100 hogs and 400 cows per hour.

Less inspection and faster slaughter and meat processing spells disaster. After dozens of people were killed, recalls were issued for hundreds of millions of pounds of potentially dirty meat. Stuff was getting through that shouldn't have been.

Irradiation offers an alluringly simple solution: instead of keeping meat free of feces, urine, pus, vomit and other bacteria havens during animal slaughter and processing, just zap food at the end of the line, killing the bacteria regardless of how much it had contaminated the meat.

However, consumers don't want to eat fecal matter or other contaminants, even if the bacteria has been killed. Consumers want to be confidant that their food is safe and clean. Rather than wringing out every possible cent of profit by moving slaughter lines at impossibly fast speeds, and reducing inspection, the meat industry needs to slow down the lines and the USDA needs to tighten up inspection.

But, the industry is looking for a silver bullet. And, with the acceleration of globalized food production, irradiation can enhance profits because it increases shelf life at the same time that it kills bacteria. This is attractive to some multinational corporations that are moving their operations to the developing world, where labor is cheap and environmental laws are often not enforced.

Imagine the excitement at a company like Dole that produces fruit in Latin America where labor costs are a fraction of those in the United States, and having the produce last up to three times as long as its non-irradiated counterpart. An auxiliary benefit is irradiation's sterilization of insects. In the past, many fruits and vegetables could not be shipped into the United States because of the fear of invasive insects, but irradiation solves that problem. No wonder some irradiation proponents view the technology as a silver bullet.

The Road to Irradiation

While industry and government have only recently begun to hail irradiation as a revolutionary technology, it was first legalized in the U.S. way back in 1963. The Army won permission from the Food and Drug Administration to irradiate bacon and serve it to military personnel. With hostilities on the rise in Southeast Asia, the Pentagon needed better ways to keep food from rotting before reaching distant battlefields.

In the first of many setbacks, the FDA yanked the Army's bacon permit when secret papers came to light documenting premature death, cancer, and other serious health problems in lab animals fed irradiated foods. At a Congressional Hearing on food irradiation in 1966, an aghast member of Congress, Melvin Price, who'd eaten irradiated food called himself a "guinea pig." Two years later, an unnerved FDA official, Associate Commissioner Daniel Banes, feared another Thalidomide disaster.

The FDA renewed its interest in irradiation in the early 1980s. But the agency's flip-flop had so far almost nothing to do with food safety, and almost everything to do with politics. The U.S. Department of Energy (DOE), a big promoter of all things nuclear, advocated using the radioactive waste left behind from making bombs to irradiate food. DOE pressured the FDA to reverse its long-held position that irradiated foods pose health risks. The experiment ended in disgrace in 1988 when a radioactive cesium-137 capsule that was being used to irradiate food sprung a leak near Atlanta, Georgia. An estimated 70,000 milk cartons, contact lens solution boxes, and other containers were shipped out from the irradiation facility after they were splashed with radioactive water. Only about 900 of the contaminated containers were recovered. The ensuing taxpayer-funded cleanup cost $50 million.

Still, the FDA went ahead and legalized irradiation—based on shaky scientific evidence—for many types of food, including fruit, vegetables, beef, poultry, pork, eggs, spices, shellfish, and fruit and vegetable juice. As of this writing, the FDA was considering legalizing irradiated ready-to-eat foods and vitamins, despite a shocking lack of research vouching for the safety of these foods when irradiated (see Appendix E for approved and proposed foods).

In addition to the U.S., irradiated foods are legal in about 50 countries scattered around the globe (see Appendix F). Exact figures are impossible to calculate, but an estimated 250,000 tons of food—500 million pounds—are zapped worldwide each year. Of that, about a third is herbs and spices, much of which is Chinese garlic.[113] A variety of irradiated staple foods have been sold to the public since the 1970s. Irradiated onions have been sold in Argentina, dried fish in Bangladesh, apples in China, potatoes in Pakistan, mangoes in South Africa and "nahm" (fermented pork sausage) in Thailand.[114]

The history is fuzzy, but irradiated foods are believed to have premiered commercially in the U.S. in March 1992, when a grocer named James Corrigan began selling zapped strawberries, grapefruit, and oranges in his family-run store, Carrot Top, in the Chicago suburb of Glenview. He stocked irradiated chicken a year later, bringing national attention to Food Technology Service. This was also the year of Jack-in-the-Box, which again thrust irradiation into the spotlight and led the FDA to legalize irradiated beef.

On May 16, 2000, frozen hamburgers irradiated by a linear accelerator in Sioux City, Iowa, went on sale in 84 grocery stores in the Twin Cities. The media devoured the story: "Incredible." "Historic." "Groundbreaking." Within two years, according to the food irradiation industry, zapped beef was on sale coast-to-coast in 5,000 stores, including Albertson's/Jewel-Osco, Giant, Pathmark, Safeway, and Winn-Dixie (though this figure could never be independently confirmed). However, it turns out that most of the media attention was hype that didn't confer economic benefits to the irradiation industry.

But, after 50 years of disappointment and humiliation, the irradiation movement puffed out its chest—and declared that irradiation's time had come. It did, at times, to disturbing and laughable extremes.

In 2003, when the USDA lifted its ban on irradiated ground beef in the National School Lunch Program, which feeds 27 million financially disadvantaged children a day, the irradiation industry seemed to have reached an important turning point. Thus far, however, the decision seems to have backfired. As if it weren't controversial enough that the government was delivering captive consumers to the irradiation industry. These consumers are poor children who have little choice but to eat what's put in front of them. Worse still, schools are not required to tell the public if they're serving irradiated foods.

Outraged parents pounded the USDA with e-mails and phone calls. About a dozen U.S. school districts were quick to ban irradiated foods, including Los Angeles, San Francisco, and Washington, DC. In a departure from decades past, the media coverage was critical to irradiation, even hostile in places. As of this writing, no U.S. school had ordered irradiated ground beef.

Beyond the smattering of irradiated burgers still on grocery store shelves, the only other zapped foods known to be irradiated in significant amounts in the U.S. are herbs and spices. No one really knows how much food is really being irradiated.

Deepening the mystery, public disclosure is also not required in restaurants, hospitals, nursing homes, schools, and other institutional settings for *any* irradiated foods.

Public disclosure has always been a slippery matter. Sales are difficult to track because the major irradiation companies almost never identify their clients, to avoid public opposition. Moreover, government officials say they don't keep track of what foods are irradiated or where they're sold.

The nuclear industry is fond of calling consumer advocates and environmentalists paranoid and suspicious. But how do some corporate executives react when asked whether they're dealing in irradiated foods?

Bashful Irradiators

"We decline to participate," said Cub Foods spokesperson Chris Murphy when asked whether Cub stores were still selling irradiated ground beef. Eustice announced at a food-safety conference in September 2004 that Cub is selling irradiated hamburger patties. The Twin Cities-based chain, which has about 75 stores in the Midwest, actually helped debut irradiated hamburgers amidst great fanfare in May 2000, making Murphy's reticence puzzling.

Another chain that at one time sold irradiated beef, SuperAmerica of Ohio, whose parent company has 1,700 convenience stores in the Midwest and Southeast, also rebuffed questions. And, the two meat processors who at one time supplied the irradiated meat—Simek's and Ellison Farms/Howard Beef, both of Minnesota—wouldn't talk to the authors of this book about sales.

Other formerly out-front companies that have gone quiet include Publix, which sells hamburgers irradiated by Richard Hunter in stores in Florida and several other Southeast states; and Schwan's, a nationwide home-delivery service, which only sells irradiated hamburgers. A Schwan's spokesperson extensively quizzed an interviewer before eventually ending the conversation.

True Believers

Two pioneers have continued their advocacy roles. Omaha Steaks announced it was completely switching to irradiated ground beef in November 2000, one month after it recalled 22,000 pounds of hamburger patties for fear of *E. coli* contamination. The company has been a believer ever since. "We've always been concerned that anything we might sell might make people sick," says spokesperson Beth Weiss. "I have kids of my own, and it they want to eat a hamburger, I rest a little easier knowing that it's been irradiated."

Omaha Steaks' hamburgers are trucked from Nebraska to Hunter's irradiation plant in Florida, a four-plus-day round trip. The company's website says all ground beef is "irradiated for your safety" and conspicuously displays the flower-like "radura," the international symbol for irradiation. Weiss said steaks are not irradiated, however, because whole cuts of meat are less likely to be contaminated than ground beef—a general rule that's well known in the industry but far less understood among consumers.

The other outspoken pioneer is Wegman's, the first chain to sell irradiated ground beef under its own label. The company, which has about 70 grocery stores in the Mid-Atlantic region, is widely respected for its family-oriented way of doing business. Company executives frequently speak at industry and food safety conferences, and are often quoted in the media praising irradiation. "We were proud of the product and didn't try to hide it," says spokesperson Jeanne Colleluori. The meat, she said, was labeled "Irradiated" in big, red letters.

Wegman's meat is zapped at Texas A&M University, for years a major irradiation research and public relations center. Now the school is in the irradiation business, treating meat for Huisken Meats of Minnesota. Huisken, which in 2000 became the first company to produce irradiated meat sold in stores, supplies patties for Wegman's and Schwan's (see Chapter 6).

The newest player in the irradiation movement has been surprisingly open, given its rough beginnings. CFC Logistics opened a cobalt-60 irradiator in rural Pennsylvania in 2003 amid massive public opposition and multiple lawsuits. A sister company of Hatfield Quality Meats, the country's fifth-largest pork producer, CFC was banking on irradiating ground beef for the USDA's school lunch program. This hasn't panned out, as the USDA isn't willing to spend enough for zapped meat. CFC, in fact, didn't wind up irradiating any food whatsoever, says operations manager Luke Trauger, just pharmaceutical materials, botanicals, and a few other items. The company shut down its irradiator in April 2005 because of a lack of demand for irradiated foods (see Chapter 7).

Always a technology that seems to bounce back, irradiation experienced yet another revival in the fall of 2006. In events reminiscent of the Jack-in-the Box tragedy, three people died and about 200 others in 26 states were sickened after eating bagged, pre-cut spinach contaminated with *E. coli*. The spinach was traced to farms in California's Salinas Valley. The *E. coli* itself was then traced to a neighboring cattle ranch, where infected manure apparently found its way into irrigation or processing water used by the spinach farms.

In familiar fashion, irradiation advocates parlayed the crisis into an opportunity. Among them was Dennis Olsen, a former vice president of the now-defunct irradiation company SureBeam and a long-time irradiation researcher at Iowa State University.

"If the spinach...had been irradiated," Olsen said, "there would not have been 199 cases of illness, 102 hospitalizations and three deaths."[115]

U.S. Sen. Charles Grassley went one step further, calling for all vegetables and fruit to be irradiated. The Iowa Republican declared that instead of devoting energy to finding the sources of harmful bacteria, food should be irradiated at the end of production lines. Grassley repeated a common misconception about irradiation, saying it would not increase the price of food.[116]

(Ironically, several members of Grassley's congressional staff in Washington, DC, became ill after handling mail that had been irradiated in the wake of the 2001 anthrax scare. Grassley himself asked for an investigation into the health problems, which included skin rashes, headaches, and eye irritation.)

Olsen, Grassley, and other irradiation boosters are overlooking the fact that vegetables are poor candidates for irradiation for several reasons. First, spinach, lettuce, and other greens wilt, lose flavor, and suffer vitamin depletion when irradiated at doses necessary to make bacteria-contaminated vegetables safe to eat. Second, there is no system in place to irradiate large amounts of vegetables and deliver them to market. Finally, very little testing has been done on whether irradiated vegetables are safe for human consumption, and no published research is known to exist on irradiated spinach or lettuce. As of this writing, the FDA had not approved the use of irradiation to kill bacteria on fresh vegetables and fruit.

Irradiating Spices

While the irradiation industry has yet to penetrate the vegetable and fruit market, the same cannot be said for spices.

An estimated 95 million pounds of spices are irradiated in the U.S. every year. Maryland-based McCormick & Company, the world's largest spice maker with more than $2 billion in annual sales, doesn't irradiate any of its consumer lines, including Club House, Ducros, Golden Dipt, Mojave, Old Bay, and Zatarain's. But a spokesperson wouldn't respond to numerous inquiries about whether any spices it sells to food processors and restaurants—such as breading, "salty snack" seasonings, and fruit and vegetable powders—are irradiated.

Lawry's, a spice company owned by London-based multinational Unilever, and The Spice Hunter of California wouldn't answer any questions at all. The American Spice Trade Association didn't want to talk either. Neither did prominent irradiation companies Sterigenics International of Illinois and STERIS/Isomedix of Ohio. Their Web sites say they irradiate spices but offer no details. Sterigenics made 10 kinds of irradiated spices in 1994 but no stores bought them. "None of us wants to take on something that will be a boycott issue," one California grocer said at the time.[117]

Federal rules require irradiated spices sold in stores to be labeled, which is why you've almost certainly never seen them on the shelf. And this is why neither C.F. Sauer of Virginia, whose labels include Master Chef and Sunrise Blend, and Tone Brothers of Iowa, which has French's, Spice Islands, Durkee, and Trader's Choice, irradiate their products. "We stay away from it," a Tone spokesperson said.

Illinois-based Griffith Laboratories actually acknowledged irradiating spices they are not required to tell the public they're selling. The company irradiates spice mixes such as rubs, meat seasonings, barbecue sauce, gravy, and pizza sauce for restaurants, processors, and food service companies. Even without a public disclosure requirement, some customers still won't buy irradiated spices, said a Griffith spokesperson. Some customers go so far as to demand the company sign an affidavit attesting it's not selling them irradiated products, he said.

Who's Doing It?

The difficulty in finding out who's making irradiated foods and where they're being sold has been a problem for consumers and consumer groups for decades. A secretive bunch has been behind irradiation for the past 50 years: nuclear scientists, military officers, government regulators, and theoretically beneficent organizations linked to the United Nations such as the International Atomic Energy Agency.

Up until only about 10 years ago, it was the nuclear industry, not the food industry that was promoting irradiation. It's a technology spawned of the post-World War II atomic craze, when Glenn Seaborg and other nuclear pioneers worshipped for their genius made predictions of atomic-powered airplanes, cars, wristwatches—even artificial suns. Finding "peaceful" uses of the technology that brought us the atomic bomb, not making food safer, was the irradiation movement's prime directive.

Chalk this up as a key reason for irradiation's sketchy performance. "The midwife attending the birth of food irradiation was nuclear fission, and Hiroshima and Nagasaki. This stigma has dogged its progress ever since," said the late Edward Josephson, who ran the Army's doomed irradiation program in the 1960s. "If food irradiation had been spawned of medical applications of nuclear energy, the public today would be enjoying its benefits."[118]

On top of perception problems, irradiation is enormously expensive and, because it uses radiation, dangerous. Many types of fruit, vegetables, and meat, along with nearly all dairy products, cannot withstand titanic blasts of radiation. Lemons turn black, lettuce shrivels, beef smells like a wet dog, pork turns red, and eggs become runny.

And there are serious logistical problems. Trucks already driving hundreds or thousands of miles would have to make lengthy detours to irradiation facilities, only a few of which are specifically designed to handle food. (Irradiators mainly treat herbs and spices, medical supplies, cosmetics, and specialty items such as gemstones, botanicals, and beehives.)

But, irradiation can also be used to mask filthy conditions in animal slaughterhouses and meat processing plants. As long as the bacteria are killed so the reasoning goes, it's not a problem that meat may contain sterile feces and urine.

Down the line, irradiation could delay comprehensive improvements to the safety and wholesomeness of our food supply. Several years of false hope could set back progress for decades. By extending shelf life, it could also advance the already monstrous global food trade, which has decimated farm economies in the developing and developed worlds alike.

And irradiation, which is done in centralized facilities, is most profitable for big, vertically integrated corporations. Irradiation facilities are expensive, and they require large capital investments. The use of irradiation is another reason that consolidation in the food industry, particularly the meat sector, is advantageous. A bundle of recent mega-mergers, featuring Smithfield-Farmland in 2003 and Tyson-IBP in 2001, have concentrated enormous economic and political power in the hands of so few people that it borders on oligarchy.

The Tyson-IBP deal has been called "deadly" for consumers and family farmers alike.[119]

But, the irradiation industry has its cheerleaders. Michael Osterholm is the movement's version of Karl Rove. "To say that irradiation is a problem," he once snapped, "is to argue that the Earth is flat."[120] It's the media's fault: "There are so many myths, misconceptions, and, frankly, outright lies being spread about."[121]

Osterholm is a legend in irradiation circles. He runs a prominent research center at the University of Minnesota. He's received numerous national awards, and written more than 300 scholarly papers. He's helped solve many medical mysteries, including a diarrhea outbreak among the Minnesota Vikings football team, and a 220,000-victim *Salmonella* disaster that put him in the national spotlight, which he has not relinquished.

People in the spotlight sometimes find themselves telling it not quite like it is. "Heat is radiation," Osterholm once said when asked to explain food irradiation[122]—implying that holding some cobalt-60 in your hand is no more dangerous than holding a light bulb.

Food irradiation advocates have built their movement on saying anything.

SureBeam Corp. called its irradiated hamburgers "electronically pasteurized" until the USDA whacked the company. SureBeam irradiated food with a linear accelerator, which uses electricity to produce ionizing radiation. But, whether the radiation comes from radioactive materials, a linear accelerator, or an X-ray machine, it is still ionizing radiation—and the effects on food are the same. While the linear accelerator does not use radioactive materials to produce radiation, its inner chamber where the irradiation takes place becomes extremely radioactive. Electronic pasteurization is an inaccurate label for a process that irradiates with ionizing radiation.

The mother of all deceptions is also the mother of all ironies. Illinois-based irradiator Sterigenics argued to a judge in 1996 that it deserved a tax break because its cobalt-60 "loses part of itself, which becomes radiation *that is absorbed and permanently retained by the customers' products*. The cobalt-60...thus is delivered to the customer."[123] (Emphasis in the original.) So in order to save on taxes, Sterigenics swore in court to the opposite of what the irradiation industry has pledged for decades and continues to say—that radiation simply passes through food. Sterigenics lost the case, and the industry's reputation took a major hit.

It is SureBeam, however, that has done more public relations damage than perhaps any other irradiation company. A spin-off of secretive defense contractor Titan Corp. of San Diego, SureBeam zapped food with linear accelerators designed for the "Star Wars" missile-defense system. SureBeam went bankrupt in 2004 and its irradiated ground beef disappeared from thousands of grocery stores nationwide. The federal government investigated questionable accounting practices. Irate stockholders filed class-action lawsuits. False advertising complaints were lodged against companies for not properly labeling their irradiated products.

Moreover, people do not want irradiation facilities built in their communities, around the world; from the Philippines and Australia to the United States, citizens are fighting to prevent cobalt-60 irradiators from being built. People also rose up in Maine, New Jersey, and New York in the late 1980s, pushing through statewide bans on irradiated foods. Bans have also been passed in Cleveland and several surrounding communities.

Behind a veil of misinformation is an industry that would have self-destructed long ago had it not been propped up by the U.S. government. Public opinion polls consistently say most Americans want to know if their food is irradiated. A 1999 poll commissioned by the American Association of Retired Persons (AARP) and the Center for Science in the Public Interest (CSPI) found that 88.6 percent of Americans wanted irradiated food labeled. Similarly, a 1997 CBS News poll found that 77 percent of Americans said they would not buy irradiated food.

Nearly all test-markets of irradiated foods over the past 20 years have ended in failure. SureBeam's rollout was so poorly executed that meat department managers throughout the country didn't know their stores were even carrying the burgers.

Like perpetual motion machines, domed cities and other great promises of the Atomic Age, food irradiation has been trumpeted by an entranced media parroting industry rhetoric without questioning any of the "facts." Many reporters seem to think the issue is too complicated, too obscure, or that it's not a "problem" yet. It may be so closely associated with the nuclear debate that it's too hot to handle for reporters or more likely their publishers, especially those with political and corporate ties that corrupt news judgment.

The industry has survived because of its close association with what Eisenhower called the "military industrial complex," and because of public unawareness, misunderstanding, and misconceptions. This confusion is understandable, given some of the irradiation movement's tactics. A South African grocery maven once said at an international conference, "We must confer with experts in the various fields of advertising and psychology to put the public at ease, and develop a more friendly feeling to irradiation." A UN consultant added that words like "radiation" that would "inspire fear and cause the product to be avoided" should not appear on labels.

Indeed, the industry desperately wants government permission to label irradiated foods "cold pasteurized" or "electronically pasteurized," despite overwhelming consumer feedback to the FDA that this would be "sneaky" and "a fake." Between 2001 and 2002, the FDA received 20,000 comments with this message. In truth, the battle over irradiation has mainly been a battle over information. From the start in the 1950s, everyone with fingerprints on irradiation has said "education" is the key to consumer acceptance. The food and nuclear industries have been spreading fantastically biased information for decades.

Clearly, this issue cannot be fully understood in isolation. Beyond food safety lies questions about the potential effects of irradiation on small-scale farmers and ranchers, its role in the global food trade, its place in broader food safety reforms, and the philosophy of science—whether it is best to conquer nature rather than work with it.

Neither irradiation nor any other technology should be permitted to enter the mainstream before a thorough public debate is held based on a complete range of analyses, not merely the assertions of institutions with financial or political stakes in the outcome.

This decision should not be made by cloistered Beltway bureaucrats whose daily existence rarely takes them beyond their own four walls, or by corporate executives who treat food like so many widgets while angling for bonuses and stock options. The decision should be made by the people who will ultimately benefit or suffer: consumers.

Chapter 3

Unleashing the Atomic Age: Irradiation's Roots

A 50-year-old German physicist named Wilhelm Konrad Röntgen opened the Atomic Age on November 8, 1895, in a way that many great discoveries are made—by accident. After two months of sleeping and eating in his laboratory at the University of Würzburg, Röntgen made a screen glow by shooting electricity through a vacuum bulb. Röntgen was shocked. Even though the bulb was inside a cardboard box, the rays penetrated the box and illuminated a screen across the room.

Each time Röntgen repeated the experiment, the invisible rays made the screen glow. He soon discovered that the rays could also pass through paper, wood, copper, and other items impervious to light. He also found that the rays could only partially pass through human bones and certain metals. For Röntgen, the next logical step was to ask his wife to place her hand between the bulb and a photographic plate. Fifteen minutes later, the plate registered her bones and wedding band, but her flesh only very faintly. The first "Röntgenogram" was taken.

Utterly mystified, Röntgen called the rays "X."

The ensuing craze was unlike anything ever before witnessed. People speculated that X-rays could cure cancer, tuberculosis, syphilis, and, if aimed at the head, criminal behavior. Doctors treated mental and physical "female problems," such as depression and excessive menstrual bleeding, by X-raying the ovaries, uterus, and other body parts.

The "fluoroscope," popularized in the 1940s and 1950s by Brooks Stevens (who also designed the Oscar Meyer Wienermobile and the Miller Beer logo), used X-rays to fit children's shoes until it was finally deemed unsafe around

1970. There was talk of using X-rays to peer through clothing, which led to X-ray-proof underwear for women.[124,125]

Despite its corruption by popular culture, Röntgen's discovery earned him the Nobel Prize for Physics in 1901.

Trouble in X-rayland

Dangers soon emerged. Shortly after Röntgen received his award, X-rays were shown to be fatal to mammals and harmful to mammal fetuses; they induced mutations in toads. X-rays also caused leukemia and other cancers in physicians who worked with them.[126]

One of the first recorded human radiation injuries befell an assistant to Thomas Edison, Clarence Dally. "Soon I found that the X-ray had affected poisonously my assistant," Edison wrote, "so his hair came out and his flesh commenced to ulcerate." Dally developed cancer. Hoping to reverse the damage, Dally's doctor treated him with yet more X-rays. It didn't work. Dally's right arm and left hand were amputated, and, in 1904, he died at age 39.

If there was a lesson to be learned from Dally's death, it escaped many. A New York physician named Albert Geyser started leasing X-ray machines to beauty parlors and teaching cosmetologists how to use the contraption to remove unwanted hair. Thousands of people—a vast majority of them women—suffered burns, cancer, and death. [127]

Also around this time, many of the first radiation researchers and their patients began to die from cancer and blood disorders—illnesses that took years to manifest. It was not until 1934, 39 years after X-rays were discovered, that international standards for radiation exposure were set. Two years later, with the trail of death and disease plain to see, the German Röntgen Society built a monument in Hamburg to memorialize the "martyrs of radiation."[128]

The Atomic Age took its next daring though dangerous big step in 1896, just one year after Röntgen's discovery.

French physics professor Antoine Henri Becquerel, who studied fluorescent materials, was inspired by Röntgen. Becquerel took bits of fluorescent rock and wood lying around his workshop and wrapped them in photographic plates to see if they would give off X-rays. Nothing happened.

Becquerel then repeated the experiment using uranium crystals, which were known to glow when exposed to sunlight. The crystals didn't glow, however, because he hadn't exposed them to the sun. Legend has it that on a certain overcast day in Paris in February 1896, Becquerel for some reason put the uranium in a drawer with the photographic plates that he had been using for his work. When he developed the photographic plates a few days later and saw an impression of the crystals, Becquerel realized the uranium was emitting radiation spontaneously. Unlike X-rays, which Röntgen generated with a device, Becquerel's rays were natural. Without really knowing what he was looking for, or what to call it, Becquerel discovered radioactivity.

Unlike Röntgen's discovery, Becquerel's did not become an international sensation; his work eventually reached a dead end and he fell into relative obscurity. Like Röntgen, however, he won the Nobel Prize for Physics, taking the award in 1903.[129,130,131] And, like Röntgen, a unit of measure of radioactivity was named after him.

Enter Marie and Pierre Curie.

Marie Sklodowska was born in Warsaw in 1867, the daughter of two educators. At age 23 she enrolled in the Sorbonne, where she struggled with French but earned master's degrees in physics and math. Torn between advancing her academic career in Paris or returning to Poland, she stayed in France, having been wooed by fellow physics wizard Pierre Curie. Their connection was professional and personal. Marie helped Pierre earn his doctorate in 1895 and the couple married later that year.[132]

Wanting a doctorate of her own, Marie picked up where Röntgen and Becquerel left off. With Pierre's help, she got permission to use an abandoned shed at the Paris School of Industrial Physics and Chemistry. Once used as a dissecting room, the leaky, poorly heated shack with a cracked floor was described as a "cross between a stable and a potato cellar." But it was free.

Marie and Pierre needed uranium to study. An Austrian government official agreed to help the two "lunatics" and gave them a ton of waste from Bohemia, where the uranium ore, pitchblende, was being mined. After years of toil, the Curies discovered two new substances: radium and polonium, which Marie named after her native country. They named the mysterious rays emitted by the substances "radioactivity." Marie became the first woman to earn an advanced research degree in France, and the first to lecture at the Sorbonne in the school's 600-year history.

The Curies shared the Nobel Prize for Physics with Becquerel in 1903. The press raved, linking their discovery to more fantastical possibilities: "Man and Wife Team Discover Perpetual Motion in Hut." Curie paid the ultimate price. In 1934 she died at age 66 of leukemia induced by nearly four decades of intimate exposure to radioactivity. Some of her notes are still radioactive.[133,134]

Like Röntgen's work, the Curies' discoveries inspired many absurdities. Radioactive toothpaste promised not just whiter teeth but better digestion. Radioactive face cream purported to lighten skin. The "rejuvenator" radium chocolate bar and "uranium wine" were said to cure stomach ulcers and tuberculosis. Perhaps the most hyped product was radioactive water—"liquid sunshine."

A medical journal naively gushed in 1916: "Radium has absolutely no toxic effects, it being accepted as harmoniously by the human system as is sunlight by the plant."[135]

This assertion would soon be proven wrong by the most gruesome episode in the early days of nuclear technology.

The Radium Girl

Margaret Looney had just graduated high school in 1923 when she got a job at the Radium Dial Co. in Ottawa, Illinois, a river town about 75 miles outside of Peoria. Known to her friends as Peg, Looney joined the rapidly growing industry of painting wristwatch faces with glow-in-the-dark radium. It was a civilian application of military technology: luminous gauges on their instrument panels helped pilots navigate their way through night skies during World War I.

Using camel-hair brushes to paint tiny numbers onto watches was tedious work but it paid well. As many as 5,000 people, a vast majority of them young women, worked in about 50 radium studios nationwide, painting not just watches but fish bait, doll eyes, and gun sights. The trick of the trade was keeping the point of the brush as sharp as possible. Using a cloth or their fingers didn't work well enough, so workers resorted to licking brush tips with their tongues and lips.

"Not to worry," workers were told. "If you swallow any radium, it'll make your cheeks rosy." That didn't happen, but the radium made their teeth, fingernails, and faces glow in the dark, providing comic relief in dreary warehouses where hundreds of workers sat at large tables lined up one after another.

Unbeknownst to her, Looney was being tested for radioactivity, and the tests were coming back positive. She was literally falling apart: some of her teeth fell out and pieces of her jaw cleaved off. She died in 1929, eight days after she quit her job. When her body was exhumed 40 years later, the radioactivity was still more than 1,000 times the level considered safe. "I'm angry because they knew years before she died that she was full of radium," Peg's sister would say. "And then they lied." Many other people were doomed to die.[136]

Soon after the "Radium Girl" tragedy, the most miraculous of all atomic discoveries was made—or the most terrifying, depending on your view of history.

The Bomb

On a fall day in 1933, a Jewish-Hungarian physicist named Leo Szilard was walking down a London street when he had an epiphany about how splitting the atom could set off a nuclear chain reaction. Szilard, who had just fled Germany, suspected his realization could lead to the construction of an atomic bomb. Not about to allow this information to fall into Adolf Hitler's hands, Szilard kept quiet.

For the next dozen years, up until the detonation of the world's first atomic bomb, some of the most notable scientists of the 20th century joined in the hunt for subatomic secrets. In 1934 Enrico Fermi of Columbia University blasted uranium with neutrons, achieving the world's first nuclear fission. Also that year, Irène Curie (daughter of Marie and Pierre) and her husband, Frédéric Joliot discovered artificial radioactivity when they "created" four new isotopes.

In the formative year of 1939, Fermi and Szilard worked together to prove that a nuclear chain reaction was theoretically possible. Maintaining his silence as he did in 1933, Szilard did not go public with his findings, abiding by a self-imposed censorship agreement among many top nuclear scientists.

On March 15, 1939—the same day Hitler invaded Czechoslovakia—Curie and Joliot published details on how chain reactions could be constructed.[137] With Hitler's military intentions now apparent, Albert Einstein sent a warning to President Franklin D. Roosevelt.

On Dec. 2, 1942, one year after the attack on Pearl Harbor, Fermi achieved the first-ever controlled chain reaction, in the bizarre setting of a squash court in the basement of a dormant athletic field at the University of Chicago.[138,139] Work on developing an atomic weapon was swift. The first test bomb, code named "Trinity," was detonated in the desert near Alamogordo, New Mexico, on July 16, 1945. President Harry Truman exclaimed, "This is the greatest day in history!" The next two bombs, "Little Boy" and "Fat Man," were dropped on Hiroshima and Nagasaki three weeks later.

At the time, Congress' Joint Committee on Atomic Energy was chaired by Sen. Brien McMahon, who was best known for bringing Baby Face Nelson and other gangsters to justice as a federal prosecutor. Always colorful, McMahon said of the events in Japan: "When the bomb bay doors of the B-29 opened over Hiroshima when the first atomic bomb exploded, in my opinion there occurred the most momentous development in the 2,000 years of the world's history since the birth of Jesus Christ."[140]

Soon after Hiroshima and Nagasaki, however, Truman saw a bleak future. With ground zero in Japan still smoldering, the U.S. political and scientific establishment, though quite pleased with the swiftness in which the atomic bomb put an end to World War II, recognized that a global arms race was afoot. Truman pushed for an international agreement to ban the military use of atomic energy and encourage peaceful applications.[141]

Atoms for Peace

"Beyond the veil of dust and smoke and searing death which was Hiroshima," the *New York Times* told readers, "there are many fascinating fields of speculation for the use of atomic power for beneficent rather than destructive ends."[142]

Fantasies about what the Happy Atom could do for society knew no end. Scientists, politicians, and journalists competed to dream up more wondrous possibilities. In hindsight, it is difficult to imagine an entire nation being deluded into thinking that atomic energy could make virtually anything possible.

John O'Neill, science editor of the *New York Herald Tribune*, suggested igniting atomic bombs in the Arctic to melt the Earth's polar ice caps, giving "the entire world a moister, warmer climate." He envisioned connecting major U.S. cities with "vacuum tubes" that could carry nuclear-powered trains going 10,000 miles per hour. He predicted using radioactive beams to mine and smelt metals, and developing "atomic-energy vitamin tablets."

Prominent science writer David O. Woodbury entertained notions of a nuclear-powered car, which he nicknamed the "atom-auto." He readily confessed, however, the impracticality of such a thing: "Our atom-autos are going to be embarrassingly heavy, carrying 50 tons or so of lead or pig iron to save us from being rayed to death by our engines." In a blithe suggestion characteristic of the day, he wrote, "But suppose they do find a weightless shield through a loophole in physics."

David Dietz, a Pulitzer Prize-winning journalist and a fellow with the American Association for the Advancement of Science wrote, "Beyond a doubt the Era of Atomic Energy will see artificial suns mounted on tall steel towers. No baseball game will be called off on account of rain. No airplane will bypass an airport because of fog. No city will experience a winter traffic jam because of heavy snow. Summer resorts will be able to guarantee the weather and artificial suns will make it as easy to grow corn and potatoes indoors as on the farm.

"The old dream of the alchemist to turn base metals—iron and lead, for example—into gold will come true. For atomic energy is not only unlimited energy but it is energy in a form that will do special things, such as transmuting chemical elements."

Dietz seemed unable to contain his exuberance: "Universal perpetual peace will reign. With energy as abundant as the air we breathe, there will no longer be any reason to fight for oil or coal. By using atomic energy to mine the ocean, every nation will be able to obtain easily all the raw materials that it needs. With even more powerful bombs than those dropped on Japan, war will become so destructive that no nation will dare begin one."[143]

Picking up on the atomic weather theme, Carnegie Institution physicist Robert Potter predicted a weather "forecast fantasy." Atomic bombs could obliterate hurricanes. Nuclear power could run huge pumps to suck out underground water; in the case of the Sahara Desert, enough irrigation water could be tapped to grow enough food to feed all of Africa and most of Europe. "Stretching the imagination a bit," wrote Potter, as though his imagination hadn't already been pushed beyond its limits, "it is even possible to visualize scientific control of some of the world's ocean currents with atomic heating."

Heading into another bizarre area, Potter predicted that atomic energy could somehow be used to create synthetic foods. Nuclear power, he said without elaboration, could run "conversion factories" where "every weed, every tree, every plant could enter at one end and emerge as food at the other end."

In a grand summation, Potter wrote: "Inexpensive food could be supplied to everyone, everywhere, so that at last mankind would no longer have worries about the necessities of life."[144]

Though his ideas were outlandish, Potter's prediction that atomic energy could advance peace ultimately became the official, although cynical, position of the U.S. government.

On Dec. 8, 1953, President Dwight Eisenhower unveiled his "Atoms for Peace" program to the United Nations General Assembly. While the arms race with the Soviet Union was in full gear, Eisenhower not only challenged the inevitability of nuclear war, he said the "terrible problem" could be transformed into a "hopeful alternative":

> This greatest of destructive forces can be developed into a great boon for the benefit of all mankind. My country's purpose is to help us move out of the dark chamber of horrors into the light, to find a way by which the minds of men, the

> hopes of men, the souls of men everywhere, can move forward
> toward peace and happiness and well being.[145]

It would be difficult to overstate the effect that Eisenhower's words and the atomic power lobby had on the American populace. Writers from across the land tried to out-hype each other. Woodbury, who named his book after Eisenhower's speech, went so far as to make nuclear war itself sound peaceful:

> Atomic war would probably not be as horrible as many excited
> people think. Principally, it would be more "efficient." There
> would probably be very little maiming and dismemberment.
> It would be decisive; one would either be dead or unharmed.
> Atomic death is, if anything, less painful and less horrible
> than death by maiming or by incineration. If we can take the
> destruction of Hiroshima and Nagasaki as valid examples, *a
> mass of people takes it remarkably in stride.*[146] (Emphasis
> added.)

The U.S. military establishment found itself caught up with the efficiency that nuclear weapons could resolve conflict. Though Atoms for Peace was the mantra of the day, there was plenty attention on using atoms for war. Many of these initiatives, however, ended in failure.

The Army and Navy wanted to build a remote-controlled "death-spray plane" powered by an unshielded atomic engine that could kill anything within a half-mile with its "glowing blue nimbus of radiation." "It could knock out an entire enemy bomber formation by simply flying close to it. It could wipe out an armored column out of existence by a single low pass. It could strafe a city in a most devilish way; if it flew low overhead, the city would become a death trap, while if it were shot down, there wouldn't be any city left."[147] The plane was never built for fear of accidents.

The U.S. eventually developed a nuclear-powered engine that could fly a plane at 460 miles per hour for 30,000 miles. Shielding and weight problems couldn't be solved, so in 1961, over the JCAE's objections, the new Kennedy administration terminated the program.[148,149]

Plans for a nuclear-powered rocket first appeared in the late 1950s, with Nuclear Engines for Rocket Vehicle Applications (NERVA). The rocket was ground-tested 31 times in the Nevada desert from 1959 to 1969, spewing radiation to California and Utah. Pieces torn from fuel rods were found 80 miles away. The project was cancelled in 1971, also over the JCAE's objections. One Congress member fumed: "The failure to include funds for the NERVA program amounts to almost a national crime against the American people."[150]

The federal government spent a lot of time and money pontificating about how nuclear technology could help humanity. With a then-astronomical half-billion-dollar budget and 60,000 employees, the Atomic Energy Commission perfected the image of the Happy Atom.

The AEC sponsored "Atomic Energy Weeks" across the U.S. The first was held in 1947 in Hyattsville, Maryland, near Washington, DC. Sidewalk informational displays were erected. Clergymen preached the virtues of atomic energy. High school students staged a play starring Miss Molecule and Mr. Atomic Energy. Grade-schoolers listened to simplified explanations about things atomic.

The effort peaked in the summer of 1948. With the help of nuclear power contractors General Electric and Westinghouse, the AEC ran a month-long "Man and the Atom" exhibit in New York City's Central Park. The main attraction, the "Theater of Atoms," included a chain reaction comprised of 60 mousetraps and a model of an atomic nucleus said to look like "a futuristic Christmas tree." *Dagwood Splits the Atom* comic books were handed out by the thousands. In all, an estimated four million people turned out for Atomic Energy Weeks.[151]

Behind this public relations juggernaut, the AEC promoted a seemingly endless list of peaceful applications of nuclear technology. Like the military endeavors, many civilian projects also flopped or were scaled back.

Just over 100 nuclear power plants have been built in the U.S., far fewer than the thousand once conceived. The infamous prediction made in 1954 by then-AEC Chair Lewis Strauss—"Our children will enjoy electrical energy too cheap to meter"—has not come true and almost certainly never will.

Many far-fetched notions were abandoned altogether:

- "Bombs for peace," which could dig second Panama and Suez Canals, excavate harbors, blast railway tunnels, and "drill" for natural gas. This latter plan fizzled because the gas was too radioactive to use in homes and workplaces. It was simply burned off at the wells, sending radioactivity skyward.

- "Atomic slaves" to do unspecified "dirty work" in industry and the home, as proposed by AEC Chair Glenn Seaborg, the Nobel Prize-winning discoverer of plutonium and other radioactive elements.

- Replacing many of the 3,000 aging U.S. merchant ships with nuclear-powered vessels.[152] Only one such ship, the *Savannah*, sailed from 1962 to 1972.[153]

- "Manpack thermoelectric generators" to keep Army soldiers warm, and plutonium-heated long-johns for Navy divers (which were considered for use by recreational campers).

- Nuclear-powered coffeepots, which Monsanto hoped would run for 100 years without refueling. And nuclear-powered wristwatches, which the Bulova Watch Co. researched during the 1960s and 1970s.[154,155]

The Atomic Age grew so absurd that *Harper's* ran a fictional story about a man in Arizona who discovered a radioactive isotope in Mexican beans called *frijolium*, which he could convert into electricity to run household appliances. "I've had it running the washing machine for three hours, and if I didn't turn it off, it would run for 72 years."[156]

The Atoms for Peace program, of course, was no joke to the Atomic Energy Commission. And while in hindsight many of its ideas were outlandish, one initiative has survived a half-century of skepticism, ridicule, and all manner of setbacks.

Food irradiation was the supreme example of how nuclear technology could help everyone: using radioactivity to extend the shelf life of food, instead of using it to obliterate human life. Unlike wristwatches and long-johns, food is something that everyone needs to survive. This made irradiation a superstar within the Atoms for Peace program.

The AEC proudly predicted in 1964: "Oranges as sweet and juicy as if just picked—strawberries firm and free of mold—yet all many miles and weeks away from harvest. How is it possible? They've been radiation 'pasteurized.' In the 1970s it is probable that a typical U.S. family, understanding that radiation-processed foods are fresh, wholesome, tasty and vitamin complete, will include them in its weekly diet."[157]

Like most of the AEC's plans to merge nuclear technologies into the mainstream, food irradiation was a tough sell. Empowered by the spirit of the age, however, the AEC was not about to allow food irradiation to follow the path of the atomic coffeepot.

It wouldn't be easy. The Council on Foreign Relations warned of "anti-radiation neurosis": "Irradiated food need not be radioactive, but it will probably be difficult to obtain general public acceptance of irradiated foods if they are so labeled. Much of the psychosis arises from the confusion of radiation danger with fallout hazards."[158]

As it turned out, the AEC and other government agencies, as well as the nuclear and food industries, would have much more to worry about than public relations.

Chapter 4

A Broken Record: The Regulators Change Their Tune

Richard Morse had a dreadful assignment on January 14, 1960. One of his first duties as the new research and development director for the U.S. Army would be to appear before Congress' Joint Committee on Atomic Energy (JCAE). It was a far cry from his civilian career, much of which he spent finding better ways to dehydrate food and refine metals, and helping to invent concentrated orange juice for the Minute Maid Corporation.[159]

The JCAE, created one year after Hiroshima and Nagasaki, was Congress' driving force behind the advancement of nuclear technologies. A crucible of Cold War thinking, the Committee was under the influence of military veterans and geopolitical strategists who worked hand-in-hand with the Atomic Energy Commission (AEC) and dozens of powerful, politically connected defense and nuclear technology corporations to advance nuclear technologies. The AEC was the Committee's counterpart in the executive branch, and it enforced the will of presidents, beginning with Truman.

The Cold War was becoming icier every day. The last thing the JCAE wanted to hear was a lack of progress—or even worse, a relapse—in the pursuit of nuclear secrets. The U.S. and Soviet Union were in competition over just about everything, and food irradiation, a poster child of the Atoms for Peace program, was near the top of the list. As one Army brass wrote to another in 1959: "There is undisputed worldwide acknowledgement of United States leadership, which should be maintained."[160]

Thinking that the Army had the most pressing need for irradiated foods, which can be stored for years without refrigeration, the AEC began funding the Army's human feeding tests in 1953. The Korean War ended that year, so the effort came too late to help the food supply chain in that conflict. As hostilities in Vietnam grew, however, the Army redoubled its research into irradiated foods, which could make the trip halfway around the world without spoiling. In 1956, several feeding experiments were conducted on Mennonite conscientious objectors at the Department of Defense Army Medical Research and Nutrition Laboratory at the Fitzsimons Army Hospital, in Denver, Colorado. Nobody who ate irradiated foods in those experiments became noticeably ill.

This was not the case with lab animals, which can serve as a bellwether of how foreign substances could be harmful to humans. It was Morse's displeasure to report to the JCAE that January day in 1960—four months after the Soviets struck a blow to the U.S. space program by landing the first spacecraft on the moon—that something had gone terribly wrong with the country's food irradiation program.

Mice fed irradiated foods died of ruptured hearts. Dogs became sterile. Rats whose parents ate the food were born blind or died from internal bleeding. The problems were so frightening that Morse told the Committee that further human tests should be stopped immediately, and that the Army should scrap its plans to build a food irradiation facility.[161]

"We have some big red flags raised here which certainly in my judgment preclude going ahead," Morse, deadpanning the situation, told aghast members of the JCAE.[162]

The Soviets had just landed an unmanned spacecraft on the moon, and the U.S. couldn't figure out how to feed irradiated foods to lab animals without them keeling over dead.

The Atomic Energy Commission was infuriated. When the Army tried to issue a press release announcing the cancellation of the irradiation facility, the AEC expunged all references to the lab animals' health problems, which the Army's original version discussed in great detail. The final release cryptically stated that "certain physiological problems have not yielded to solution in the laboratory."[163]

Taken in isolation, the AEC's meddling with one press release may not seem significant. During its nearly 30 years of existence, however, the AEC was notorious not only for its hasty, evangelical approach to nuclear technology, but also for its sometimes less-than-forthcoming dealings with the public.

The AEC's public relations strategy became clear during a meeting between AEC and military officials held in December 1950 to discuss the location of atomic bomb tests in Nevada. According to meeting minutes, the central feature of the strategy was to "make the atom routine and make the public feel at home with atomic blasts and radiation hazards. The idea of making the public feel at home with neutrons trotting around is the most important angle to get across."[164]

In 1969, AEC physicist John Gofman accused the agency of censoring a report in which he stated the risk of getting cancer from radiation exposure was "20 times greater than was being said in official circles." Gofman said, "To continue the present guidelines is absolute folly."[165] Gofman would go on to become one of the most renowned and influential radiation health experts of the late 20th century, authoring several seminal books on the subject.

Most notably, the AEC persistently downplayed the effects of radioactive fallout from atomic bombs exploded in Nevada, the Marshall Islands, Hiroshima and Nagasaki, and elsewhere. Based on AEC findings, Eisenhower said in 1956: "The continuance of the present rate of H-bomb testing, by the most sober and responsible scientific judgment does not imperil the health of humanity."[166]

By 1964, however, the truth had begun to surface. President Lyndon Johnson said in a televised address one year after the signing of the Nuclear Test Ban Treaty, which outlawed nuclear explosions in the atmosphere, under water, and in space: "The deadly products of atomic explosions were poisoning our soil and food and the milk our children drank and the air we all breathe. Radioactive deposits were being formed in increasing quantity in the teeth and bones of young Americans. Radioactive poisons were beginning to threaten the safety of people throughout the world. They were a growing menace to the health of every unborn child."[167]

By the time the AEC went back before the Joint Committee on Atomic Energy to talk about food irradiation in 1966, the reluctance of the AEC to discuss the health effects related to the use of nuclear technologies was clear. Rather than discussing exploding hearts, blindness, or infertility in lab animals, JCAE members were treated to the presentation: "An Apron on the Atom: Irradiated Foods for Tomorrow's Dinners."

The Promise of Ease

Though irradiated foods were nowhere near reaching grocery store shelves, much less had they been shown safe to eat, the publication promised: "Housewives of the world, take heart! Your day of liberation from kitchen chores is in prospect. When her husband telephones at 4 p.m. and says, 'Dear, the boss is in town and I'm bringing him home to dinner,' she can coolly look over her stock of irradiated meat, fish and vegetables, and heat and serve a company dinner."[168]

With the disastrous 1960 congressional hearing safely fading into the past, the AEC and the Army were once again in a favorable position. The agencies had won permission from the Food and Drug Administration to irradiate bacon, wheat flour, and potatoes. Applications had been filed for ham, oranges, lemons, grapefruit, strawberries, and several types of fish. And, the AEC and Army were working on applications for dozens of other foods, including beef, pork, poultry, seafood, and various fruits.[169]

Major progress was also being made on the hardware side of things. The AEC had several irradiation machines in operation, however gadgety they may have been. Among them was the "Mobile Gamma Irradiator," which was hauled around central California farmlands in a tractor-trailer; the "Portable Cesium-137 Irradiator," which made a truck tour of 12 food companies in four states; and three "Shipboard Irradiators," which were aboard fishing boats that trolled the Gulf of Mexico and the coasts of Massachusetts and Washington.[170]

Just as in the 1950s, the good tidings were short-lived. The AEC and the Army—and the entire food irradiation movement, for that matter—were struck a major blow in 1968 from which it took more than a decade to recover. (Some would argue that the movement still has not recovered, and never will.) Once again, the stage was the Joint Committee on Atomic Energy. And once again, ugly laboratory findings were the source of the trouble.

In an unusually blunt discussion, JCAE members grilled AEC, Army, and FDA officials about the sudden emergence of previously withheld Army documents indicating serious health effects among lab animals fed irradiated foods. These problems included fewer living offspring among rats, a finding that then-FDA Commissioner James Goddard said was "highly unlikely to be due to chance."

In other tests using irradiated diets, more rats died, dogs and mice gained less weight, dogs and rats had blood disorders, and rats developed more malignant tumors including pituitary cancer. "Since this is a rarely occurring type of cancer," Goddard wrote, "this could be very significant."[171]

"We Were Guinea Pigs"

Promptly after the damning information surfaced, the FDA revoked the Army's 1963 permit to irradiate bacon and serve it to military personnel. The decision was a shocker. Soldiers already risking life and limb serving in Vietnam, the FDA determined, should not also be exposed to the potential hazards of eating irradiated bacon. The scandal shook Congress to the core.

JCAE member Chet Holifield, a Democratic representative from California once portrayed as "the most pivotal individual controlling the destiny of atomic energy in the United States,"[172] felt betrayed: "This is a complete repudiation of what this committee has been told by what we thought were expert people."[173] Rep. William Bates, a World War II Navy veteran, felt deceived: "We were told several years ago that bacon was all right. We proceeded to eat it."

Rep. Melvin Price, himself an Army veteran, had the last word: "We were guinea pigs."[174]

So unsettled was Daniel Banes, the FDA's associate commissioner, that he raised the gruesome prospect of another Thalidomide-type disaster. A sleeping and anti-nausea pill marketed to pregnant women, Thalidomide caused hundreds of deaths and more than 10,000 birth defects in the late 1950s and 1960s in countries throughout the world, including Brazil, Canada, England, Germany, Italy, Japan, and Sweden.

The FDA never approved Thalidomide, thus sparing American women from that tragedy. It was more than clear that the FDA wanted to make the right decision about food irradiation, too. As events would have it, the FDA did not approve another food irradiation application until 1983.

Addressing Rep. Price at the JCAE hearing, Banes said: "Our knowledge eight or 10 years ago about the [birth defect-causing] effect of drugs—for example, Thalidomide and its effects on the embryo—was sketchy. In fact, it was practically nonexistent. The questions we ask now about the effects of drugs on the reproductive process and the biochemistry of the body are far more subtle and far more advanced. I submit, sir, that the same situation obtains with respect to irradiated foods."[175]

The tough talk didn't stop there. Banes' boss, FDA Commissioner Goddard, scolded AEC Chair Glenn Seaborg regarding shabby research the Army used to support its request to irradiate ham and serve it to soldiers, which the FDA rejected: "I was most disappointed. Too much time and effort has been wasted on poorly executed studies, on incomplete studies, and on an inadequate evaluation of the results."[176]

Seaborg was not accustomed to receiving tongue-lashings. One of the most influential scientists in recent history, Seaborg won the Nobel Prize for Chemistry in 1951 for co-discovering plutonium and other radioactive elements. He developed the plutonium used in the atomic bomb dropped on Nagasaki. He became the first living person after whom an element was named—seaborgium. And he is listed in the *Guinness Book of World Records* as having the longest biography in *Who's Who in America*.

In hindsight, it is little wonder that Goddard found fault with Seaborg's research on food irradiation. Though his discoveries in the field of nuclear physics are perhaps unmatched, many of Seaborg's views about applying nuclear technology to real-life situations were far-fetched. His ideas are reminiscent of the X-ray and uranium crazes of the early 1900s, when speculation lost all rationality.

"The Earth, a slightly flawed planet, is a unique and generous home for man, but it is not perfectly suited to his aspirations," Seaborg once wrote. "The weather is not what we would like it to be, despite millennia of sacrifices to the gods and tons of dry ice and silver iodide crystals. All of humanity's efforts to restore the Garden of Eden have been futile so far. Man's machines have not been powerful enough to compete with the forces of nature."[177]

Seaborg spoke at length about using "peaceful nuclear explosions" to dig shipping canals, construction sites, reservoirs, "instant" harbors, and underground caverns to store oil and water. Bombs could be used to extract coal, copper, water, natural gas, and other underground resources. Giant underground "chimneys" could be used to dispose of liquid waste. [178]

Nuclear bombs positioned along seismic fault lines could forestall earthquakes. Blasts could close the Strait of Gibraltar, turning the Mediterranean Sea into a freshwater lake that could irrigate the Sahara Desert—though this benefit, Seaborg wrote, "would have to be weighed against the loss of Venice and other sea-level cities.[179]

Massive nuclear-powered facilities called "Nuplexes," which Seaborg only vaguely described, could somehow serve as the "nuclei of a nation's major industrial areas responsible for most of its products and power."

Seaborg's imagination seemed to have gotten the better of him.

Just as many of Seaborg's ideas have not passed the test of time, food irradiation was also running into trouble. Less than a year after the humiliating 1968 hearing before the Joint Committee on Atomic Energy, the AEC decided to drop its food irradiation program altogether. The Army decided to pull the plug on its own initiative in 1970.

After spending more than $40 million and putting in 15 years' worth of research, and despite consistent assurances that success was just around the corner, the AEC and the Army failed to demonstrate that irradiated foods are safe for people to eat.

Army brass speculated that irradiated foods would never take hold in the marketplace: "There is no evidence to indicate that our efforts will be successful in removing the FDA questions and the emotional public doubts."

The decision to stop food irradiation research was met with the usual Cold War bluster. AEC Commissioner James Ramey said "the Soviet Union is moving ahead and one can expect that they may try to take over the leadership we have been exercising."[180] A food irradiation "gap" was out of the question.

In explaining the AEC's decision to drop its program, John R. Totter, who headed the AEC's Division of Biology and Medicine, told the JCAE that "this action was taken solely for reasons of budgetary stringency, and does not imply any adverse wholesomeness and safety findings."[181] This, of course, ran contrary to the scientific record, which contained ample evidence that irradiated foods could be hazardous, and had been presented to Congress in open sessions dating back to 1960.

Secret Human Experiments

As disingenuous as Totter's remark was, it was in keeping with AEC's approach to public policy. The division's interest in radiation extended far beyond food. Experimenting on humans was one of the pursuits of this division—research that the AEC liked to call "peaceful applications" of atomic energy.

Many of these human experiments remained a secret for decades. The top was finally blown off in 1986, when U.S. Rep. Edward Markey (D-MA,) released the report, "American Nuclear Guinea Pigs: Three Decades of Radiation Experiments on U.S. Citizens."

Markey's findings were met with shock and revulsion. His report detailed how the AEC and kindred government agencies funded, supervised, and otherwise facilitated dozens of radiation experiments on hundreds of people at universities, hospitals, and research centers throughout the U.S. from the 1940s through the 1970s. Many of these people were in little or no position to refuse: some were in prison, some were elderly, some had terminal diseases, and some simply were not told they were being experimented upon.

With this sort of experimentation occurring in secrecy, it is little wonder that the AEC's food irradiation research, which also lacked transparency, didn't impress the FDA and members of Congress once it was finally made public.

Enter the IAEA

Despite a series of embarrassing failures, despite almost no interest from food companies, and despite the fact that food irradiation research proved that ingesting irradiated food caused negative unintended consequences, the advocacy for food irradiation continued at the international level. And just as food irradiation research and policy was shaped by the AEC and JCAE, both of which had little or no food safety experience, it would be the International Atomic Energy Agency (IAEA) that elevated irradiation to the international stage.

In the summer of 1957, the superpowers had agreed to form IAEA under the auspices of the United Nations—allegedly to encourage constructive uses for nuclear technology.

The IAEA's stated mission was broad: "Take any action needed to promote research on, development of, and practical applications of nuclear energy for peaceful purposes."[182] Note the word "any." Like its cousins the Atomic Energy Commission and Joint Committee on Atomic Energy, the IAEA has stopped at nothing to promote atomic energy. On paper, at least, the IAEA was charged with trying to save the world from nuclear holocaust. (About 100 organizations in more than 25 countries urged the IAEA in 2005 to drop the promotion of nuclear technology from its mission.[183])

Upon its birth, the IAEA immediately began to exert its authority. In 1959, just two years after it was founded, the IAEA won an agreement with the World Health Organization (WHO), another United Nations agency, that handed the IAEA "the primary responsibility" to research peaceful uses of atomic energy.[184]

Getting the WHO out of the way was no small achievement. The WHO's job is preserving "a state of complete physical, mental and social well being" for the entire population of the world.[185] As far as atomic energy was concerned, that responsibility now belonged to the IAEA—an agency that does not put the health of people first, but the health of the nuclear industry.

Under closer inspection, the WHO's decision to back away from nuclear issues made perfect sense. In 1958, the year before the WHO signed its agreement with the IAEA, the WHO published the report, "Mental Health Aspects of the Peaceful Uses of Atomic Energy." In it, the WHO dismisses public concerns over the dangers of atomic energy as unwarranted, delusional—even as a sign of mental illness:

"When the evidence of abnormal emotional response to atomic energy is checked against reality, it is clear that the response is quite unjustified. There is reason to believe that certain emotional responses must, in many cases, be considered as pathological."

Bizarrely, the WHO goes on to compare the public's fear of atomic energy with a child's fear of the world: "As atomic energy is so gigantic a force emanating from exceedingly small quantities of matter, it easily provokes irrational phantasies. Such phantasies may well be related to those of early childhood—of magical power, the casting of spells, the working of miracles and so on—dreams by which children compensate for their felt smallness and weakness."

Instead of ensuring that the public received accurate, complete information about the potential dangers of atomic energy, the WHO, in a prescription familiar to the day, concluded: "It is clear that the public will need protection from undue anxieties and fears."[186]

In 1961, two years after the IAEA-WHO agreement was signed, the two agencies, along with the United Nations' Food and Agriculture Organization (FAO), met in Brussels for the first major international conference on food irradiation. More than 100 delegates from 28 nations raised many in-depth questions they said needed to be resolved before the safety and wholesomeness of irradiated foods could be established—including whether irradiated foods are radioactive, whether they could cause cancer or birth defects, and whether they are nutrient deficient.[187] The safety assessment being conducted by the world's leading medical experts was off to a good start.

Three years later, however, when the three agencies met in Rome, a dramatic reversal took place. Discussions no longer focused on health and safety issues. Instead, the top priority was convincing governments around the world to legalize irradiated food and persuading people to eat it.[188] The cart had been placed before the horse: the agencies began promoting irradiated foods even before they had been declared safe to eat. The mark of the IAEA was beginning to be made.

In 1969, the IAEA, WHO, and FAO took their first step on the issue of safety, endorsing irradiated wheat and potatoes. In a sign of things to come, the agencies did so in the face of evidence that irradiated foods could be hazardous. In a joint report, "Wholesomeness of Irradiated Food with Special References to Wheat, Potatoes, & Onions," they discussed studies that detailed health problems in animals fed irradiated food.[189]

Mice fed irradiated flour died younger and had more tumors than mice fed non-irradiated flour.[190] The report went on to discuss a study where hens fed irradiated wheat hatched fewer eggs and lost more embryos than hens fed non-irradiated wheat.[191]

Further, in the joint report, the agencies acknowledged that irradiated foods could contain chemicals that could cause genetic and cellular damage, and that they only had a "paucity" of information on the problems.

In 1976, the IAEA, WHO, and FAO endorsed irradiation of eight common foods, including rice, onions, chicken, and strawberries, despite yet more disturbing evidence. For instance, studies by Drs. Vijayalaxmi and K.V. Rao in India showed that well-fed rats developed genetic damage after eating irradiated foods.[192] The Technical Report Series 604 of the World Health Organization, a joint report by WHO, IAEA, and FAO after their 1976 meeting, mentions other studies, including one where ovary damage was observed in rodents fed irradiated potatoes.[193]

The meeting report fails to discuss many of the core issues that were raised in 1961 at the first meeting of these institutions on irradiation. No follow up was done by WHO, IAEA, or FAO on irradiation's effect on protein, fat, and carbohydrates, on the likelihood of irradiated food causing cancer, or on irradiation inducing radioactivity in food.[194]

It is worth noting that the breakthrough decision by these prestigious international institutions to endorse irradiation was based largely on research by the International Project in the Field of Food Irradiation in Karlsruhe, Germany.[195] The program was established by the pro-nuclear IAEA, and funded by the IAEA and the U.S. Department of Energy.

In 1979, J. Barna reviewed food irradiation studies for the Hungarian Academy of Sciences. He classified study results as adverse, neutral, or beneficial. He found 1,414 adverse effects, 185 beneficial effects, and 7,191 neutral effects. [196]

In 1980, representatives of the WHO, IAEA, and FAO met in Geneva and concluded that *any* food could be irradiated up to a certain dose and still be safe to eat. Despite a vast and growing amount of data to the contrary, the agencies said that all the toxicological studies "have produced no evidence of adverse effects as a result of irradiation."[197] They completely ignored numerous studies conducted over a more than 20-year period that revealed health problems in animals that ate irradiated foods. Some of these experiments were performed by the U.S. Army. It also directly contradicts the report from the 1976 meeting of the agencies, which references studies in which chromosomal aberrations developed in several animal species.[198]

Public Relations

It became obvious that international deliberations over food irradiation had very little to do with safety, and very much to do with the proliferation of irradiated foods throughout the world. In the 1980s, the IAEA turned completely away from health issues and toward the problem of public relations. To lend assistance, the IAEA hired various consultants to craft a strategy to enhance the image of irradiated foods. The meeting in Vienna at which the consultants findings were presented, "Marketing, and Consumer Acceptance of Irradiated Foods," featured some very frank and revealing discussions. Quoting from the report that was issued:

> Any word or statement containing the word 'radiation' or 'radiate' would inspire fear of a nonexistent danger...and therefore will cause the product to be avoided. The consultant group does not recommend that the label carry a statement of the process."[199]

Among the people attending the meeting were Edward Josephson, the former director of the U.S. Army's food irradiation program, Jan Leemhorst, a high-ranking officer with the Association of International Industrial Irradiators, and Jacek Sivivnski, an engineering consultant with CH2M Hill, a prominent energy and nuclear technology company.

"Any word or statement containing the word 'radiation' or 'radiate' would inspire fear...and therefore will cause the product to be avoided," the consultant said. "Identification of the process should not be required on the label." Absurd suggestions to call irradiated foods "processed with electrons" or "gammatized" were entertained.

Also speaking at the 1982 meeting was an executive with a large retailer in South Africa, whose propagandist notions bordered on the Orwellian:

We start from a totally negative situation because nothing
has threatened mankind so completely as total destruction
through nuclear holocaust. Therefore, it is difficult for the ordinary person to accept that anything that is associated with
radiation, even indirectly, is not going to cause terrible death
or disaster... We have to know and understand the ordinary
people. We must confer with experts in the various fields of
advertising and psychology to put the public at ease, and develop a more friendly feeling to irradiation. Symbols must be
developed not to look like radiation symbols. Names must be
simple and not necessarily related to the words 'irradiation'
or 'radiation.'[200]

In 1984, the Raltech Scientific Service conducted animal feeding studies
for the federal government, under the supervision of the Department of Agriculture. Two of the studies had adverse findings. One study, which was supposed to last two years, had to be terminated after nine months because of
excessive mortality among offspring in the group.[201] However, the results were
dismissed by Donald Thayer, the Department of Agriculture's chief reviewer,
even though he chronicled the problems in his report.[202]

The IAEA, WHO, and FAO ultimately endorsed the irradiation of all foods
at any dose, no matter how high—a monumental decision handed down in
1999. But just as problems plagued research by the Atomic Energy Commission and the Army, the endorsement by the three international agencies was
also flawed.

In 2002 Public Citizen and the Global Resource Action Center for the Environment published *Bad Taste*, a study of key IAEA/WHO/FAO reports endorsing food irradiation in 1994, 1995, and 1999.[203,204,205] A disturbing pattern
emerged. On 33 occasions, the agencies took studies that revealed health problems in lab animals that ate irradiated foods and re-classified the studies as
negative—meaning that there was no correlation between irradiated foods and
health problems. The health problems the agencies tried to conceal included
increased mortality, fatal internal bleeding, decreased fertility, mutations,
liver damage, and stunted growth. On 19 other occasions, the agencies simply
omitted "positive" studies that had been referenced in earlier reports.[206]

It would seem that the IAEA—by dismissing substantial evidence questioning the safety of irradiated foods, resorting to misleading public relations
tactics, and engaging in scientific sleight-of-hand—has indeed taken "any action needed" to promote nuclear technology, as its original charter empowers
the agency to do.

Chapter 5

The Next Phase:
The Reagan Revolution's
Helping Hand

With virtually no food irradiation activity occurring in the U.S. during the 1970s, yet another nuclear agency stepped forward to lend a hand as the 1980s opened. The interest in food irradiation exhibited by the Atomic Energy Commission, the Joint Committee on Atomic Energy, and the International Atomic Energy Agency had little, if anything, to do with actual food safety. Such was the case when the U.S. Department of Energy (DOE) emerged with its own scheme to promote atomic energy under the guise of making food safer to eat.

The DOE was one of two agencies formed to replace the Atomic Energy Commission in 1974, when it became clear that the AEC's dual role of promoting and regulating nuclear technology created a rather blatant conflict of interest. The DOE took over the promotional work, while the Nuclear Regulatory Commission was founded to regulate the nuclear power industry—which by most independent accounts it has done unsatisfactorily.

In addition to thousands of nuclear warheads, the DOE also inherited from the AEC a tremendous amount of radioactive waste left over from producing plutonium and tritium for nuclear weapons. Most of the waste was being stored (and continues to be stored) at the Hanford bomb factory in eastern Washington state, and the Savannah River bomb factory in South Carolina near the Georgia border.

The Nuclear Waste "Solution"

One of the DOE's solutions to the waste problem was to extract the most radioactive, or "hottest," substances—cesium-137 and strontium-90—and find "beneficial" uses for them. It was Atoms for Peace all over again, only this time it was called the "Byproducts Utilization Program." Twenty-five years earlier, cesium-137 was used in some of the AEC's first food irradiation experiments, though the results were not promising because this radioactive isotope is water soluble. This can lead to major safety problems, because a leak can potentially contaminate water sources. Despite the potential problems, DOE officials thought their prayers had been answered. An examination of the troubling events that unfolded over the next two decades provides a rare, up-close glimpse into government at its cynical, deceptive worst: placing its own interests and the interests of the nuclear industry over the well being of the American people. All the while, officials told the public that irradiation, a failed technology for 25 years, was a major discovery.

DOE officials announced their plans to use cesium-137 for food irradiation to Congress in March 1981[207], six weeks after President Ronald Reagan was sworn in. The timing appears to be other than coincidental. Later that year, Reagan overturned President Jimmy Carter's 1977 ban on reprocessing spent fuel rods from commercial nuclear power plants. Reprocessing the rods could not only provide Reagan the weapons-grade plutonium he wanted to expand the U.S. nuclear arsenal as the Cold War droned on, but it would also yield huge amounts of cesium-137.

Under enormous pressure from the new Reagan administration, the FDA changed its position on food irradiation. Just three weeks after the DOE unveiled its cesium-137 scheme, the FDA formally announced it was reconsidering its position that irradiated foods might be hazardous. The Reagan Administration was already putting its mark on the FDA.

Changing its position on food irradiation was the FDA's first official act on this issue since it rescinded the Army's bacon irradiation permit in 1968. Despite clearly disturbing evidence on safety, the government had all but shut down funding for studies on irradiated food by 1980.

Ignoring the Science

Most FDA decisions to reassess the safety of products or processes come at the request of businesses. But this decision to reassess the safety of irradiated foods was not made at the behest of a food company, medical organization, or public health organization. It was initiated by the Reagan administration and the nuclear industry.

Support within the FDA was not unanimous. A staff scientist named Krishna Misra wrote in an internal memo that the agency's plan to test the safety of irradiated foods was inadequate: "I have <u>serious</u> reservations. I believe we need still more continuing research. The proposed recommendations need to be shelved aside for the time being. They do not provide assurance for safety."[208] (Misra, now retired, declined an interview.)

Misra's misgivings about the plan seem to have merit. An internal FDA panel appointed to reassess the safety of irradiated foods said in 1980 that further toxicity testing was not needed for foods irradiated at relatively low levels, nor for foods comprising a small portion of the typical American's diet, such as spices. And, in the case of high-level irradiation, the panel recommended lab animal tests that were far less comprehensive than the battery normally required by the FDA.[209]

Moreover, the 1980 panel stated—without any supporting evidence—that any new chemicals formed in the process of irradiating foods would likely not cause health problems in people because the chemicals *probably* would be similar to those found in non-irradiated foods.[210] The panel ignored a groundbreaking Army-funded study that concluded: "The possible presence of undetected substances can never be excluded."[211] (This statement would prove prophetic, with the later discovery of toxic chemicals in irradiated foods linked to colon cancer in lab rats.)

Two years later, in 1982, another internal FDA panel announced it had identified just seven studies, out of the more than 400 it reviewed, in which lab animals fed irradiated foods came through the experiments unscathed. Like the 1980 committee, however, this panel's findings were gravely flawed.

The findings of both panels were reviewed by Public Citizen, the Cancer Prevention Coalition, and the Global Resource Action Center for the Environment in the October 2000 report, *A Broken Record*. None of the seven studies came close to meeting the FDA's own standards for how lab animal experiments are to be conducted. Dozens of critical observations—including complete autopsies of adults and fetuses, organ and tissue exams, blood tests and body-weight measurements—were not conducted.

Further, in two of the studies, researchers added nutrients to lab animals' diets for the specific purpose of reversing the well-known harmful effects of irradiated foods. Vitamin E, for example, was fed to rats after "very high losses" (deaths) were observed in the first two generations of offspring. And, three of the seven studies were written in French, which, inexplicably, the FDA did not translate into English. Public Citizen eventually translated the studies, and found them badly flawed.[212]

It appears that under political pressure, the FDA decided not to bother assessing the large body of research that had been done. Instead, it focused on finding some studies that seemed to suggest that irradiation was safe, without having to deal with years of data.

With the scientific foundation in place, however unstable it was, the government was free to implement its plan to dispose of radioactive waste behind the front of food irradiation. The developments were fast, furious, and well coordinated.

In March 1983, a high-ranking DOE official went to Congress to announce that the agency's cesium-137 food irradiation program was going full-steam ahead: "The utilization of these radioactive materials simply reduces our waste handling problem, in that we get some of the very hot elements out of the waste," said F. Charles Gilbert, a DOE deputy assistant secretary. "I frankly would like to see us use everything, including the squeal, if you want to refer to pork, we possibly can."[213]

Pushing it Through

Reagan's next move was designed to remove any chance of the initiative's failure and indicates just how important food irradiation was to the administration. One week after Gilbert appeared before Congress, Margaret Heckler was sworn in as secretary of the U.S. Department of Health and Human Services, which oversees the FDA. Among the reasons that Heckler was chosen is that as a member of Congress for 16 years, she represented a Massachusetts district that was home to the Army's food irradiation research facility in Natick, near Boston.

In July 1983, just four months after Heckler was sworn in, the FDA legalized irradiated spices and seasonings—the agency's first irradiation approval in 19 years. Again, the request did not come not from a food company, medical organization, or public health agency—this time it came from an irradiation company that used radioactive cobalt-60, Radiation Technology, Inc. (which soon became embroiled in the most notorious scandal in irradiation history).

Heckler then set about to do what the South African retailer suggested to the IAEA in 1982: "To put the public at ease, and develop a more friendly feeling to irradiation."

"Some education will be necessary," Heckler said, "but once the public realizes that ionizing energy is just another form of energy, completely safe, leaving no residues, I am confident there will be widespread agreement on the need for this important technology."[214]

Heckler's preferred method of educating the American people was to withhold information from them. In February 1984 the FDA proposed with splendid doublespeak to completely remove labeling requirements for irradiated foods: "The word 'radiation' may be confusing to consumers because it could convey an erroneous impression."[215]

Heckler felt it would be less erroneous to call irradiated foods "picowaved," which she formally proposed to the White House. The idea was so ludicrous that a top FDA official, Stanford Miller (one of Heckler's own people), said it flunked the "hee haw test. It's like going out in the sun and saying I'm going to be nanowaved.'"[216] (Heckler's deception is immortalized in Rutgers professor William Lutz's book *Doublespeak*, along with crashed Cruise missiles that "ceased to fly" and the U.S. "rescue mission" in Grenada.[217])

A private consultant hired by the DOE made the whole irradiation process sound like just another day in the warehouse. "All it takes to irradiate something is a half-horsepower motor to drive the conveyor belt, and fork lifts to bring things in and out."[218]

The DOE's Gilbert was soon back before Congress, laying out an elaborate plan to use enormous quantities of cesium-137 for food irradiation. More than 75 million curies of cesium-137—enough to fuel about 15 food irradiation facilities—was available at the Hanford bomb factory, and much more was in the pipeline. Reprocessing spent fuel rods from commercial nuclear power plants would free up an estimated 11 *billion* curies of cesium-137 through 2021, enough for about 2,000 facilities.[219] (This never took place, as President Bill Clinton reinstated Carter's reprocessing ban in 1993.)

In a replay of the Atomic Energy Commission's aborted plans of the 1950s and 1960s, the DOE wanted to irradiate citrus fruit, pork, apples, cherries, almonds, raisins, and shellfish, among many foods. (There was even talk of irradiating human sewage and feeding it to livestock.) And just as the AEC had planned, the DOE wanted to build irradiators all over the country—in Alaska, California, Florida, Hawaii, Iowa, Oklahoma, and Washington state.[220]

U.S. Sen. Tom Harkin (D-IA), a long-time cheerleader for industrialized agriculture, whose state produces one-fourth of the nation's pork, stumped for the DOE's irradiation program. Harkin told Congress that he once ate irradiated lunchmeat the Army zapped 10 years earlier: "I found it very pleasant and tasteful. And as you can see, I'm still in pretty good shape today—didn't hurt me a bit."[221]

Harkin also supported industry-backed legislation to reclassify food irradiation from an "additive" to a "process," which would have greatly streamlined the FDA's approval process.[222] In an indication of just how important food irradiation was to the nuclear waste industry, the bill was sponsored by Rep. Sid Morrison, whose Congressional district included Hanford, and Sen. Slade Gordon, who represented all of Washington state. The bill also would have encouraged the sale of cesium-137 waste to private irradiation companies. The legislation failed but the government didn't let up.

A year later, in 1985, the FDA legalized irradiated pork, much to Harkin's delight. This request also came from Radiation Technology. In 1986 the FDA followed through on its own plans to legalize irradiated fruit and vegetables.

The People React

However, the proponents of irradiation did not count on the David and Goliath scenario that played out as public opposition began to boil over. They couldn't conceptualize that the plans of the Department of Energy, the Food and Drug Administration, and the irradiation industry could be stymied by the combined efforts of an activist couple, and the hundreds of people that they mobilized.

Kitty Tucker was born an activist. She was moved by the tragic story of Karen Silkwood, an employee of a Kerr-McGee uranium and plutonium plant in Cimarron, Okalahoma, who was murdered on November 13, 1974, at the age of 28 while driving to meet a reporter from the *New York Times* to give him documentation about plutonium fuel rod tampering at the plant. As Legislative Coordinator of the National Organization for Women (NOW), and a student at Antioch Law School in Washington, DC, Kitty began investigating the circumstances of Karen Silkwood's death. She became instrumental in coordinating the research and investigation that allowed a case to eventually be brought against Kerr-McGee. Karen Silkwood's parents obtained a $1.38 million settlement in January 1985.

Meanwhile, hundreds of people filed objections to the FDA's rulings. Several consumer and environmental groups also entered the fray, including Dr. Sidney Wolfe of Public Citizen's Health Research Group, Kathleen Tucker of the Health and Energy Institute, Robert Alvarez of the Environmental Policy Institute, and Denis Mosgofian of the National Coalition to Stop Food Irradiation. The FDA rejected their requests for public hearings, arguing that their objections did not meet the agency's arcane standards, which make successful citizen challenges almost impossible. The opposition, however, did pressure the FDA into dropping its proposal to eliminate the labeling requirement.

The FDA faced more opposition in 1987, when federal legislation was proposed to drastically restrict food irradiation. The bill sought to revoke the FDA's approval of irradiated fruit, vegetables, and pork; block approval of any additional irradiated foods; study the health and environmental hazards of irradiation; require labeling for irradiated foods served in restaurants and for irradiated ingredients; and require irradiation companies to report their activities to the government. Numerous influential members of Congress supported the bill, including Democratic Sen. George Mitchell of Maine, the soon-to-be majority leader. In a direct slap, Mitchell said, "I am not convinced that irradiation has been sufficiently proven safe by the FDA."[223]

The bill failed, but more trouble for irradiation advocates lay ahead.

Big Trouble

The DOE's first full-scale attempt at using cesium-137 for irradiation—which had been renamed the "Advanced Radiation Technology Program" to counter public outrage—ended in near catastrophe. In June 1988, a so-called "fail-proof" capsule of cesium originating from Hanford sprung a leak at an irradiation facility near Atlanta, in Decatur, Georgia.

Because the plant's owner, Radiation Sterilizers, Inc., had not been monitoring the facility properly, "extensive" radioactivity spread throughout the plant. The fact that cesium-137 can dissolve in water aggravated the situation. More than 70,000 boxes, reportedly to be used for contact lens solution and other consumer products, may have been contaminated and shipped into the marketplace. Ten employees were exposed—three of them to the point that they contaminated their homes and cars.

The resulting taxpayer-funded cleanup cost $47 million. Eventually it was revealed that the U.S. Nuclear Regulatory Commission suspected the cesium capsules were unsafe, but the agency allowed them to be used anyway. The accident has gone down in history as the "Three Mile Island of the irradiation industry."(See Chapter 10 for more on this fiasco.)[224,225,226,227]

The mishap put an immediate halt to the DOE's cesium-137 scheme; Congress cut funding for the program in 1989.[228] The accident, however, did not prevent the FDA from legalizing irradiated poultry in 1990, acting on yet another request from Radiation Technology (whose president, Martin Welt, by this time had been sentenced to federal prison for trying to cover up safety violations at his facility in Rockaway, New Jersey).

The next irradiation request, filed for beef in 1994 and approved in 1997, came from another company that used cobalt-60, Isomedix (which got into trouble for flushing radioactive water down the toilet into the public sewer system at its facility in Parsippany, New Jersey). (Chapters 9 and 10 discuss irradiation accidents in more detail.)

The Decatur accident also has not stopped the U.S. Department of Agriculture from providing financial and technical assistance to a New Jersey company called Gray*Star, which is attempting to design an irradiation machine that uses cesium-137. Thus far, the NRC has rejected Gray*Star's design because it is not "adequate to protect health and minimize danger to life and property."[229] Glenn Seaborg took an active interest in Gray*Star, whose founder, Martin Stein, worked for Seaborg on food irradiation projects at the AEC. Seaborg invested in the company and wrote a letter of support to then-DOE Secretary Hazel O'Leary in 1995,[230] to no avail.

The FDA's latest approval came in 2000, when the agency legalized irradiated eggs. The request came from Edward Josephson, who directed the Army's ill-fated food irradiation research program for more than a decade. He won FDA approval despite presenting no toxicological evidence that irradiated eggs are safe for human consumption.[231]

This blemish on the FDA's record is just one among many.

Public Citizen's *A Broken Record* also reported that in the course of legalizing irradiated fruit, vegetables, poultry, beef, and eggs from 1986 to 2000, the FDA relied on 79 research studies that the agency's own expert scientists had declared deficient. The FDA has also failed to study whether the dozens of toxic chemicals formed in irradiated foods could pose health risks, which the agency's 1980 panel strongly recommended.

And, officials of the FDA, U.S. Army, and other federal agencies have consistently misled Congress about the potential hazards of food irradiation. Based on these and many other flaws, Public Citizen requested an investigation by an independent panel comprised entirely of members who have not been involved with the FDA's food irradiation program.[232]

Over a period of 30 years, from the Army flop to the DOE failure, U.S. government agencies were consistently unable to demonstrate that food irradiation is a technology that can work. The collapse had much in common with the overly optimistic X-ray and uranium frenzies that played out with comical and at times disastrous results decades earlier.

Scientists and government officials thought they had stumbled upon a miracle. Based on preliminary observations—the fact that radioactivity can be fatal to living organisms—they theorized that radiation could be used safely and effectively to kill harmful bacteria in food and extend shelf life. Such speculation may have seemed reasonable at the outset, just as it seemed logical to some that X-rays aimed at the head could stop criminal behavior, that radium-laced water could cure diabetes, and that "uranium wine" could treat tuberculosis.

As the earlier discussion of the history makes clear, many Atomic Age fantasies were based not so much on finding solutions for well-defined problems, but finding perceived problems that scientists believed radiation could solve. As history demonstrates, many boosters of nuclear technology, blinded by faith, were willing to believe that atomic energy could solve virtually any problem.

Such has been the case with food irradiation. The work of the Atomic Energy Commission, the Joint Committee on Atomic Energy, and the Department of Energy had almost nothing to do with food safety. More than anything else, these agencies were searching for opportunities to demonstrate that radiation could make positive contributions to society—that Hiroshima and Nagasaki represented aberrations in what ostensibly was a noble pursuit of understanding the subatomic world. Despite one failure after another, the agencies remained in a delusional state, somehow convincing themselves that success was just around the bend.

The history of food irradiation is still unfolding. It will be years before society will learn whether this technology will lead to folly, like the nuclear-powered car, or, as was the case with the Radium Girls, tragedy.

Chapter 6

The Good, The Bad, And The Die-Hards: The Struggle Over Irradiation

As a teenager, Francesca de la Rosa walked the picket line with her mother, a Los Angeles school teacher whose union had gone on strike. Her father, a musician, and her grandfather, a railroad worker, were both active union members.

She attended Belmont High, a predominantly Latino school located in a low-income neighborhood near downtown L.A. Belmont is notoriously overcrowded and underachieving—half of its students' parents lack diplomas of their own.

"I couldn't help growing up politically conscious," de la Rosa says.

After studying political science and philosophy at Mount St. Mary's College close to home, de la Rosa planned to move out of L.A. to become a lawyer specializing in *pro bono* political and social work. Instead of leaving town, however, she took organizing positions with hotel and service employees unions. Then came an organizing job with Coalition LA, a multi-ethnic grassroots organization that advocates on housing, transportation, open space, and other neighborhood issues.

Gradually, it became clear to de la Rosa that she should stay put. "I had an intention to get away from L.A. But there is so much activism here, and there have been so many historic social justice campaigns fought here. There is too much work to be done."

Facing so many options, de la Rosa chose an area that she had never worked in before and knew very little about: food and nutrition. "I was taking a risk. I did not have a background in these issues," she says. "I grew up in L.A. I was lucky if I even *saw* anything green."

In 2001, de la Rosa joined the Center for Food and Justice at L.A.'s Occidental College, a liberal arts university known for its work on community political and social issues. "I honestly did not think that food and nutrition would resonate with people. Who is going to get excited about food?" she says. "But this has been one of the easiest things I have ever organized around. Within weeks people were jumping at it. You can't tell someone that they don't deserve good food."

This is especially true for children, which is why de la Rosa helped start the Healthy School Food Coalition.

Working with students, parents, teachers, and school administrators, de la Rosa persuaded the Los Angeles Unified School District (LAUSD) to ban soft drinks from the district's 700 campuses. Passed in August 2002, the ban became a model for school districts throughout the country.

The staff at Public Citizen heard about her successful organizing and contacted her about the possibility of banning irradiated meat in the school system. Public Citizen had been engaged in a long battle with the USDA over its policies regarding irradiated meat, and was organizing a national campaign to stop the agency from helping the industry commercialize irradiated hamburger by selling it to school children. This involved a massive outreach effort to get the word out to parents about the USDA scheme. One of the main goals of the campaign was helping parent groups to organize bans or restrictions for school purchases of irradiated meat.

With one victory behind her, de la Rosa was ready to take on the irradiation industry and the USDA.

In May 2003, the USDA lifted its ban on serving irradiated ground beef in its subsidized meal programs, including the National School Lunch Program. The program serves 27 million low-income children nationwide, including three-fourths of the 720,000 students within the LAUSD, the second-largest school district in the country. It's being called the largest food experiment in history, and one whose subjects are particularly vulnerable—poor children who already have problems getting proper nourishment.

The ban was lifted at the behest of U.S. Sen. Tom Harkin (D-Iowa), who, as we have seen, has close ties with large meat companies and other agribusinesses, and with the food irradiation industry. The move was seen as a bailout for irradiation companies that were having trouble getting consumers to buy their products in grocery stores, where, unlike schools, irradiated foods must be labeled. Having particular difficulty cracking the public market was Sure-Beam Corp., which ran a huge irradiation facility in Sioux City, in Harkin's home state. A spin-off of a major weapons contractor, SureBeam irradiated food with linear accelerators originally designed for the "Star Wars" missile defense program.

To battle the forces trying to put irradiated meats on school lunch menus, de la Rosa and Public Citizen organizer Tracy Lerman began putting together a campaign for Los Angeles. De la Rosa contacted LAUSD member Julie Kortenstein, who wrote a resolution to ban irradiated ground beef from the district's cafeterias. Like de la Rosa, Kortenstein has a long history of political and social activism, having worked on anti-nuclear and environmental-protection campaigns during the 1970s and 1980s. "Obviously, with irradiated foods, we're talking about radiation one way or another," says Kortenstein, who also co-sponsored the ban on soft drinks in the schools.

In short order, a huge grassroots movement of parents, teachers, and consumer and environmental groups united to support Kortenstein's resolution. It passed unanimously in September 2003. "The consequences of using our children as guinea pigs are very frightening to me," Kortenstein said at the time. "I believe we need to err on the side of caution."[233]

In October 2003, just one month after the irradiated foods ban was passed, Kortenstein led an effort to eradicate junk food and serve salads, vegetarian foods, soy milk, and other healthful items in schools. The measure is part of the "Farm to School" initiative that, ironically, is partially funded by the USDA, which simultaneously is pushing irradiated ground beef. Next, de la Rosa wants fast-food chains banned from L.A. campuses: "A lot of kids come from low-income communities littered with fast-food restaurants. School is the only place where they can get healthy food."[234]

And a "No!" from the North

Five hundred miles to the north, along the hilly, wave-brushed coastline of Mendocino County, a town of 400 known for its high-brow counter-culture is taking its own stand.

Point Arena is a proud community. Its century-old lighthouse, rebuilt after the Great 1906 Earthquake, attracts tens of thousands of people every year. Locals are trying to save the endangered mountain beaver, of which only several hundred are left in existence. It has a vibrant arts community with a bevy of painters, sculptors, jewelry makers, and other craftspeople.

It is also a community that thinks for itself. In 2000 Point Arena became the first U.S. city to declare that corporations should not enjoy the same legal rights as people, stating in hard-to-argue-against language that corporations "are not naturally endowed with consciousness."

The city has also come out against the Patriot Act, especially its provisions on searching library and bookstore records, and spying on religious and political organizations. And, the city has banned genetically modified foods.

The place even has its own poet laureate.

So when Bill Myers heard about irradiated school lunches, he knew what to do.

"I thought that feeding irradiated foods to kids was way over the top," says Myers, the School Board's president. "This was something that fit into a pattern in my life of caring about the environment and people's health."

The Point Arena School Board allowed ubiquitous food irradiation advocate Christine Bruhn to speak in support of the USDA's plan. A prolific marketing professor at the University of California-Davis and a household name in the food industry, Bruhn for years has spoken fervently in support of irradiated foods, appearing at dozens of industry and government conferences, and being quoted countless times in newspapers and magazines throughout the country.

Bruhn's specialty is persuading people to eat irradiated foods by withholding negative information about the products. Her marketing programs play up the "benefits" of irradiation while omitting or downplaying problems such as vitamin loss, ruined flavor and odor, and the formation of toxic chemicals. "Irradiated foods are safe and wholesome," Bruhn once wrote, continuing, "Irradiated food is nutritious and flavorful."[235]

Bruhn's appearance before the School Board fell flat. "The people who attended the meeting were overwhelmingly against the idea," says Myers.

In February 2003, Point Arena became the second U.S. city, after Berkeley, California, to reject irradiated foods.

"Banning irradiated food was an empowering thing for the community," says Myers. "It helped push forward the idea that we have the power locally to determine what kind of food is served here. We went against the policy of the entire federal government."

In addition to Los Angeles, Point Arena, and Berkeley, other California districts that have banned irradiated food are San Francisco, Ukiah, and Grant Elementary in Redding. Other U.S. cities that have passed bans include Washington, DC; Iowa City, Iowa; Shawnee Mission, Kansas; Farmington, Maine; and Morris, New York.

California State Assembly Member Loni Hancock (D-Berkeley) and Tracy Lerman initiated a statewide campaign on the issue, which included forming a coalition of consumer and teacher organizations. After a tremendous organizing effort, the California legislature passed legislation requiring school board approval, public disclosure, and parental notification before irradiated foods could be served in California schools. However, Republican Gov. Arnold Schwarzenegger, under the influence of the irradiation industry, vetoed the bill in September 2004. Evidently, California's governor does not believe that parents have a right to know that their children are eating irradiated food.

Several hundred schools in eight states—California, Illinois, Minnesota, Nebraska, Oklahoma, Tennessee, Texas and Washington—ordered irradiated ground beef for the School Lunch Program in 2004. But the orders weren't filled because the USDA couldn't find a company to produce the beef cheaply enough. Promises from the food industry that irradiated beef would cost just 13-20 cents more per pound than regular beef were grossly understated. The USDA received bids at 30-80 cents more per pound, which the agency rejected before it gave up trying to find a supplier.

Taking it to the Hill

Six months after the Point Arena ban went on the books, Public Citizen food irradiation campaign lobbyist Tony Corbo pushed the school lunch battle into the halls of Congress. As a result, Rep. Barbara Lee tossed the "Right to Know Child Nutrition Act" into the hopper. A Democrat whose district includes Oakland and Berkeley, Lee has championed numerous public health issues, including HIV/AIDS, comprehensive health care coverage, drug abuse, mental health and adolescent pregnancy.

When she heard that irradiated ground beef was headed for the National School Lunch Program, Lee, a member of the Congressional Food Safety Caucus, stepped forward. "The school lunch program was begun to ensure the good health of our students," she said. "Now, this program could possibly sacrifice our students' health and nutrition. That's a dangerous policy."[236]

Lee's legislation did not go as far as the bans in Los Angeles and Point Arena, but it would have required irradiated foods to be labeled and school boards to offer non-irradiated alternatives. It also would have made irradiated foods available only to states and school districts that specifically requested them. Detractors, including food industry executives and their Capitol Hill lobbyists, wondered why irradiated meat—which is perfectly legal to produce and sell—would have to be labeled at all.

Tony Corbo's advocacy in Congress eventually paid off. Legislation based on Lee's proposal, and sponsored by fellow California Democratic Reps. George Miller and Lynn Woolsey, eventually was passed by Congress and signed into law by President Bush in June 2004. Opposition by Republicans and food industry lobbyists watered down the bill somewhat, but the key provisions remained intact.

But how did irradiated meat make its way into the National School Lunch Program in the first place? As is often the case in Washington, a small, closed circle of powerful people and organizations was responsible for dramatically altering public policy.

Under pressure from the American School Food Service Association and major meat industry groups including the American Meat Institute, the USDA in March 2001 tried to reverse a policy requiring all ground beef served as part of the school lunch program to be tested for *Salmonella*. Instead, the USDA wanted to allow students to eat irradiated ground beef, which theoretically would be free of the bacteria that sickens 1.4 million and kills 600 people in the U.S. each year.

The Clinton administration ordered the *Salmonella* testing for the school lunch program the previous summer, in response to a federal court ruling forbidding the USDA from shutting down meat plants with *Salmonella* problems. (Fittingly, the ruling benefited Supreme Beef of Dallas, then a major supplier of beef to the school lunch program.)

Clinton's new *Salmonella* tests were aggressively opposed by the meat industry, which favors vaguely written, "science-based" policies that emphasize sticking to a company-written plan for containing hygiene problems, instead of government inspectors performing bacteria tests and other oversight.

The meat industry waited until Clinton left office to plan its response. Within weeks after President Bush was sworn in, the industry persuaded newly installed Agriculture Secretary Ann Veneman to stop the *Salmonella* tests, arguing that they were too expensive and caused schoolchildren to eat less meat.

This latter effect was not necessarily a bad thing. In the first year of testing alone, five million pounds of potentially *Salmonella*-contaminated meat was culled from the USDA's school lunch supply—nearly five percent of the total 111 million pounds.

Senator Richard Durbin, an Illinois Democrat, was one of several members of Congress to accuse the Bush administration of weakening health and environmental policies. "First, it's arsenic in water. Now it's *Salmonella* in school lunches. Where will this end?"

Representative Rosa DeLauro, a Democrat from Connecticut, offered a personal story. "When I was two years old, I got *Salmonella* poisoning and ended up in isolation for two weeks. For two weeks I couldn't even see my parents. No parent should have to face that. Yet the [Bush] administration chose to roll back food safety protections for children."

A red-faced Veneman withdrew the proposal just several hours after it became public, meekly stating it was "released prior to receiving appropriate review."[237,238,239,240]

Stymied in the executive branch, the meat industry took its case to Congress. In February 2002, less than a year after the Veneman debacle, Harkin proposed overturning the USDA's ban on irradiated ground beef for school lunches. Harkin also wanted to allow irradiated foods to be called "pasteurized." This would eliminate a major barrier to marketing the products, which must be labeled "Treated by Irradiation" and are thus avoided by most consumers.

Harkin's proposals literally came at the last minute, on the final day of debate on the 2002 Farm Bill. At such a late stage in the game, the proposals were almost certain to be approved. They were.

Harkin was seen as carrying water for SureBeam. Harkin, in fact, attended the opening ceremony of the facility two years earlier. The company that founded SureBeam, Titan Corp., gave Harkin $5,000 the same month the Farm Bill was passed.[241] A year earlier, Titan CEO Gene Ray gave Harkin $1,000 as a campaign contribution.[242]

As the top-ranking Democrat on the Senate Agriculture Committee, Harkin wields enormous power on Capitol Hill. Though generally considered pro-consumer on many issues, Harking is cozy with the industrialized agriculture and food processing industry.

For his proposal to serve irradiated ground beef to schoolchildren, Harkin had some powerful allies within the Bush administration who helped ensure his idea would take hold.

Mention the Muranos to anyone in the food safety world—whether in industry, academia, or government—and they'll know exactly who you're talking about. Elsa and Peter Murano have built much of their careers teaching, researching, and promoting food irradiation. Elsa oversaw, and Peter worked on, the food irradiation research program at Iowa State University (in Harkin's home state) with Dennis Olson, a food safety expert who went on to become a vice president at SureBeam.

In 1995 the Muranos landed new jobs at Texas A&M University, where Elsa eventually developed a relationship with SureBeam—and where a deep pattern of cronyism began to take shape. In 2000 she helped broker a deal that delivered two SureBeam irradiation machines worth $10 million to the school.[243]

Around this same time, Texas A&M issued a press release in which Elsa Murano highly praised food irradiation—though not without using some of the irradiation movement's most misleading language. She used the well-worn and deceptive comparison of radiation to microwaves. She said foods can be irradiated "without affecting the way they look, taste or smell," which contradicts 50 years' worth of research. And, employing a morsel of spin often used by the industry, she said irradiation "has a negative connotation to some people who don't know what it means."[244]

This press release was issued May 16, 2000, the very same day that Sure-Beam's irradiated hamburgers debuted in the Twin Cities.

The Muranos were on their way. One year later, in July 2001, President George W. Bush nominated Elsa to be the USDA's under-secretary for Food Safety, which gave her a bully pulpit for numerous food safety issues. She used her position numerous times to promote irradiation. That December, Peter became a deputy administrator of the USDA's Food and Nutrition Service, which runs the National School Lunch Program. The Muranos were in influential positions to promote food irradiation within the USDA and to the American people.

A Public Citizen report, *The Plan of Ten Thousand Mistakes: Minnesota's Misguided Food Irradiation 'Education' Program*, details numerous questionable relationships and conflicts of interests in a series of events that soon followed. Even before Harkin's proposal was signed into law, the American School Food Service Association wrote to Peter Murano and asked him to launch an "educational" program to spread information about irradiated ground beef to school districts throughout the country. Murano quickly agreed.[245]

More cronyism appeared. The association's top lawyer, Marshall Matz, at the time was also lobbying the FDA, USDA, and members of Congress on behalf of SureBeam.[246] Matz also lobbies for the National Meat Association, the National Food Processors Association, and the United Fresh Fruit & Vegetable Association—powerful industry groups that strongly support irradiation.

The plot thickened. Peter Murano's program was rolled out in Minnesota, apparently because of the state's central role in promoting irradiated foods. The first test-marketing of irradiated beef took place in the Twin Cities two years earlier. The company that produced the beef, Huisken Meats, is based in Minnesota. And, two of the country's most prolific food irradiation advocates live there: Ron Eustice, the globetrotting head of the Minnesota Beef Council, and Dr. Michael Osterholm, formerly the state's chief epidemiologist.

Murano's program was a failure. First off, the people running the program were hardly non-biased, raising questions about whether the initiative was truly "educational." The cronyism ran thick. The program's organizers included none other than SureBeam; Eustice's Minnesota Beef Council, which received financial support from SureBeam; and International Dairy Queen, which at the time was serving SureBeam-irradiated hamburgers in dozens of its restaurants. The program was actively promoted by Osterholm, who now runs a research center at the University of Minnesota that has received funding from SureBeam.[247]

For reasons that remain unclear, the three Minnesota school districts that the program initially targeted were Spring Lake Park, in the Twin Cities area; Sauk Rapids, near St. Cloud; and Willmar, a rural district in the central part of the state. Whatever Peter Murano was thinking by choosing these three districts, he thought wrong.

After parents became upset about the prospect of their children eating irradiated meat and a subsequent assessment of the USDA's "educational" materials, officials at all three Minnesota districts refused to serve irradiated ground beef to their students. Sauk Rapids Superintendent Greg Vandal said he felt pressured into buying the USDA's irradiated ground beef, when all he thought he was doing was reviewing the agency's materials: "We realized we were stepping further into this than what we agreed to," Vandal said.[248] Despite all the resources at the USDA's disposal, and despite the support of some of the most powerful food irradiation advocates in the country, the Minnesota experiment was a flop.

Having underachieved at the USDA, Elsa and Peter Murano left the agency in December 2004 and moved back to Texas. Elsa became a vice chancellor and dean of the agriculture program at Texas A&M, and Peter resumed his teaching. Not long after quitting the USDA, Elsa Murano was back in DC lamenting the sluggishness of the food irradiation industry.[249]

Enter Ron Eustice

The Minnesota defeat was also bitter for Ron Eustice of the Minnesota Beef Council. Born of hardy stock, Eustice has always been an achiever.

Eustice was raised on a cattle, pig, and sheep farm in Steele County, a sparsely populated area in southern Minnesota near the Iowa border. His father's side of the family fled the Irish potato famine and arrived in 1869. Life in Steele County was not for the faint of heart. The country was smoldering from the Civil War and stained with blood from battles with the Santee Sioux. Planting season is often tormented by tornadoes, pests, and violent storms.

Eustice worked the land with his parents, and three brothers and sisters. "I'm pleased to say that my roots are in agriculture." His family still owns 200 acres of ranchland.

But Eustice left family farming behind and threw his lot in with big agribusiness. He studied agricultural journalism and international relations in college. He's been on the road ever since. Eustice has traveled to more than 80 countries, drumming up business for major agricultural corporations including American Breeders Service of Wisconsin, the largest supplier of bull semen in the world.

Eustice is a proud man. Proud of the fact that he's fluent in Spanish, Indonesian, and German. Proud of the fact that he's head of the Minnesota Beef Council. And especially proud of the fact that his name has become virtually synonymous with food irradiation.

In the fall of 1997, Hudson Foods of Arkansas, supplier to Burger King and Boston Market, had just recalled 25 million pounds of ground beef because of possible *E. coli O157:H7* contamination. Sixteen people were sickened in what remains the largest ground beef recall in U.S. history. Eustice got a call from Michael Osterholm, then chief epidemiologist at the Minnesota Department of Health.

Osterholm suggested starting a campaign to promote irradiation, particularly as a way to eradicate bacteria in meat. For years, Osterholm had been on a mission to push irradiation and dispense with any opposition. Around the time he called Eustice, Osterholm testified to Congress: "We cannot let the junk science so often voiced by those opposed to irradiation stand unchallenged any longer."[250]

Osterholm became a media superstar in 1994, when he helped trace a *Salmonella* outbreak that sickened tens of thousands of people to contaminated ice cream sold by home-delivery service Schwan's. "Bad News Mike" has also made headlines working on toxic shock syndrome, dirty beef from cattle necks, Legionnaire's Disease, poisonous nutritional supplements, and diarrhea-stricken Minnesota Vikings.

He is not much interested in the health effects of the chemicals or technologies used by industrialized agriculture. But, once a victim of bacterial infection himself, the man does not like things on the other end of his microscope. He's had a sign up in his office, "The Bug Stops Here." Osterholm also doesn't think too highly of people who disagree with him on food irradiation. "Anyone who opposes this from a scientific standpoint is a nut."[251] But even he confesses that humans can't always control their own creations. "Technology at its finest improves the quality of life, but sometimes there is a price."[252]

Osterholm wanted to make food irradiation his latest triumph, and Eustice agreed to help. They obtained 1,500 samples of frozen, irradiated ground beef from their friend Dennis Olson, who ran a linear accelerator at Iowa State University (before becoming a vice president at SureBeam). As he'd done for many years selling bull semen, Eustice hit the road to sell irradiated ground beef—"one toothpick at a time," as he likes to say. Conveniently, the U.S. Food and Drug Administration legalized the irradiation of beef that December.

The following February, Eustice handed out bite-sized beef samples on toothpicks at the Minnesota Restaurant Association's trade show, and he hasn't stopped since. Eustice has gotten a lot of financial and other help from his friends, such as SureBeam and several companies that at the time sold irradiated ground beef, including multinational food producer Cargill, fast-food giant Dairy Queen, and national home-delivery service Schwan's. Taxpayers have also supported Eustice, in the form of assistance from Minnesota's Department of Agriculture and Department of Health.

Eustice travels almost non-stop throughout the U.S., speaking at food safety conferences in front of government regulators, academics, and food industry executives. He shows a well-rehearsed PowerPoint presentation that explains everything from how radiation splits the DNA of bacteria, to how Americans are already buying products that have been irradiated, such as pet treats, cosmetics, and computer chips.

Limping on a broken foot wrapped in a cast and wearing a Birkenstock on the other, Eustice brought his message to the Illinois Food Safety Symposium in Peoria in September 2004. "I hope that irradiation will become the fourth pillar of public health, with pasteurization, immunization and chlorination," delivering an oft-repeated line to an audience of about 500.

Not all of what Eustice told the crowd is entirely true. He said sales of irradiated ground beef are "holding steady or growing," despite the fact that the country's largest meat irradiator, SureBeam, has gone out of business. He said irradiation doesn't reduce the nutritional value, change the flavor, or alter the chemical composition of food, despite irrefutable evidence that it does. And he said irradiation will not result in "filthy" food reaching the market, despite the fact that the very purpose of irradiation is to kill *E. coli*, *Salmonella*, and other bacteria that are the product of unhygienic feeding, slaughtering, and processing practices. Eustice cryptically dismissed these and other concerns of irradiation skeptics as "blue smoke."

Eustice also told the crowd that he's been responsible for distributing more than one million samples—thousands of pounds—of irradiated ground beef. His oddball campaign has attracted some curious people.

Hosted by a wisecracking TV newscaster, the Fido Fashion Show featured Trudy the Labrador dressed as Snow White, and Tala the collie done up as Superman. You could buy red hats with purple feathers, perfect for women over 50 who want to join the Red Hat Society. You could buy Wonder Brooms, Bath Ice Cream, and Magic Dryer Balls.

And, just around the corner from the Spam Mobile, you could get a free sample of irradiated ground beef, cooked on a George Foreman grill and served on a toothpick.

Welcome to the Southern Women's Show, held in Charlotte, North Carolina, in September 2004. "You'll feel like a new woman!" organizers of the annual event promised. "It's no wonder women love this show!"

Dressed in red and black overalls, the four women running the booth were members of the American National CattleWomen, foot soldiers in Ron Eustice's campaign to get irradiated food into the mouths of as many people as possible. His favorite venues are women's shows, women's expos, and home fairs. The Charlotte show was a perfect outlet, held in two enormous convention halls and attended by thousands of women who drove in from all over the South to get the latest beauty tips, fashion ideas, and, of course, food and beverage breakthroughs.

The irradiated ground beef was up against some stiff competition, including low-carb frozen yogurt, sweet potato casserole, and a tangy concoction of black-eyed peas and onions called redneck caviar. Still, the CattleWomen managed to attract a steady flow of takers. They sliced up 696 hamburgers and actually ran out of the 4,500 toothpicks they arrived with, so they had to buy 750 more and borrow yet more from a neighboring booth.[253]

"Would you like a sample?" CattleWoman Jean Barton asked a passerby who already had something to nibble on. "It'll go good with your apple!"

Some took Barton up on her offer. "Tastes pretty good," said one man, smiling. Others didn't. "It won't kill you, will it?" asked a woman, grimacing. "No thanks."

Barton is a fourth-generation rancher who raises about 200 head of cattle on her family's 1,600-acre spread in Red Bluff, California, not too far from Mount Shasta in a scenic, historic area known as Tehama Country—"Where Mother Nature and Father Time are Still an Item." She said she came all the way from California "on her own nickel to educate the public about irradiated ground beef." Three other CattleWomen came in from Arizona and Nebraska.

Like Eustice, however, Barton did a little bit more than educate. Part of her rap was one of the irradiation industry's favorite lines, however factually challenged it may be, that irradiation "does not change the flavor, texture, or nutritional value." She even told one passerby that "the government irradiates all of our spices," a wild notion, considering that only about 10 percent of spices sold in the U.S. are irradiated and that the government does none of it.

Barton said she'd been to four women's shows in the previous year. All told, CattleWomen have handed out irradiated beef samples at some 50 shows in more than 15 states. The initiative is funded by what's known as the "Beef Checkoff," a one-dollar fee charged on every head of cattle sold in the U.S. that pays for beef promotion and research projects. The Checkoff program, which the USDA oversees, is controversial, in part because it funds "education" efforts that, in actuality, might not be in the best interest of American consumers, or even family-owned cattle ranches.

The CattleWomen are the soft, friendly face of the heavily male-dominated beef industry, which is anything but soft and friendly. Among its many anti-consumer efforts, the corporate beef industry is trying to weaken inspection of slaughterhouses and processing plants, keep consumers in the dark about where their meat comes from, and block increased testing for mad cow disease. Meanwhile, the CattleWomen hold contests for the best beef recipe ("Grilled Steaks Balsamico" is the latest winner), sell children's books (such as *Cowboys, Kids & Critters*), and select teenage girls to become beef spokeswomen at beauty contest-style events ("Skirt length must be to the knee").

Ron Eustice is a member of a small yet well-organized clique of food irradiation advocates who have devoted all or part of their careers to the movement. Along with developing government connections, consulting with private industry, and speaking at conferences, they also do low-level tasks like writing letters to the editor and calling radio talk shows.

Some in the clique, like Dennis Olson, who left Iowa State University to join SureBeam, have cashed in on their expertise by moving from the public sector to the corporate world (though Olson has yet to resurface since SureBeam went under).

Others have gone through the revolving door. Michael Osterholm left the Minnesota Department of Health to start his own consulting firm, which went bust after two years. Curiously, Osterholm hired as his chief financial officer Mark Payne, a peripatetic corporate operative who has alternately sold Internet products, business advice, snowmobiles, reclining chairs, and barbecue sandwiches. Payne quit as president of Famous Dave's restaurants after reporting a seven-digit loss one quarter, cutting expansion plans.[254,255,256] His snowmobile company went bankrupt one year after it went public.[257] And his home-shopping network was sued for abandoning a $150 million deal to buy an infomercial company.[258]

Osterholm is back with the government, running a research center at the University of Minnesota that SureBeam briefly funded. Payne is back on TV, selling jewelry, watches, and beauty products.[259]

Still other members of the club work for public agencies but have not stopped themselves from becoming strident irradiation supporters.

Enter Christine Bruhn

You need a special stapler to bind Christine Bruhn's *curriculum vitae*, it's so thick. Some of the many food safety and marketing issues she's written, taught, and consulted on seem harmless enough, like the vitamin content of yogurt and the quality of stone fruit. Others aren't so benign, such as plotting ways to get consumers to buy genetically modified foods and vouching for the safety of agricultural pesticides. And she's been hostile toward organic food. "It's a market philosophy that's built on a house of cards," she said recently.[260]

Bruhn runs the Center for Consumer Research at the University of California-Davis, one of the leading agricultural universities in the country, and the recipient of millions of dollars in grants and other forms of funding from the food industry and the government. She's often the first person reporters call when they need to talk to somebody on the "pro" side.

Though she frequently speaks about the safety of irradiated foods and presents herself as a food science expert, Bruhn is not a scientist. She holds bachelor's and master's degrees in home economics, and a Ph.D. in consumer behavior. Bruhn is a marketing expert, and she has built a career on finding ways to persuade people to buy and eat irradiated foods despite the evidence that they are unhealthful. Among many pro-irradiation organizations she has worked for are the California Cattlemen's Association, the American Meat Industry, and the International Atomic Energy Agency, the world's leading irradiation advocate over the past 50 years.

Bruhn hit the big-time in 2001, when she received a $598,000 grant from the USDA for a "Consumer Food Safety and Food Irradiation Education Program." The program is being run in nine states, including irradiation hot-spots Florida, Minnesota, and Texas. Just as Peter Murano's "education" program in Minnesota did very little instruction, Bruhn's program is actually an advertising campaign designed to promote irradiated foods.

Bruhn states this plainly in "Objective 1" of her program, which is "increasing consumer acceptance of foods processed by irradiation." Among other tactics, Bruhn paid "volunteers" from community groups such as Rotary, Kiwanis, League of Women Voters, and Parent Teacher Organizations to watch pro-irradiation videos.

She's not just trying to expand knowledge but also sales: "More participants are expected to be interested in purchasing irradiated meat after viewing the videotape." This, she hopes, will put irradiated foods on the shelf: "If consumer response is shown to be positive, processors and supermarkets may be more likely to offer irradiated products."[261]

As a marketing expert, Bruhn is adept at gearing her message to achieve the desired response. She has expressed concern about a recent study in which 50 people were shown "positive" and "negative" information about irradiated foods. The negative information included statements that irradiation produces carcinogenic chemicals, destroys essential vitamins, eliminates the warning signs of botulism, and puts workers and nearby communities at risk due to radioactive materials—all true statements. Of the 50 people surveyed, only one preferred irradiated over non-irradiated foods.[262]

Bruhn's solution to this problem is simply to withhold negative information from consumers. In one study, for example, showing a video containing positive information about irradiation increased people's willingness to buy irradiated foods from about half to 90 percent.[263]

Sometimes, withholding all information from consumers is the best route. One of Bruhn's collaborators said telling people that meat is irradiated was a "relatively trivial matter." Bruhn is also fond of referring to irradiation as "cold pasteurized" and "electronically pasteurized," misleading euphemisms that public opinion polls indicate are deceptive, but which she says will lead to "easier consumer understanding."[264] And she's developed a disdain for irradiation critics: "I think they're using scare tactics, McCarthyism," she once said.[265]

Bruhn has predicted for years that people would jump at the chance to buy irradiated foods if they showed up on the shelf. "Marketing studies," she wrote, "clearly demonstrate that many consumers prefer irradiated food and will select it over non-irradiated when given the opportunity."[266]

Try telling that to the SureBeam Corp.

From Star Wars to SureBeam

During the 1960s and 1970s, as the Cold War raged on, a young physicist named Gene Ray worked for the U.S. Defense Department and private defense contractors, studying better ways to build and launch nuclear weapons. From humble beginnings in a four-room farmhouse in Murray, Kentucky, Ray soared to improbable heights. One night in April 1981—so the story goes—Ray and a former colleague were having dinner at La Bergerie, a palatial French restaurant in the Old Town section of Alexandria, Virginia.

Ronald Reagan, known somewhat derogatorily as "ray-gun" for his strong support of the military, had just been sworn in as president. Ray thought this was "arguably the best time ever to start a defense company." At dinner that night, Ray and his friend sketched out their plan on a napkin. Thus was born Titan Corp.

Ray quickly won contracts to work on Reagan's Strategic Defense Initiative, better known as "Star Wars." His first job was to study new ways to deploy the Minuteman and MX nuclear missiles. The company worked on several communications and intelligence projects. Eventually, Titan developed linear accelerators to study the effects of nuclear weapons."[267,268,269]

Things were rosy for Ray and Titan until the Cold War ended in 1991. "I think there's a real fear [among investors] that peace may break out," one analyst famously groused. Having lost hundreds of millions of dollars in weapons-related business, Ray needed to bring in money in other ways. He had heard that linear accelerators could be used to irradiate food. After all, radar systems developed during World War II provided the inspiration for microwave ovens. Why couldn't Ray cash in on his defense work, too? Especially since he was well connected politically, and could use his network to promote irradiation.

On Oct. 25, 1999, SureBeam opened a food irradiation facility in Sioux City, Iowa, with a scaled-down version of its Star Wars linear accelerator. U.S. Sen. Tom Harkin and Rep. Tom Latham, both from Iowa, attended the grand opening and tasted irradiated ground beef and chicken.[270] The meat had been blasted with electrons traveling near the speed of light—or "e-beams."

The grand opening was also attended by renowned food irradiation researcher Dennis Olson of Iowa State University, where he ran linear accelerators. "The SureBeam technology," Olson said that day, "will revolutionize the way we safeguard our food supply."[271] Nine months later, in July 2000, Olson was off the public payroll—taxpayers paid for his training—and was on SureBeam's payroll, as vice president of research. Olson has always been bullish on irradiation. He proclaimed several years earlier, "Every test market that's been done has sold irradiated product with success."[272]

By this time, SureBeam had made history by becoming the first company to test-market irradiated ground beef in U.S. grocery stores. In May 2000, family-owned beef producer Huisken Meats of Chandler, Minnesota, began selling frozen, SureBeam-irradiated hamburgers in 84 stores in the Twin Cities area. The event made national news, from *USA Today* on down. Public Citizen and local groups in Minnesota organized protests and garnered some of the attention.

Within two years, SureBeam-irradiated hamburger patties were reportedly on the shelves in some 5,000 grocery stores in about 40 states in all regions of the U.S. Many prominent chains picked up Huisken hamburgers, including Albertson's, Giant, Kroger, Pathmark, Price Chopper, Safeway, Stop & Shop, and Winn-Dixie.

SureBeam had a well-oiled public relations strategy, which successfully hyped its progress. As a result, it also signed up several major food producers, either wanting to sell irradiated products or wanting to experiment with the process, including Cargill, Del Monte, IBP, Kraft, Omaha Steaks, SYSCO, Tyson, and United Food Group. Omaha Steaks, an upscale mail-order company, eventually began selling SureBeam-irradiated hamburgers exclusively, as did home-delivery service Schwan's. Dairy Queen began serving irradiated hamburgers in several dozen restaurants in the Midwest, Northeast, and Southwest.

There seemed to be nothing SureBeam couldn't kill. The company suggested that its linear accelerators could decontaminate biological and chemical weapons, including nerve gas.[273] On the lighter side, an Australian company asked whether e-beams could be used to stop wool from growing where the sheep's defecation was sticking and causing infection. SureBeam never did the work, which the company nicknamed "ROBOS"—Radiation of the Butts of Sheep."[274]

SureBeam was riding high. It signed up more grocery stores and food producers, its stock price was on the rise, it was receiving flattering media coverage all over the country, it received numerous industry awards for its innovation, and it persuaded former San Diego Mayor Susan Golding to join its board of directors. It sold several e-beam machines to medical supply manufacturers and landed its own contracts to irradiate medical equipment. On March 16, 2001, SureBeam joined the NASDAQ stock exchange, which displayed the company's blue-and-yellow logo on its marquee.

SureBeam also scored a major victory in Congress. In June 2001, Rep. Marcy Kaptur, a Democrat from Toledo, proposed spending $500,000 for additional research into the safety and wholesomeness of irradiated foods, which could have proved damaging not only to SureBeam but to the entire irradiation industry. Enter Rep. Randy "Duke" Cunningham, a hawkish Republican from San Diego (where SureBeam is headquartered) and a former Navy pilot whose escapades were depicted in the movie *Top Gun*.

Cunningham thinks highly of Ray: "Through his initiative, Titan has been able to do wonders. Our personal security is enhanced through his vision."[275] Ray has enhanced the security of Cunningham's campaign war chest over the years, donating $7,000 from 1999 to 2004.[276]

What did Cunningham do for his friend? He killed the research funding.

Public Citizen lobbyist Tony Corbo witnessed a scene straight out of *The West Wing*. Moments after the funding was eliminated at a hearing on Capitol Hill, a Titan lobbyist walked up to Cunningham, handed him a note with Ray's private phone number and said, "Do you want to give Gene the good news?"[277]

SureBeam even found a way to cash in on the 2001 anthrax scare. After anthrax spores were found in letters mailed to U.S. Sens. Pat Leahy and Tom Daschle around the time of the September 11 attacks, the U.S. Postal Service bought eight linear accelerators from SureBeam in a no-bid contract for $26 million. Sen. Harkin went to SureBeam's Sioux City plant and sniffed a piece of freshly irradiated mail; the picture became the stuff of legend around the Beltway. Titan went so far as to start an "Office of Homeland Security."

From here, however, it was all downhill for SureBeam. It turned out that the linear accelerators the Postal Service bought weren't strong enough to irradiate mail. The Postal Service donated the machines to Idaho State University and several governmental agencies, including two nuclear research centers and the Army's Picatinny weapons-production facility in New Jersey.[278,279]

Around the same time, the FDA conducted a series of focus groups in which participants were asked whether irradiated foods should be labeled "electronically pasteurized" or "cold pasteurized." SureBeam and other irradiation companies, as well as Sen. Harkin, want this changed because they think "Treated by Irradiation" deters would-be buyers. Public Citizen and the Center for Food Safety, a consumer protection group, had a dialogue with the

FDA about how the focus groups would be conducted and were eventually allowed to view them.

The results of the focus groups weren't pretty. Participants unanimously opposed the idea. "That's deceitful," said one participant. "They're pulling the wool over your eyes," said another. "I think it's nasty, trying to mask this," said another. The outcome of the research supported the findings of an FDA poll in which 98.2 percent of respondents said they wanted federal labeling regulations that require the use of the term "irradiation."

Also in 2001, Public Citizen and the Center for Food Safety filed false advertising complaints against SureBeam with the Federal Trade Commission and U.S. Securities and Exchange Commission (SEC) for calling irradiation "electronic pasteurization" in advertisements and in press releases.

In apparent retaliation, staffers of Public Citizen became the target of a smear campaign. In an article about the stormy relationship between consumer advocates and SureBeam, *Forbes* wrote an article on irradiation because it had received a "stack of investigative reports on individual staff members of Public Citizen that was sent anonymously and included alleged personal dirt and tales of supposed ethical conflicts, such as owning an organic farm and advocating against irradiation."[280] The source of the materials could not be determined.

Also that year, the Illinois Food Safety Coalition forced state environmental officials to require SureBeam to obtain an air pollution permit for its new irradiation facility in the Chicago suburb of Glendale Heights because of its ozone emissions. "The way SureBeam tried to ignore the law—or perhaps even failed to find out what the law is—illustrates the need to closely monitor this company's activities," said coalition Director Paul Fehribach.[281] SureBeam publicly stated—just a few weeks after the 9/11 attacks—that the group was trying to "terrorize" citizens,[282] a characterization that would soon lead to a gruesome irony.

As sales of SureBeam's irradiated hamburgers began to stagnate, and some grocery stores pulled the products because of poor sales, the company suffered staggering losses. "There has been absolutely no consumer acceptance," said a spokesperson for Pick 'n Save in Milwaukee.[283] SureBeam lost $74.4 million in 2001 and $35.1 million in 2002.[284]

Reports of fuzzy math then began to surface. In April 2002, *Forbes* reported that SureBeam was crediting revenues even before sending out invoices: "SureBeam needs a little disinfectant on its balance sheet."[285]

Many SureBeam higher-ups didn't seem to be hurt by the financial troubles. From 2001 to 2003, 11 executives and other parties collected $27 million in profits via insider trading. Seven pocketed more than $1 million apiece. Dennis Olson, the former Iowa State researcher, collected $964,000.[286] Though perfectly legal, the profits raised eyebrows on Wall Street and, along with accounting irregularities that drew an SEC investigation, became grist for numerous class-action lawsuits filed by irate investors.

Olson's pledge that SureBeam would "revolutionize" the food industry failed to come true. In October 2003, SureBeam was kicked off the NASDAQ stock exchange. On January 12, 2004, SureBeam filed for Chapter 7 bankrupt-

cy. Some 3,600 shareholders lost all of their equity in the company.[287] Once
a true believer in the company, Olson finally confessed after SureBeam went
under that it never had a chance to succeed: "We needed to grow 300 to 400
percent to cover the overhead," he said, adding that there is "no momentum at
all" in the irradiation business.[288]

Meanwhile, SureBeam's parent company, Titan, has suffered its own trials. Five months after SureBeam went bust, defense contractor giant Lockheed
Martin called off its proposed buyout of Titan because of a federal government
investigation into millions of dollars in alleged bribes by Titan to government
officials in Africa, Asia, and the Middle East, where the company was aggressively competing for business. Titan pleaded guilty to federal bribery charges
in March 2005 for funneling money to the president of Benin, in West Africa,
and paid a $28.5 million fine.[289]

At the same time, translators hired by Titan to work in the Abu Ghraib
prison in Iraq were accused of torturing Iraqi detainees. One Titan employee
allegedly held down three Iraqi prisoners who were "nude, handcuffed to each
other and placed in sexual positions."[290]

Misleading Irradiation "Endorsements"

Private companies are not alone in pushing irradiated foods into the marketplace and onto the plates of consumers. Many governmental, quasi-govern-
mental, and ostensibly non-biased agencies and organizations have issued endorsements. The food industry is quick to roll out these statements to support
its case that irradiated foods are safe to eat, but these endorsements crumble
upon close inspection. For example:

- The U.S. Department of Agriculture (USDA) is not statutorily empowered to assess the safety of irradiated foods.

- The International Atomic Energy Agency (IAEA) is not a health, food
  safety, or agriculture organization, but rather has a mission to "accelerate and enlarge the contribution of atomic energy."[291]

- The World Health Organization (WHO) handed to the IAEA the "primary responsibility" to research and develop nuclear technologies, and
  promised to consult with the IAEA when working on overlapping projects, thus compromising its independence and credibility.[292]

- The American Medical Association (AMA) endorsed food irradiation
  at a meeting in 1984. The endorsement was not a regular item on the
  meeting agenda, however, and was approved without any discussion.
  Further, an internal AMA memo reveals "unresolved" questions on the
  issue, including whether there are any "potential long-term effects on
  humans;" whether irradiated foods "create any adverse offspring effects
  to animals;" and whether irradiation "will initiate radiation-resistant
  strains of bacteria and viruses."[293]

- The American Dietetic Association endorsed food irradiation in 2000. It did so, however, based on the false statement that "it is difficult to design a test to determine whether a food has been irradiated."[294] In truth, there is an internationally recognized test that can detect chemicals formed in irradiated foods called 2-ACBs, which do not occur naturally in any foods.[295]

- The Mayo Clinic, which the food industry often contends has endorsed food irradiation, in reality has not. The Clinic told New Jersey State Assembly Member John Kelly in 2000: "The Mayo Clinic does not endorse processes or products, and has not made any institutional endorsement of food irradiation."[296] Kelly, a Republican from Essex, and aide Michael Perrone led a successful effort to ban irradiated food in New Jersey from 1989 to 1991.

- NASA, which the food industry often says feeds irradiated foods to Space Shuttle crewmembers, told Kelly that irradiated steak and turkey make up only two percent of astronauts' diets. Further, NASA said that crewmembers are not required to eat irradiated foods: "It is strictly optional."[297]

Among the food industry organizations that trumpet these purported endorsements are the Food Products Association, Grocery Manufacturers Association, National Cattlemen's Beef Association, American Meat Institute, and the Food Marketing Institute.

This tactic, of course, is just the beginning of how these and other industry organizations attempt to shape public opinion and public policy. And no organization does this better than the Food Products Association (FPA).

The Powerful FPA

The self-endowed leader of the $500 billion-a-year food processing industry, the FPA is among the most ubiquitous and powerful trade groups in the United States. Its board of directors is a Who's Who of the food industry, packed with executives from dozens of huge multinational corporations, including Archer Daniels Midland, Cargill, ConAgra, Del Monte, Dole, General Mills, Kraft, Nestle, and Tyson. (Terry Bruggeman, CEO of the now-defunct irradiation company SureBeam, also served on the board.)

Most industry groups are sheepish about their lobbying activities, in order to remain below the radar of the media and public interest groups. The FPA does the opposite, stating outright in its Annual Report: "We use our leadership and influence with legislators to ensure that industry's priorities are reflected at the highest level."[298]

The FPA weighs in on virtually every food safety issue under consideration by every federal government agency and by every member of Congress. The group has been particularly busy of late, as concerns over foodborne illness, the global food trade, genetically modified foods, and diet and obesity have reached an all-time high.

It is the FPA that petitioned the FDA in 1999 to legalize irradiated ready-to-eat foods. This category of food is potentially huge, encompassing a range of processed foods, such as baby food, hot dogs, frozen dinners, condiments, and pre-bagged salads. The request was made a year after a massive *Listeria* outbreak linked to Sara Lee hot dogs and deli meat caused 15 deaths, six miscarriages, and 100 illnesses in 22 states.

The FPA filed the petition as the "Food Irradiation Coalition," an in-name-only collection of 30 industry groups and irradiation companies, including the American Meat Institute, Society of the Plastics Industry, Institute of Shortening and Edible Oils, and STERIS/Isomedix. The petition contains no updated research on the safety of irradiated foods, relying instead on a few studies dating to the 1950s.[299] The FDA has yet to take action on the petition as of this writing; agency officials have publicly acknowledged that opposition from Public Citizen and the Center for Food Safety has slowed the process. These organizations plan to take legal action if the FDA legalizes irradiation of ready-to-eat foods.

While saying the answer to dirty food is irradiation, the FPA is also working to keep consumers in the dark about where their food comes from. The organization is vigorously opposing a new federal law that requires "country-of-origin" labeling for many imported foods, including beef, pork, seafood, fruit, and vegetables.

Known as "COOL," the law was passed by Congress in 2002 to give consumers who prefer domestic foods the ability to avoid imported products, and to give U.S. farmers and ranchers a marketing edge over imports. In particular, the law came in response to growing concerns over mad cow and foot-and-mouth diseases. Public opinion surveys show that 80 percent of Americans support such labeling and would pay more for food made in the USA.

The FPA boasted of killing a COOL bill in 1999, saying that its "vocal opposition helped defeat" this "onerous legislation."[300] Though the FPA lost the COOL battle in 2002, it and other industry groups persuaded Congress to postpone implementing the law for two years, to 2006. The FPA hasn't stopped there, however. "A two-year delay is nice," FPA lobbyist Tamara Somerville said, "but we want this thing repealed."[301] And the industry is working to effectively kill the program by making it voluntary.

The FPA is generally hostile to making food labeling more helpful for consumers. It opposes mandatory labeling for genetically modified foods, opposes complete information on *trans* fats, supports labeling that includes unproven health claims, and supports a national food-warning law that would override tough state laws. On the issue of irradiation, the FPA, like Christine Bruhn, supports labeling irradiated foods "electronically pasteurized" or "cold pasteurized." And, like the CattleWomen, the FPA says that irradiation "does not significantly change a food chemically or physically," and that "its original appearance, taste, smell, and texture are preserved."[302]

The FPA is also fighting to weaken federal regulations on *Listeria*, a dangerous bacteria that kills 500 people and hospitalizes 2,300 each year. It was *Listeria* that caused 26 deaths, 12 miscarriages and 200 illnesses, and the recall of 79 million pounds of hot dog and other processed meat in three separate episodes from 1998 to 2002. Following the recall of 27.4 million pounds of turkey and chicken from a Pilgrim's Pride plant in Pennsylvania in 2002, the Bush administration pledged to strengthen inspection and testing of meat processing facilities for *Listeria*. The FPA successfully pressured the USDA to back away from its plan.[303]

Now, the FPA—along with 14 other industry groups including the American Meat Institute and Grocery Manufacturers of America—wants to completely gut federal *Listeria* regulations by eliminating the government's zero-tolerance policy and allowing food to contain a certain amount of the bacteria.

What the Food Industry Is Feeding Us

Collectively, food industry groups have adopted a seemingly endless agenda aimed at weakening consumer protections across the board. To name just a few of its positions, the food industry:

- Opposes increased government inspection of slaughterhouses and meat processing plants;

- Opposes giving the USDA the authority to shut down meat processing plants that can't control bacterial contamination;

- Opposes giving the USDA the power to order recalls of potentially contaminated meat. (Currently, recalls are voluntary and up to the discretion of food companies.) It also opposes telling consumers where potentially contaminated meat is being sold;

- Opposes comprehensive testing of beef cattle for mad cow disease, and opposes banning some substances that could be infected with the mad cow prion from animal feed;

- Opposes restricting enormous factory-style farms (known as "concentrated animal feeding operations") that cause air, water, and soil pollution by releasing trillions of pounds of animal waste;

- Opposes restricting "captive supply" agreements, under which small-scale farmers and ranchers are essentially forced to sell their products to huge agribusinesses at below-market prices; and

- Opposes labeling food grown with fertilizer made with human sewage.

It comes as little surprise that food industry groups contribute handsomely to the campaigns of Congressional candidates, particularly to Republicans, who are traditionally more responsive to the concerns of large agribusiness corporations and less interested in consumer protection than Democrats. From 1998 to 2004:

- the FPA donated $246,000, of which 88 percent went to Republicans;

- the Food Marketing Institute contributed $1.7 million, of which 87 percent went to Republicans;

- the National Cattlemen's Beef Association gave $1.2 million, of which 84 percent went to Republicans;

- the American Meat Institute donated $659,000, of which 84 percent went to Republicans; and

- the Grocery Manufacturers gave $347,000, of which 85 percent went to Republicans.[304]

It also comes as little surprise that food industry groups have managed to place many of their own people in high-ranking jobs within the USDA. Chief of Staff Dale Moore, Deputy Under-secretary Chuck Lambert, and Communications Director Alisa Harrison, all came from the National Cattlemen's Beef Association. Deputy Under Secretary, Kate Coler, worked for the Food Marketing Institute. And Deputy Under Secretary, Floyd D. Gaibler, worked for the National Cheese Institute and American Butter Institute.[305]

Perhaps more than any other food-related issue, the industry, government officials, health groups, and international organizations have allied themselves in a decades' long effort to convince food producers to make, grocery stores to sell, and consumers to eat irradiated foods. Advocates are quick to point out that no food technology has been studied more thoroughly. "Irradiation is the most extensively researched food treatment process in the history of mankind," says irradiation pioneer John Masefield of STERIS/Isomedix of Mentor, Ohio, who got his start irradiating animal hides in the 1960s.[306]

For years, advocates have promised that if only consumers were given the option, they would eagerly choose irradiated over regular foods. No one has made this pledge more loudly and clearly than Christine Bruhn: "Stores need only offer it and consumers will be willing to buy it and pay a premium," she once said.[307]

Note the contradiction with their stand on labeling: If it is true people would pay a premium for irradiated food, then labels would be big and proud—as a way of touting their difference. But given that they are trying to do away with labeling requirements suggests that the irradiation industry has a much clearer view of the public's desire for irradiated food than it is letting on.

The irradiation industry, however, continues to find itself in the margins, despite the full weight of governmental agencies including the FDA, USDA, and Department of Energy; powerful members of Congress such as Sen. Tom Harkin; multinational corporations including Cargill and Tyson; and industry groups such as the FPA and National Cattlemen's Beef Association.

The industry has had a lot to overcome: technological challenges that have made the process unreliable and expensive, reluctant food producers and grocery stores that try to avoid negative publicity, and suspicious consumers who have a visceral reaction against eating something that's been exposed to radiation, which, however imaginary, conjures images of Three Mile Island and atomic bombs.

Try as it may to persuade or even trick people into thinking that irradiation is no different than cooking or pasteurization, the bad news for the irradiation industry is that the technology has the word "radiation" in it. This is a stubborn reality that calling irradiated foods "cold pasteurized," giving millions of dollars to industry-friendly political candidates, running "educational" campaigns, slipping irradiated foods into school lunches, and handing out toothpicked beef samples will never be able to change.

Chapter 7

Food Irradiation Plants: The Plot Thickens

Bucks County hadn't seen the likes of it since that near-freezing morning in Point Pleasant 20 years earlier.

On January 11, 1983, Abbie Hoffman and more than 100 other people were arrested for blocking bulldozers and dump trucks from entering the construction site of "The Pump." The mammoth Point Pleasant Water Diversion Project was being built to suck 100 million gallons of water a day from the Delaware River to cool the Limerick 2 nuclear power plant on the Schuylkill River, a short drive north of Philadelphia.

"Dump the Pump" became a national crusade. Bucks County Judge Isaac S. "Zeke" Garb—about whom one local lawyer said, "his fury has no limitations with regard to anybody"—jailed protesters while granting legal freedom to water and nuclear interests to do as they wished.[308] Hoffman called the campaign "the most important environmental battle in the country."[309]

On August 1, 1989, The Pump was turned on.

Meanwhile Bob Sugarman, activist lawyer, was fighting The Pump in the Bucks County Courthouse in Doylestown, Pennsylvania. He faced the short-fused Judge Garb, arguing that The Pump was an environmental disaster. Representing Bucks County and a citizens' group, Sugarman delayed the project for several years and won some key improvements to the project. Though he didn't stop The Pump, he considers the effort a success.

"We were working toward a conscious objective of getting more citizens involved. People should be taking the reins of government when the government is not being responsive," says Sugarman, a *magna cum laude* graduate of Harvard and former tax attorney who became politicized in the 1960s. "Fortunately, when powerful entrepreneurial groups try to impose their will on communities through coercion, there are people out there who stand up for themselves."

Sugarman has been involved in many battles. He helped stymie Disney's plans to build a theme park near the Manassas National Battlefield in northern Virginia. He stopped the Philadelphia Phillies baseball stadium from going up in Chinatown. He halted the Philadelphia Crosstown Expressway, saving 2,000 homes and preventing the segregation of low-income, predominantly African-American neighborhoods. He took on a notorious polluter that fouled groundwater with arsenic and selenium. And he is an out-front opponent of "SLAPP" suits, which are used primarily by large corporations to frighten and silence dissenters.

Twenty years after tangling with Judge Garb in the Point Pleasant case, Sugarman was back at the Bucks County Courthouse. In 2003 he became a front man in a campaign against an unlikely project for a rural village that is proud of its history.

It's where General George Washington crossed the Delaware River on Christmas 1776. And it's where an armed mob led by John Fries in 1799 revolted against a federal tax on property, buildings, and windows in a rebellion that bears his name. Pearl S. Buck and James Michener are among the many notable writers who have tapped their muses while living here.

Today, residents of Milford Township have organized themselves to block something with a history yet unwritten—an irradiation facility that zaps food and medical supplies with highly radioactive cobalt-60.

Like the Crosstown Expressway would have done to Philadelphians if it were built, "The Irradiator," as locals call it, could forever change Milford and its residents.

The irradiation facility represents more than just unwelcome growth. Milford residents will tell you with great urgency about many things they believe could go wrong. They fear the facility—which actually has a detailed map on the company's Web site—is a bull's eye for terrorists, who could make it a kamikaze target or steal its cobalt-60 to fashion "dirty bombs." A small "No Trespassing" sign, which you have to slow down in order to read, is the only deterrence.

"To build this so soon after 9/11 is insane," says Judy Szela, a retired psychotherapist and a leader of NoCobalt-4-Food, one of two grassroots organizations formed to oppose the irradiator. "We are very quiet, very simple people—but we are very pissed off." Szela was so incensed that she ran for township supervisor under the Green Party in 2003, though unsuccessfully.

Because there's no nuclear reactor, the irradiator won't melt down like nearby Three Mile Island did in 1979. But opponents fear hurricanes, tornadoes, or even earthquakes might trigger an environmental catastrophe that would overwhelm Milford's volunteer fire department. Or, trucks carrying cobalt-60 to and from the facility could crash, a not-uncommon occurrence.

"Why are they forcing an unwelcome and potentially unsafe technology upon this trusting, loyal, and supportive community?" says Max Geisler, a high school science teacher and a leader of another local grassroots organization, Concerned Citizens of Milford Township.

When the Clemens Family Corporation chose to build its irradiation plant near Fries Highway, a rebellion seemed inevitable. No one's been hurt, but near-fisticuffs, threats of violence, nasty phone calls, slashed tires, and other ugliness have fissured a community that has survived 300 years of intermittent strife.

Until recently controversy was a foreign concept to the Clemens Family Corporation, headquartered about 20 miles south of the irradiator in Hatfield. Dating to 1895, CFC owns Hatfield Quality Meats, the nation's fifth-largest pork producer with $400 million in annual sales throughout the U.S. as well as Mexico, Asia, and Eastern Europe. When baseball fans go to Citizens Bank Park, they eat Hatfield's Phillies Franks.

Many locals wonder why CFC would imperil its good name by building something that assuredly would cause a backlash. While no one knows for sure, it likely has something to do with Board Chair Phil Clemens' relationship to the American Meat Institute (AMI), where he recently served as chair. AMI is a big promoter of irradiation.

In many ways, it's surprising that the company would take a chance on such a marginal technology. While fruit, vegetables, beef, poultry, pork, eggs, and spices can all legally be irradiated in the U.S., very few zapped foods have ever reached grocery stores because required labels repel consumers.

The USDA, however, has permitted irradiated ground beef in the National School Lunch Program since 2003, though none is known to have been served to students. It is likely CFC had reason to believe in the beginning that it would have the opportunity to irradiate hamburger for school lunches.

Qualipaq of Smoyersville, Pennsylvania, just down the road from Milford, had a contract with USDA to provide non-irradiated hamburger from October 1, 2003 through September 30, 2004. The company was the second-largest provider of frozen hamburger patties during this period. Eventually, Qualipaq did receive a contract to supply irradiated hamburger, and it was announced that CFC would do the irradiation.

Chris Sommers, who replaced the well-known advocate of irradiated food, Donald Thayer, as the lead scientist for USDA's Agricultural Research Services, was instrumental in designing the irradiation protocol at CFC Logistics for ground beef destined for the National School Lunch Program. Sommers has followed in Thayer's footsteps, continuing to research irradiation, particularly on ready-to-eat meat and poultry products.

In 2004, Sommers made a slide presentation at the annual meeting of the American School Food Service Association in Indianapolis entitled, "Food Irradiation: The Role of the USDA's Agricultural Research Service." His slide show characterized organizations opposing irradiation as "radical anti-technology and anti-globalization groups."[310]

Sommers claimed in a private conversation with a Public Citizen staffer that it was Peter Murano, who then oversaw the USDA's school lunch program, who originally told him to work with CFC on the irradiation protocol. Murano is a vocal proponent of irradiation as described in Chapter 6, and obviously he viewed CFC as important for the commercialization of irradiation.

And CFC staked its future on the success of irradiated school lunch meat.

CFC is viewed as a family-friendly business. It was named the Family Business of the Year by Penn's Wharton School of Business in 1997. The company phone list is loaded with the Clemens name—third-, fourth-, and even fifth-generation family members.[311]

Another interesting fact about CFC is that its executives say that they hold themselves to the highest authority. "It is the Clemens Family Corporation's goal to own profitable diversified enterprises that honor the Lord Jesus Christ," Phil Clemens recited his company's creed to the AMI at the Hilton Riverside in New Orleans in October 2002.[312]

Clemens' term as AMI's chair ended that day. One of his last official acts was to urge the USDA to allow irradiated ground beef into the National School Lunch Program. The USDA made the announcement the following day. The agency usually listens to the AMI, to which Phil Clemens personally donated $4,500 from 1999 to 2004.[313]

It's all part of a divine plan. "As I sit here today, I am convinced that this is where God wants me to be. If he gave me a call tomorrow, I would be willing to move where he would have me to be," wrote Clemens, who says he accepted Jesus Christ as his personal savior at age five. "We need to be the salt and light God has called us to be. We will be held accountable for how we have conducted his business."[314]

Township officials claim that when CFC opened the warehouse in October 2002, they were not told about the irradiator. Around Christmas, CFC finally told Milford officials about the cobalt. The company applied for a permit to dig the cobalt pit, which the Township granted the following February. "We thought this was over and done," said Milford's attorney, Terry Clemons (no relation). "We didn't know this was going to push anyone's buttons."[315]

According to CFC, it includes a 4.4-million-cubic-foot warehouse with 17,500 pallet positions, 18 dock doors and super-powered blast freezers. And then there's the steel- and concrete-lined pit of water—seven feet across, eight feet wide and 20 feet deep—that can hold about 60 rods of radioactive, blue-glowing cobalt-60, innocuously called "pencils" by the nuclear industry. That's one million curies of radiation, equal to the zapping power of up to two million medical radiation therapy units, or about one-hundredth the radiation released at Chernobyl.

The town went haywire. It didn't take long before local activists and Public Citizen were sharing information and organizing strategies. In short order, weekly meetings were being held at a local church. Hundreds of anti-irradiation signs were planted in front yards. People spread information door-to-door. Web sites appeared. Press release upon press release flew out to newspapers, and TV and radio stations. Whole Foods, the natural-foods grocery store chain, donated money to the cause.

The story spread like wildfire: daily newspapers in Philadelphia and Allentown covered the issue. U.S. Sens. Arlen Specter and Rick Santorum, and U.S. Rep. Robert Wonderling urged the NRC to listen to the citizens' concerns.[316]

"When something this heinous comes into the community, or if there is a corporate assault, you've got to get ready," says Kim Haymans-Geisler, a public relations writer and a co-leader of CCMT with her husband, Max Geisler. "Did they think that we would roll over and die?"

In his AMI speech, Clemens said: "I believe we should always treat our opponents with respect and listen to their views."[317]

In a laughable grade-school analogy, CFC Logistics President Jim Wood wrote in a local newspaper that gamma rays from cobalt-60, capable of doing ultimate harm to living things, are "similar" to sunlight, and TV and radio signals.[318]

Not since The Pump had the Pennsylvania community been so red-hot with activism.

Township Manager Jeff Vey and the township's three part-time supervisors were held accountable for their decisions at a series of meetings in the summer of 2003. Local media coverage was intense. Then TV cameras from Philadelphia started to show up.

Vey, essentially the Township's mayor, decided he couldn't sit there and do nothing. Testifying to the activism of the local citizen organizations, he says, "I've gotten 40 to 60 e-mails a day about this. I'm a wailing wall. This place is Hooterville!" Vey wrote a zoning ordinance that would have zoned CFC's irradiator out of existence by establishing buffers around homes, schools, and churches.

On top of that, the Township told CFC that it would block cobalt shipments to the plant until a dispute over permits was cleared up. "They're trying to put us out of business," groused Wood, who has been derided for his many blunt public statements. "We think what they did is illegal."[319]

Enter the attorneys. CFC sued Milford in county and federal courts. In the federal case, CFC literally argued that the company is a "person" that cannot be denied equal protection under the Fourteenth Amendment of the U.S. Constitution.[320] Milford sued back. The citizens' groups, under the legal guidance of Bob Sugarman, filed its own county suit and asked the NRC to suspend CFC's cobalt license, which was issued a month earlier in August 2003.

Dozens of hearings and court filings later, little was settled. Both sides agreed to disagree, and no significant legal conclusion was reached. The citizens' groups, however, achieved a near miracle. The NRC, easily among the federal government's least responsive agencies, agreed to hold a public meeting. When 500 mostly riled people showed up, NRC officials were shamed into holding another one. Agency officials said they had never experienced anything like it before.

Worn down by Sugarman, the NRC appointed a special judge to mediate the situation. Finally an accord was reached in November 2004—two years after CFC opened its warehouse. CFC agreed to install two safety measures: a backup generator for the cobalt pit and an alarm designed to prevent cobalt rods from being dropped and damaged. CFC's Wood later announced the company wouldn't install any additional irradiation machines, a decision no doubt reached in part to avoid more protest and litigation.

Sugarman rightfully chalked it all up as a victory: "It's almost impossible to get anything out of the Nuclear Regulatory Commission." The controversy and expense that CFC experienced will certainly act as a deterrent to other corporations considering building an irradiation facility.

Despite the partial success with the NRC, local activists continue to lament the naïveté of township supervisors who have spent more time and effort debating a new convenience store and extending an airport runway than approving an irradiator packed with enough cobalt-60 to endanger the health of millions of people.

The irradiator itself, a $1.5 million item, was made by Gray*Star of Mt. Arlington, New Jersey. The machine was designed by Martin and Russell Stein, a father-and-son team that carries a pock-marked reputation.

Martin Stein, who worked with Nobel Laureate Glenn Seaborg at the old Atomic Energy Commission, started an irradiation company in Mine Hill, New Jersey that went bust in 1987. The NRC fined Stein a few months later, due to "the apparent lack of sufficient technical knowledge"[321] and for failing to adequately monitor a leaking cobalt-60 tank.[322] Stein blamed Mine Hill's activist mayor for driving his company to ruin: "The mayor said his No. 1 goal was to put us out of business. And he succeeded."[323]

Fourteen years later, in 2001, the NRC rejected Stein's design for an irradiator using nuclear-bomb waste cesium-137, a highly radioactive substance that had caused the worst U.S. irradiation accident in history. NRC officials said Stein's experimental machine might not be able to "protect health and minimize danger to life and property."[324]

Stein failed despite a personal letter Seaborg wrote in 1995 to then-Energy Secretary Hazel O'Leary, saying he was "particularly intrigued" by the machine and had invested in Gray*Star.[325] Babcock & Wilcox, which made the doomed nuclear reactor at Three Mile Island, joined the venture. Stein worked his government connections, receiving financial and technical assistance for his cesium machine from the USDA.[326]

Beginning anew with cobalt-60, the Steins created the "Genesis" irradiator.

After losing a reported $6,000-8,000 per week during its legal limbo, CFC started up its irradiator in October 2003. The first items to be irradiated included 13,000 pounds of herbs, plants, and mint and other seasonings.[327] Ground beef soon followed, in January. CFC won't name any clients for fear of protests and critical media coverage.

On a chilly but pleasant morning a few days before Thanksgiving 2004, Jim Beer, a Native American activist from the Lena'pe Nation of Pennsylvania, and many other local activists met at Judy Szela's stone farmhouse, where she lives with her husband, dentist Philip Stein. It was the second annual International Anti-Food Irradiation Day, which coincided with speaking tours, protests, workshops, press conferences, and other events in Australia, Canada, Denmark, Italy, the Philippines, and Brussels, the capital of the European Union. Like other grassroots activists around the world who are active on irradiation issues, the Milford group committed itself to continuing to watchdog the industry.

Beer, the Lena'pe Nation's spokesperson, is one of CFC's most passionate opponents: "This food irradiation plant has sprung up like a weed. We hate it," says Beer. "We hate what it stands for. We hate what it does. To the community standing here, it is unacceptable."

Around the time of the November 2004 activist gathering, Bob Sugarman said he believed the community would win its fight against CFC Logistics. After all, that's what has happened with The Pump. In the end, Bob Sugarman's arguments against The Pump have largely prevailed, as water officials in recent years have relied less on Delaware River water to cool the Limerick 2 nuclear plant.

Sugarman says it's all in the struggle. "Quality of life is built one brick at a time. I think people here are doing the best thing they can do. If they don't fight for the health of their community, who will?"

Sugarman is beginning to look like a prophet. On April 25, 2005, Jim Woods of CFC announced, "We have made a decision to shut down the irradiator." He went on to say, "The market for irradiating meat never materialized and the cold storage business has exploded and is a much more profitable business for us to be in."

One month later, in May, the cobalt "pencils" were removed from the water pit and trucked back to MDS Nordion, the Canadian company that manufactured them.

"I am so thrilled," says Kim Haymans-Geisler. "We worked so long and hard and so many people have cared about this issue for so long." [328]

Milford residents are sustaining a national movement begun 20 years earlier by the likes of California's Denis Mosgofian. "Food irradiation," Mosgofian says, "is a disposal plan, disguised as a food treatment plan." [329]

Mosgofian co-founded the National Coalition to Stop Food Irradiation in San Francisco in the mid-1980s. He helped expose the inclusion of irradiated dried mushrooms in Rice-a-Roni, which led to an FDA investigation and Quaker Oats' decision to stop the practice. An erstwhile leader of a newspaper press workers' union, Mosgofian helped block a cesium-137 irradiator from being built in the Bay Area. [330,331,332]

The Bay Area facility was one of six the U.S. Department of Energy planned for its "Byproducts Utilization Project." The DOE wanted to irradiate food with cesium-137, an extremely radioactive waste, from the Hanford nuclear bomb factory in Washington state.

The DOE was highly motivated: two-thirds of the nuclear waste at Hanford is cesium-137, packed into 2,000 capsules stored in a concrete pool. Currently, the DOE is responsible for the waste. Their strategy for "disposal" is diffusion. If they can facilitate having waste used in irradiation facilities, it will no longer be their responsibility. The Bay Area facility, nicknamed "Kaycee," could have irradiated 500 tons of fresh fruit and vegetables daily.

Faced with mass opposition, the DOE shifted gears to Alaska. But after legislation banning irradiated foods was introduced, then-Governor Steve Cowper, a former boat captain, nixed the irradiator because he feared it would harm the seafood industry's reputation.

Dissent also flourished in Washington state, where apples, cherries, asparagus, potatoes—even famed Walla Walla sweet onions—were eyed for irradiation just down the road from Hanford, at the Port of Pasco.

Connie Wheeler started Consumers United for Food Safety and challenged the irradiator at every turn: "We may have to tolerate radioactive wastes at Hanford, but I hope we will not become a national nuclear dumpsite—nor the home of nuked fruit and veggies."[333] She said Hanford wanted to "improve their image by making something other than bombs."[334] As a result of Wheeler's organizing, 6,000 people wrote to the Washington State Apple Commission, urging it to reject irradiation, which it did.

The prominent Washington Environmental Council lost a court battle against the irradiator but DOE funding had already dried up. Public opposition, along with the serious accident at a cesium-137 plant in Georgia, eventually led the DOE to abandon the scheme entirely in 1990. Facilities in Oklahoma and Hawaii were also scrapped. Dissent also led to temporary bans on irradiated foods in Maine, New Jersey, and New York, and proposed bans in many other states.

Before the federal tap ran dry, Florida and Iowa had enough money to go ahead with irradiators. Officials backed down to public resistance in those states, however, and electron-firing linear accelerators were built instead of cesium-137 machines—at the University of Florida in Gainesville and Iowa State University in Ames.

The government and irradiation industry didn't give up in Hawaii, though. Hawaii County officials came up with $2 million to help Isomedix of New Jersey build a cobalt-60 irradiator on the Big Island. (The county also spent $90,000 on a public-relations campaign run by a firm also working for the pro-irradiation Grocery Manufacturers of America.) Isomedix, founded by irradiation pioneer John Masefield, had been irradiating Hawaiian papayas at its plant in Morton Grove, Illinois since 1995. The logical next step was to build a facility right in Hawaii.

Hawaiians concerned about food safety and the environment mounted an opposition. The issue went on the November 1998 ballot and voters approved the funding—though by just 473 out of 51,000 votes. The dissent did the trick, as Isomedix chose to avoid controversy and nix the plant.

The government came to the rescue again. In 2000, U.S. Sen. Daniel Inouye coaxed a $6.75 million loan out of the USDA for a company called Hawaii Pride. The word "irradiation," however, does not appear in Inouye's press release that announced the loan, instead calling it "post-harvest disinfestation treatments" and "pasteurization."[335]

The plant, near Hilo on the Big Island, opened four months later, and began irradiating papayas with a linear accelerator and shipping them to the mainland. If Hawaii Pride defaults on the USDA loan, taxpayers will pick up the tab. This is possible, as Hawaii Pride's partner, SureBeam of San Diego, declared bankruptcy in January 2004. Despite all of the problems in Hawaii, and despite warnings that it's not necessary, state officials said in October 2004 that they hope another irradiator would be built.

The state officials might see their wish come true, but not if the Concerned Citizens of Honolulu can help it. In July 2005, Honolulu residents became aware that a fruit company called Pa'ina Hawaii, LLC planned to build and operate an irradiator along the Pacific shore near Honolulu International Airport's Reef Runway. The facility, which is also near Pearl Harbor, would use up to one million curies of cobalt-60 to eradicate fruit flies from tropical fruit and vegetables. The citizens' organization is worried the facility could be subject to the risks of aircraft crashes, tsunamis, and hurricanes. Pa'ina Hawaii, however, refused to do an environmental review for the project.

In response, the non-profit public interest law firm EarthJustice filed a petition with the Nuclear Regulatory Commission (NRC) on behalf of the Concerned Citizens of Honolulu. In January 2006, the NRC's Atomic Safety and Licensing Board granted EarthJustice's request for a hearing on the proposal, which will examine aviation and other safety issues related to the facility. Meanwhile, the NRC's Atomic Safety and Licensing Board has ordered NRC staff to conduct an environmental assessment of the irradiator proposal. While the wheels turn at the NRC, Concerned Citizens are continuing to organize.

It's relatively easy, perhaps too easy these days, to find irradiation facilities. The U.S. has about 50, and about 35 other countries have at least one machine—their addresses in plain view on the Internet. From an Old South town in Florida better known for orange groves and phosphate mines, to the all-industry Los Angeles outskirt of Vernon, the U.S. has scattered from coast-to-coast about half the number of irradiation facilities as there are nuclear power plants.

The largest chain was, until recently, owned by IBA/Sterigenics. IBA (formerly Ion Beam Applications) is a Belgian company that owned about 40 irradiators, including 16 in the U.S. and nine in Europe. Among the U.S. plants, 13 use cobalt-60 and three use linear accelerators; some sites have multiple types of machines. IBA recently opened a cobalt-60 plant in Schaumburg, Illinois, and linear accelerator facilities in Bridgeport, New Jersey and Edgewood, New York. The company has annual revenues of $300 million and 1,300 employees in 12 countries.

Located about 20 miles from Brussels in Louvain-La-Neuve—fittingly on Avenue Albert Einstein—IBA has one-third share of the global market in medical device sterilization.[336] The company also manufactures radiation therapy equipment and particle accelerators that make radioactive isotopes used in medicine. In 1999 IBA purchased Sterigenics, which had acquired several facilities owned by two other companies. Sterigenics originally was called Radiation Sterilizers, which operated the doomed cesium-137 facility in Decatur, Georgia, where a leak led to millions of dollars in damage (recounted in Chapter 10).

In March 2004, IBA sold its sterilization business for $311.5 million to Prudential plc, a London-based financial services conglomerate that manages $250 billion in insurance and investment funds. Prudential renamed the company Sterigenics International.

A year before the sale, IBA stunned the irradiation industry when it asked the FDA to increase the maximum X-ray dose for food by 50 percent.[337] The FDA quietly announced its approval two days before Christmas 2004, when the attention of most citizens and reporters was tuned elsewhere. The decision was highly flawed. The agency ignored substantial evidence showing many chemicals commonly found in food could become radioactive at this higher dose. And a notable food irradiation researcher predicted that more people could get cancer if they ate food zapped with the higher dose.[338]

A close second in size to IBA is STERIS/Isomedix, a $1 billion-a-year company that has 11 cobalt-60 irradiation facilities in the U.S. and one in Canada. Based near Cleveland, the company makes irradiation machines for health care, scientific research, and industrial markets. It also makes sanitizing lotion, soaps, and skin cream.

Unlike some of its more out-front industry brethren, STERIS is the quiet company, trying to stay out of the media, and avoid run-ins with government officials and consumer advocates. This reflects the style of John Masefield, an irradiation pioneer who in 1972 founded Isomedix, which STERIS bought in 1997.

It was Masefield who created a stir during the 1960s when he irradiated cattle hides with a mobile irradiator made by the U.S. Atomic Energy Commission that used cesium-137. Irradiation eliminated the first steps of the tanning process, which creates toxic chemicals. "People were not afraid of radiation in those days," he says. It was Masefield who designed the first U.S. commercial irradiator, for Johnson & Johnson in 1964. He co-chaired an international committee that set standards for irradiation of medical supplies.

Perhaps most notably, it was Masefield who petitioned the FDA to legalize irradiation for red meat shortly after the Jack-in-the-Box *E. coli* disaster of 1993. The several-hundred-page document became an industry standard. The format and research from this petition has been used in many subsequent legalizations.

The FDA approved the petition in 1997, leading to the emergence of SureBeam and commercialization of irradiated ground beef. "I think everyone's happy that Isomedix stepped in," Masefield said at the time.[339]

Masefield has also been active internationally, encouraging other countries to legalize irradiation and build facilities. (For more discussion of irradiation internationally, see Chapter 12, and for a complete list of irradiation facilities, see Appendix C.)

Chapter 8

Two Competing Technologies: But It's Still Ionizing Radiation

The irradiation industry is good at spin. It works to present cobalt-60 as pretty, blue-glowing stuff shaped like "pencils" that are kept perfectly safe in pools of fresh water. They don't want consumers to know the rest of the story.

Cobalt-60 is made from naturally occurring, non-radioactive cobalt-59, which is mined in about 20 countries, chiefly Botswana, Canada, Congo, Cuba, Russia, and Zimbabwe. To make cobalt radioactive, it is compressed into small cylindrical pellets and placed inside stainless steel tubes called "pencils," 18 inches long and a half-inch in diameter. The tubes are then entombed for a year or more inside a nuclear reactor, where they are blasted with countless neutrons.

With cobalt-60 now on your hands, you've got to be careful: Gamma rays—packets of massless, speed-of-light photons fired from the nuclei of radioactive isotopes—can only be stopped by lead, water, and concrete.

In an irradiation facility, cobalt is held in racks and stored in a subterranean pool of water usually about 20 feet deep. Food travels along a conveyor belt and is irradiated when the cobalt rack is hoisted out of the water into the air. Workers may be inside the cobalt chamber when the cobalt is submerged but, obviously, not when it is unshielded. Being blasted for even few seconds by cobalt-60 can be fatal.

The Suppliers

About 80 percent of the world's cobalt-60 is made by MDS Nordion, based in Kanata, Ontario, Canada. The Canadian government started a cobalt operation in 1954 and achieved fame through its pioneering work on cancer treatment. The government, however, sold the operation in 1991 to MDS International, a far-reaching multinational conglomerate that researches and manufactures pharmaceutical drugs, surgical supplies, and cancer therapy and disease detection equipment. MDS also has a venture capital arm with $1 billion invested in drug, biotechnology, and other medical companies.

While it was part of the government, Nordion was administered by Atomic Energy of Canada Ltd (AECL). Over the past 50 years, AECL has become infamous through its leading role in proliferating nuclear technology worldwide, most notably with its "CANDU" reactor.

AECL has been deaf to worldwide concern that its aggressive marketing tactics are making efforts to limit the expansion of nuclear technology all the more difficult. As violence and tensions have risen since 9/11, these concerns have deepened.

AECL is also a notorious polluter. Its Chalk River research complex, in eastern Ontario's Ottawa Valley, is an international lightning rod for controversy, with its huge store of radioactive waste. Among the waste are untold quantities of spent cobalt-60 rods retrieved from irradiation facilities throughout the world.

Though MDS Nordion is officially separate from AECL, MDS's roots in the nuclear-industrial complex are difficult to ignore. As the company itself has said, "MDS Nordion enjoys a strong relationship with the Canadian nuclear industry."[340] Case in point: AECL has provided $100 million in no-interest loans to MDS Nordion to build two reactors at Chalk River.[341]

MDS Nordion is a global force in the irradiation industry. Its executives frequently speak at conferences throughout the world. It teamed with Belgian competitor IBA to open a food irradiation facility near Mexico City. And MDS is a founding member of the Food Irradiation Processing Alliance, established in September 2000 with IBA and U.S. irradiators Food Technology Service, Gray*Star, and STERIS/Isomedix.

MDS has installed more than 100 cobalt-60 irradiators in more than 45 countries, and has supplied 75,000 sources of cobalt-60 to more than 170 irradiators. MDS supplies cobalt to, and co-owns, Food Technology Service in Florida.

"Electric" Irradiators

To distance themselves from this nastiness, SureBeam Corporation executives ran out of breath explaining to consumers and the media that their linear accelerators and X-ray machines used *electricity*—not radioactive materials. They talked it up so much that "gamma vs. e-beam" became a topic of serious debate in the business pages and at conferences during SureBeam's brief heyday. Although SureBeam used electricity to create ionizing radiation to irradiate the food rather than actual radioactive waste, it is true that it did not have to use radioactive materials at its facilities.

Ukrainian physicist George Gamow gets the credit for being the first to envision a particle accelerator, in the late 1920s. Scientists probing the very nature of reality needed a machine to help them learn more about the subatomic world. Electrons zoom at the speed of light through a tube, being pushed and pulled by electric fields and electromagnetic waves. The interactions among electrons and other particles are recorded to determine their properties. The largest such device is the two-mile-long Stanford Linear Accelerator Center in California.

To bring things down to Earth, scientists like to say that a television screen is a simple, low-energy version of an electron accelerator.

As mentioned previously, SureBeam's accelerators were originally designed for the "Star Wars" program to help study the effects of nuclear weapons. Much smaller models are used to treat cancer. Take a linear accelerator, put a sheet of tungsten in front of it, turn it on and you've got X-rays. X-rays are essentially identical to gamma rays, with very high frequencies and very short wavelengths, but they are artificially generated.

X-rays can be used to illustrate just how much of a jolt food gets when it is irradiated. A chest X-ray is about three millirads (three-thousandths of a rad, or "radiation absorbed dose"). In the U.S., spices legally can be irradiated with up to three million rads. That's the equivalent of one *billion* chest X-rays—enough radiation to kill a person 5,000 times over.

Again, somebody who eats irradiated food is not also being irradiated. The food, however, undergoes an infinite number of molecular changes, including the possible production of chemicals that could cause cancer and birth defects. As Dr. Samuel Epstein, Professor Emeritus Environmental Medicine at the University of Illinois School of Public Health says,

> Irradiated meat is a very different product than natural meat. This is hardly surprising as the Food and Drug Administration's (FDA) approved irradiation dosage of 450,000 rads is approximately 150 million times greater than that of a chest X-ray. Apart from high levels of benzene, new chemicals known as "unique radiolytic products" were identified in irradiated meat in U.S. Army tests in 1977 and recognized as carcinogenic. Later tests identified other chemicals shown to induce genetic toxicity. In sharp contrast to FDA's claims of safety, based on grossly inadequate testing which fails to meet the agency's minimal standards and which were explicitly rebutted by its own expert committees, there is well-documented scientific evidence that eating irradiated meat poses grave risks of cancer and genetic damage.[342]

However, the danger is not just from eating irradiated food. The facilities can be dangerous, especially to workers. It is in the irradiation facility, protected by concrete walls at least six feet thick, where the irradiation occurs. And linear accelerators, such as the ones that SureBeam used, can be dangerous, too. They must also have thick walls, because ionizing radiation is produced within, just like in a facility using Cobalt 60. Any facility that uses radiation can be a safety nightmare—particularly when the people running it tell lies and cover up accidents.

And as we shall see in the next chapter, there have been significant safety lapses at irradiation facilities.

Chapter 9

Profit Over Safety: The Accidents

From her raised position, U.S. District Judge Maryanne Trump Barry told the convicted criminal standing before her: "I cannot say with confidence that Dr. Welt really understands what he did wrong."[343]

Martin Welt was not accustomed to being talked to that way. He has four university degrees, including a Ph.D. in physics. He was a reactor physicist at the Atomic Energy Agency under Glenn Seaborg. He taught at North Carolina State, George Washington, and Southern Methodist University.[344] He'd been named Chicago's Entrepreneur of the Year.

But what had Welt learned about ethics? When faced with a choice between telling the truth and risking a small fine, and telling a lie that would put his livelihood, reputation, even his freedom at risk, Welt chose the lie.

In a federal courtroom in Newark, New Jersey, on Oct. 11, 1988, Martin Welt—four days after his 55th birthday—was sentenced to prison for conspiracy, violating the Atomic Energy Act, and lying to the Nuclear Regulatory Commission. The 125 letters written to Judge Barry pleading for mercy—one of which said Welt was a "missionary who has been effectively crucified"—didn't work.

Welt is easily among the top 10 most influential figures in the history of food irradiation. He started Radiation Technology Inc., (RTI) in 1968 while in his mid-20s. By the 1980s Welt had built four irradiation plants, two in New Jersey and one each in Arkansas and North Carolina. He mainly irradiated spices and medical supplies but planned to irradiate pork and other foods.

A master at working the system, Welt almost single-handedly convinced the FDA that irradiated foods are safe for human consumption. Though not a food company *per se*, RTI won six FDA approvals from 1983 to 1990 to irradiate spices, vegetable seasonings, enzyme preparations, pork, and poultry. RTI was literally bringing an industry into existence: the FDA approvals allowed anyone, not just Welt, to irradiate these foods.

Swept up in his success and notoriety, Welt made a proclamation that would come back to haunt him: "This is the safest food-preservation method man has ever come to grips with."[345]

Welt's vision began to crumble in December 1974, when NRC inspectors spotted untrained employees handling nuclear byproducts at Welt's facility in Rockaway, New Jersey. The following October, the pool of water holding radioactive cobalt-60 was found to be contaminated. In October 1976 inspectors filed a slew of violations.[346]

Events climaxed on Sept. 23, 1977, when RTI employee Michael Pierson, then 32, walked into the cobalt-60 chamber without realizing the radioactive material was unshielded. He was blasted with a near-fatal dose of 150-300 rem; he was hospitalized for a month. It turned out that a RTI manager routinely disabled a radiation warning system designed to protect workers, in order to prevent the production line from shutting down. The NRC suspended Welt's license for three weeks.[347]

The NRC pulled RTI's license twice in 1986, again for willfully allowing workers to enter the cobalt-60 chamber under dangerous circumstances. In a twist of fate, Welt that year was named Chicago's Entrepreneur of the Year, for "creativity and innovation in the use of science and engineering for the benefit of mankind."[348]

Humbling forces grew. The NRC gave RTI its license back only under the condition that Welt be barred from all company activities, along with five other top managers. That year, the New Jersey Environmental Federation named RTI one of its "Terrible 12," a list of the state's worst polluters.[349]

Eighteen years after he started the company, Welt was forced to leave RTI in July 1986. In another bizarre series of events, the U.S. Department of Energy hired him two months later to consult on six cesium-137 irradiators—at $100 per hour.[350] The DOE had confidence in Welt, even though cesium-137 is far more dangerous than the cobalt-60 he handled in Rockaway.

Welt, however, couldn't outrun his past. After more than 30 NRC violations, a federal grand jury charged Welt in March 1988 with seven crimes, including lying to the NRC and trying to cover up safety violations at the Rockaway plant. Two other RTI employees were also charged.

Welt was defiant, saying he'd done nothing wrong. His attorney snorted, "Isn't it true that when you deal with government, you find a rigidity of the brain?"[351]

The evidence doomed Welt. Among the details revealed at trial, Welt threatened RTI workers with firing if they didn't lie to NRC investigators. He lied about installing a new safety device. He contrived back-dated memos falsely stating that safety measures had been taken.[352] Later it was discovered that RTI buried radioactive waste and dumped radioactive fluids on the ground, leading to "significant" contamination. For some unknown reason, the facility was even contaminated with cesium-137.[353]

For two years, Welt and other higher-ups told employees to enter the cobalt-60 chamber under potentially unsafe conditions in order to keep production moving. When one worker asked Welt about going in, Welt told him, "Go ahead, do it."[354]

The jury found Welt guilty on six of seven charges on July 13, 1988. He was sentenced to two years in federal prison, of which he served eight months. He could have gotten 27 years. The other two RTI employees were placed on probation and fined, and the company itself was fined $100,000.

Judge Barry lambasted Welt at sentencing: "I perceive the underlying reason for the case getting here to be one of arrogance from the very beginning to this very day." Welt responded in a broken voice, "I have never hurt anyone in my life. I got caught up in something."[355]

Just three years earlier, Welt declared that food irradiation was the safest food treatment ever invented. As inmate #09076-050, Welt had eight months to think about whether it was worth lying in order to make his declaration seem true.

Welt claims to still operate a food irradiation company, Alpha Omega Technology in Cedar Knolls, New Jersey. In a rare interview, Welt, in his early 70s at this writing, berated environmental and consumer advocates: "There are make-believe dragons hurting the irradiation field. I do not take environmental groups as being fair combatants. They are holier than thou. Those people prove to be a very formidable foe. Many consumer groups do it for the money. These groups are anti-technology, anti-science, anti, anti, anti, anti... These people have an axe to grind."

Welt abruptly ended the conversion when asked about his time in prison.

Welt is certainly an unusual character, tempting the conclusion that his unsafe actions are the result of character flaws that are unlikely to happen at other companies. But the presumption that safety is important to the irradiation industry is a leap that is not supported by the facts, as another incident reveals.

...And More Scandal

New Jersey is often the butt of jokes about its abundance of polluting industries and toxic waste dumps. The food irradiation industry fits right in with that line of thinking.

Just a few miles down U.S. Route 46 from Welt's plant, around the same time that Welt was toppled, a scandal broke out at another cobalt-60 irradiation facility.

Eugene O'Sullivan, vice president of Palo Alto, California-based International Nutronics, was convicted on Oct. 29, 1986 of conspiracy and fraud for covering up a spill of radioactive water at his plant in Dover, New Jersey, four years earlier. Although he could have received a 39-year prison sentence, and indeed a federal judge told O'Sullivan, "The crime you have committed warrants and deserves jail," O'Sullivan got two years' probation.[356]

Like the Welt affair, the O'Sullivan's case is etched in food irradiation lore. When several hundred gallons of water from the cobalt-60 tank were pumped onto the floor on Dec. 3, 1982, workers were ordered to carry it in buckets to a bathroom and flush it down the drain. Medical supplies, animal feed, and semi-precious stones were being irradiated at the time.

The deception did not stop there. Workers were ordered to rig their radiation-detection badges to conceal the amount of radiation to which they were actually exposed. Company executives delayed NRC inspections. And, in order to mask radioactivity, the company drilled holes in walls and floors, filled them with lead and painted over them.

Federal law required International Nutronics to tell the NRC about the accident with 24 hours. The company was able to keep a lid on the story for 10 months, until an employee called the NRC in September 1983.[357,358,359] The federal prosecutor who handled the case, who also prosecuted Welt, said O'Sullivan "bamboozled" the NRC.[360] Taxpayer money funded some of the $2 million cleanup.

The experience seems to have left O'Sullivan a changed man. The same year the whistleblower reported the spill, O'Sullivan was ordained a deacon of the Catholic Diocese of San Jose.

Like Welt, O'Sullivan came out of the nuclear field, having worked for the Atomic Energy Commission, General Electric, and the Hanford nuclear bomb factory in Washington state. "He was a visionary," his oldest daughter Pat, said at O'Sullivan's funeral in July 2002. "Always looking for answers."[361]

The Dover irradiator site was eventually cleaned up to the point that new businesses could move in—though not without a friendly warning to tenants. Said the new property owner, "We always refer to it as the 'glow building'."[362]

Dozens of other mishaps have been reported at irradiation facilities throughout the world. William McKimm was exposed to a near-fatal dose of 400 rem in 1974 at a cobalt-60 facility in Parsippany, New Jersey, owned by Isomedix. Within the next few years, a cobalt-60 container sprung a leak, fire broke out at the plant, and workers flushed radioactive water down a toilet.[363]

Remarkably, the facilities owned by all three companies—RTI, International Nutronics, and Isomedix—were located in Morris County, about 30 miles from New York City.

The NRC recorded 50 accidents and violations between 1974 and 1988.[364] Some were fatal (none in the U.S.). Workers exposed to cobalt-60 died in Italy in 1975, Norway in 1982, El Salvador in 1989, Israel in 1990, and Belarus in 1991. Electron beam irradiators have also caused serious damage: a worker had several fingers amputated in Maryland in 1991, and a facility director lost a hand and several fingers in Vietnam in 1992.[365]

As awful as these stories may be, the nightmare scenario that came to pass in the Atlanta suburb of Decatur in the summer of 1988 will go down in history as the "Three Mile Island of the irradiation industry."

The causes of these "accidents" isn't lack of competence, character, or luck. It's the drive any business has to cut corners in order to maximize profits. Doing so may be harmless in certain industries, but here it can clearly be lethal.

These incidents reveal a profound irony. To be safe, current food preparation needs to be heavily regulated and supervised to prevent proliferation of deadly bacteria and other mishaps. The central argument of irradiation is that it creates a safe food chain and eliminates the need for onerous inspections and regulations that currently are aimed at insuring safe food. Even if it were true—that irradiation creates safe, edible food—these incidents and the dynamic of cost cutting make it clear that an irradiation industry would have to be far more heavily regulated and supervised than our current food preparation industry needs to be. Irradiation would, in the best of circumstances, shift the focus of regulating to stop the build up of bacteria, to regulating in order to prevent a major nuclear disaster, a far more serious and difficult task to accomplish.

Our record of regulating the current industry has been mixed at best and desperately needs to be stepped up. How can we assume that regulation of radiation would be any better when evidence suggests it would likely be worse?

As U.S. Attorney Thomas Greelish said about International Nutronics trying to cut corners, "The genesis of the spill was an effort to make the company more profitable."

Chapter 10

Spinning Nuclear Waste: "Cesium is Your Friend."

Robert Higbee, who oversaw waste programs at the Hanford Nuclear Reservation in eastern Washington state, believed that cesium was his friend.[366] But faith can only take you so far.

Under the DOE's Byproducts Utilization Program, which sought creative uses for nuclear-bomb waste, 252 capsules of cesium-137 were leased to Radiation Sterilizers, Inc., which wanted to irradiate surgical gloves, bandages, and other medical supplies. The company hoped to use cobalt-60 but none was available when the plant was due to open in 1986. The DOE had plenty of cesium—75 million curies' worth, enough to fuel two or three dozen irradiators.

The blue-glowing material can also be your enemy: it's among the most radioactive, or "hottest," wastes at Hanford. And it's water soluble, which could turn the smallest leak into a disaster.

The government ignored its own advice. The NRC said RSI's plan to repeatedly dunk the cesium capsules into water could cause them to leak, so the agency required the capsules to be tested for one year. Anxious to dispense with the cesium as quickly as possible, however, the DOE convinced the NRC to waive this requirement.[367] The DOE proceeded to call the 21-inch-long capsules, made of double-walled stainless steel, "fail-proof."

This cesium was no friend. DOE's reckless waste disposal plan began to unravel on June 6, 1988. After only a year in service, a leak was detected; one of the capsules had cracked. Four others bulged precariously. Inexplicably, a DOE-commissioned report published in August 1988—two months *after* the leak was detected and following widespread media coverage of the accident—stated that "no evidence of cracking was found."[368]

Federal and Georgia state investigators described a program that seemed destined to fall apart. For starters, the cesium capsules used by RSI were not designed for commercial use. A DOE official said the cesium was "lying in the [cooling] pool in Hanford, and then somebody decided that, hey, it would be a good idea to use these things for some other purpose."[369]

And, RSI did not have a plan for what to do in the event of a malfunction.[370] On the contrary, the DOE found RSI's practices were "characteristic of a risk taker intent on maximizing profit."[371]

More than 70,000 boxes, reportedly for contact lens solution and other consumer products, may have been contaminated and shipped into the marketplace. It is unknown how many of the boxes were recalled, if any. According to one report, some milk cartons arrived in Florida radioactive.[372]

Contamination was found on three RSI employees, who tracked it into their homes and cars. Carpet and car seats were ripped out and dumped at a hazardous waste dump in neighboring South Carolina.[373]

The inquiry was particularly enlightening to state officials, who did not even know that RSI was using radioactive materials. Neither did the businesses neighboring RSI at the Snapfinger Woods Business Park, including a child day-care center.[374]

In the end, Georgia officials said RSI should never be allowed to use hazardous materials again.[375] The cleanup that initially was expected to take a year and cost $1 million was completed more than four years later, in January 1993, and set back taxpayers $47 million.[376]

RSI ceased to exist, at least on paper. The Decatur plant was acquired by Sterigenics of Oak Brook, Illinois, which also bought Martin Welt's fouled Rockaway facility. Sterigenics took the offensive by filing a $200 million claim with the federal government, arguing that the cesium capsules were poorly made. "I would say that we were almost a victim in this incident," a Sterigenics spokesperson said.[377]

With the DOE fearing more problems, cesium capsules were also removed from RSI's plant in Westerville, Ohio, and from facilities in Northglenn, Colorado and Lynchburg, Virginia owned by other companies. (The Colorado plant was owned by IOTECH, a subsidiary of the politically well-connected consulting firm CH2M Hill, which helped the DOE put together the cesium irradiation program in the first place.) It took more than four years to truck about 1,000 capsules back to Hanford, testing the nerves of residents in Idaho, Oregon, Utah, Wyoming, and several states along the route.

Naturally, DOE officials wanted to put this mess behind them as quickly as possible. Their solution was to send the cesium to France, according to a DOE official, "as long as they would not make us take it back." Scoffed a French attaché: "We have enough nuclear wastes of our own. We don't need nuclear wastes from other countries."[378]

With cesium essentially out of the picture, though, things are looking up for cobalt-60. Theoretically, it isn't as bad as cesium because it is not water soluble, so it poses less risk to the water supply.

Unfortunately, the irradiation industry, some government agencies, and many academics are trying to resuscitate a burned-out Atomic Age fantasy that has never been successfully commercialized, while telling people what they love to hear: "Welcome to the Future," in the words of MDS Nordion.

Chapter 11

The Jungle Revisited: Do You Know Where Your Meat Has Been Today?

When Fred Keilitz discovered feces on a piece of beef at the ConAgra slaughterhouse where he worked as a company inspector, the last thing he expected to hear from company higher-ups was that he should pretend it never happened.

"They told me, 'You didn't see it.' They told me not to tell the USDA about what I saw. They covered it up," says Keilitz. "It really hit me hard—it pissed me off. I wanted to make sure that the meat was safe. ConAgra didn't seem to care."

Knowing that his job was at stake, though, he didn't always speak up. "If you argue with the company, you're fired."

Keilitz eventually quit, but not before witnessing the one of the largest beef recalls in U.S. history. ConAgra, the country's third-largest beef producer, recalled 18.6 million pounds of meat from its processing plant in Greeley, Colorado, in July 2002 because of an outbreak of *E. coli* O157:H7, a potentially fatal bacteria that lives in feces. A 68-year-old Ohio woman died and about 50 other people who ate tainted meat fell ill in more than 20 states.

Keilitz says he did all he could to keep dirty meat from leaving the plant. "I was very tough on the company. If I saw too many errors, I was not afraid to shut down the slaughter line. Once, I shut down the line when the president of company was at the plant on a tour."

Keilitz now works on the other side of the fence, as an inspector for the U.S. Department of Agriculture, accountable to taxpayers, not a for-profit enterprise. One would think that publicly funded USDA inspectors carry more clout than "quality control inspectors" who work for under-scrutinized private companies, but this isn't always the case. And it is becoming less so.

The recurring dangers in slaughterhouses are alarming in and of themselves, but as will become clear, this history plays right into the agenda for irradiation. The USDA inspectors see it differently. Their union, the National Joint Council of Food Inspection Locals, signed on to the campaign against food irradiation organized by Public Citizen, because they believe cleaning up slaughter facilities is the answer to dirty meat, not masking the filth through irradiation. Most people would agree, they don't want to eat fecal material or other filth, even if the bacteria is dead.

Meanwhile, the inspectors don't want to see irradiation as the solution to the problem touted by their bosses at USDA. They also know, it's the meat companies that are the power behind the throne.

USDA Divided

Gary Dahl is the local president of the union that represents more than 100 USDA meat inspectors in Colorado, the National Joint Council of Food Inspection Local. A meat inspector for 22 years, Dahl says the USDA's new policy of giving more power to meat companies shackles government inspectors. Essentially an industry honor system, the new policy has been roundly criticized by USDA inspectors, consumer groups, and even federal investigators.

"The USDA wants to prove the point that companies can self-regulate," Dahl says. "What are our inspectors supposed to do when they find feces and other contamination? They're told by USDA managers to let the system work." The system, he says, often puts corporate interests above the public interest.

On top of that, Dahl says, company employees who speak up when they see hygiene problems do so at their own risk. "If they're told to do something, they'd better do it. Otherwise, they're out of a job," he says. "Companies couldn't care less about safety. It's all about money."

Dahl is disturbed by many things he sees in today's lightning-fast slaughterhouses and processing plants, where safety often takes a back seat to efficiency. He's especially appalled by a rule that allows a smear of feces up to 16-square-inches to simply be washed off instead of cut away from carcasses.

"By using water, you're just embedding the feces into the meat and making it invisible. This was a problem at Greeley," he says. "They were washing shit but this wasn't working well enough. You can still have dangerous levels of feces. So it's all ground up into hamburger meat—the solution to pollution is dilution."

Quick with a joke and a smile, Dahl is a charmer. This is some feat, given the wretchedness and filth on the kill-floor, where blood and guts from rapidly hacked-up carcasses splatter everywhere. "The conditions are unreal," he says.

Dahl is one of the union's superstars. He's often quoted in the national media criticizing the USDA's slackening inspection system and warning consumers about filth in the food supply. He frequently takes his case to the halls of Congress. When necessary, he files unfair labor practice complaints against the USDA, which he says sometimes punishes inspectors who report violations instead of going after the violators. Its upper echelon loaded with former meat company executives, the USDA is notorious for siding with the industry.

"The USDA is so hell-bent on destroying the union that they've lost sight of consumer protection," he says. "The USDA big-house in DC has only two people we're aware of who have worked their way up from being an inspector. The USDA is so disconnected from the field that they rely on industry to give them direction."

Dahl surely isn't taking on these burdens for the money, which amounts to $240 a year—a refund of his union dues. He's on a personal mission: "I do what I do because it's about giving something back. I want to be known as someone who cares. If I can keep one person from getting sick, I have succeeded."

Perhaps more than any of the high-profile bacterial outbreaks that have struck the U.S. over the past decade, the ConAgra recall illustrates how meat company self-inspection can fail.

If it weren't for the nauseating stench in the air and the chatter in taverns and diners, you'd probably never know that Greeley, about an hour's drive north of Denver, is home to one of the largest cattle slaughterhouses and pro-cessing plants in the country. The double-decker trucks that enter the Greeley facility laden with live animals and leave empty are hidden from public view. (Meat workers joke that cattle on top ride in first class, while those on the bottom, sprayed with excrement, ride in coach.) Without special credentials, passersby can only see a plain concrete facade, which could be taken for a man-ufacturing plant of any sort.

You'd think that a concentration of 2,500 workers would translate into a healthy local economy, but the community is strewn with decrepit homes, empty storefronts, and beat-up cars. Well-paid jobs are a thing of the past. Today's low-wage work is mainly done by Mexican-Americans who rotate amongst the many meat operations in Colorado, Kansas, Nebraska, and throughout the Heartland. As economic immigrants trying to scratch out a liv-ing because there are no jobs at home, they are often undocumented, enabling meat companies to cheat and abuse them with impunity because the workers have no legal recourse available to them that doesn't risk jeopardizing their lives in the U.S.

When New York journalist/politician Horace Greeley famously pro-nounced "Go west, young man" in 1853, he never could have imagined some-thing of the mind-boggling scale as the ConAgra plant. Here in the town that bears his name, more than one million head of cattle are slaughtered and "dis-assembled" every year—one every 10 seconds, about 5,200 animals every day. Two million pounds of finely processed beef and 1.3 million pounds of assorted meats, including head meat for fast-food hamburgers, are cranked out here daily.

Walking the halls inside the immense structure, one is overpowered by the alternating smells of cleaning solutions and meat byproducts being cooked down—rendered—into fats used for various industrial purposes. It's strangely quiet, the air still and lights numbing. Men and women wearing hardhats and bloodied aprons move in orderly fashion throughout the complex. They file into the facility through a passageway that leads under U.S. 85. A huge sign greets them: "The People Who Walk Through This Tunnel Are the Best Meat Packers in the World."

That very well might be true, but something went terribly wrong at the ConAgra plant in the spring of 2002. Meat destined to become ground beef tested positive for *E. coli* 46 times that April, May, and June.[379] This culminated an 18-month period during which beef on 58 occasions was found to be smeared with feces, milk, and partially digested food, all of which can harbor *E. coli* and other hazardous bacteria.[380]

Instead of ConAgra and the USDA taking steps to fix the problems—some of which violated federal regulations—what followed was a complete breakdown of the country's meat inspection system.

Two USDA inspectors suspected *E. coli* contamination at the plant and called for an investigation in February 2002, but their bosses within the agency denied the request.[381] ConAgra's internal tests began detecting *E. coli* in April but, inexplicably, because the company had not officially deemed the bacteria a "hazard," it was not required to tell the USDA about the tests that it had done..

USDA officials did manage to get their hands onto some of ConAgra's positive *E. coli* tests. In perhaps the most startling failure, USDA officials didn't know whether they could force ConAgra to clean up its operations because they were unsure whether they could even legally know about the positive *E. coli* tests.[382] This is akin to a doctor treating a patient for a sore throat finding out that the patient has cancer, but doing nothing about it.

"The more we learn, the worse the situation appears," Rep. Henry Waxman of California said as the extent of the outbreak gradually became known.[383] Waxman led a Congressional investigation into failures by the USDA and ConAgra.

The situation did get worse as more was learned. A recall that began with 354,200 pounds on June 30 steadily grew to 18.6 million pounds within three weeks, as details about inadequate inspection and bacteria testing went public. Ironically, it was during this period that the federal government released a harsh report on the USDA's meat inspection system (see below).

The sorry fact is that the outbreak may have been preventable. In February 2002—four months before the recall—the owner of a small meat processing company in rural Montana told a high-ranking USDA official that ground beef he bought from ConAgra tested positive for *E. coli*. Instead of acting on the message, the USDA went after the messenger—John Munsell of Montana Quality Foods and Processing, about 100 miles west of Billings in Miles City.

Even though Munsell says he had proof that the contaminated beef came from ConAgra's Greeley plant, the USDA suspended his license and declared his company's food an "imminent threat to public health." Meanwhile, the USDA—siding with corporate interests—allowed ConAgra to continue to produce potentially contaminated beef until the recall began.

His story written up in newspapers and magazines throughout the nation, Munsell became an overnight celebrity. "The USDA didn't care one bit that I had proof the meat came from ConAgra,"[384] he said. "The bottom line is the meat inspection program is politically motivated."[385]

Munsell lost so much business that he put the company, which his father started in 1946, up for sale.

As for ConAgra's Greeley plant, the USDA didn't shut it down until November 2002—five months after the recall began, *E. coli* having been detected 62 times,[386] and the company written up 20 times for meat contaminated with feces, milk, or partially digested food.[387] Why the delay? Perhaps it had something to do with the close ties the Bush administration has with both ConAgra and the firm that bought the company's red meat division shortly after the recall.

By this time, ConAgra had sold its beef and pork operation for $1.4 billion to a group of buyers headed by Dallas investment firm Hicks, Muse, Tate & Furst (HMTF). Although the operation was renamed Swift & Co., ConAgra maintains a 46 percent share and top management is still comprised of former ConAgra executives.

HMTF is one of the most prominent and aggressive investment firms in the U.S. It owns the nation's two largest radio chains, Clear Channel and Chancellor Media. It owns a big portion of the nation's largest movie theater chain, Regal Cinemas. It controls many name brands, including Stetson and Chef Boyardee. Its CEO, Tom Hicks, owns the Dallas Stars hockey team and Texas Rangers baseball team, which he bought from then-Texas Gov. George W. Bush in 1998.

Hicks' and HMTF's connections to the Bush family and the Republican Party run deep. The details are too tantalizing to ignore, and provide insight into the events surrounding ConAgra. The firm has given about $300,000 to Bush spanning his political career, ranking fourth among all donors. Henry Kissinger, secretary of state under President Nixon, serves on HMTF's European advisory board.

While governor of Texas in 1995, Bush created the University of Texas Investment Management Company (UTIMCO), which assumed control of $9 billion in university investments. Bush named Hicks, who had just given $146,000 to his gubernatorial campaign, UTIMCO's chair. UTIMCO proceeded to invest hundreds of millions of University dollars in operations run by Hicks' friends and business partners, and to Bush supporters and major Republican donors—two groups of people who overlap.

The university, for instance, invested $10 million in the Carlyle Group, a stealthy Washington, DC-based investment firm chaired by Frank Carlucci, secretary of defense under President Reagan. Carlyle's partners include James Baker III, secretary of state under Bush's father and Reagan's chief of staff, and Richard Darman, the senior Bush's economic advisor. The senior Bush himself has been paid to speak at events sponsored by Carlyle.[388,389,390,391,392]

ConAgra's connections with the Republican Party may be part of the story. CEO Bruce Rohde and his wife Sandra gave $6,000—the legal maximum—to Bush during his 2000 and 2004 presidential campaigns. All told, ConAgra employees and affiliates donated $3.1 million to federal campaigns from 1989 to 2003—79 percent of which went to Republicans. Among food producers,

ConAgra has consistently ranked among the top 10 contributors to Republicans over the past 15 years.[393]

Bush's USDA didn't shut down Rohde's Greeley plant until November, two months after the HMTF takeover, and only for five days—despite numerous findings of *E. coli*, feces, and other contamination.

Disasters like the Greeley recall were supposed to have been a thing of the past. Most people believe the matter was settled when populist journalist Upton Sinclair's exposé-style novel *The Jungle* was published in 1906. The book, which described the wretched hygienic and working conditions in Chicago slaughterhouse and meatpacking plants, led to the almost immediate passage of two federal laws intended to clean up the meat supply—laws that stood for 80 years.

Federal investigators confirmed nearly all of what Sinclair wrote. He researched the book by living in "Packingtown," a decrepit neighborhood of Poles, Germans, Lithuanians, Czechs, and other recent European immigrants who came to the U.S. looking for wealth but who wound up living and working in filth. In one of the more sickening passages, the protagonist's father, Antanas Rudkus, prepares meat destined for canning:

> The beef had lain in vats full of chemicals, and men with great forks speared it out and dumped it into trucks, to be taken to the cooking-room. When they had speared out all they could reach, they emptied the vat on the floor, and then with shovels scraped up the balance and dumped it into the truck. This floor was filthy, yet they set Antanas with his mop slopping the "pickle" into a hole that connected with a sink, where it was caught and used over again forever; and if that were not enough, there was a trap in the pipe, where all the scraps of meat and odds and ends of refuse were caught, and every few days it was the old man's task to clean these out, and shovel their contents into one of the trucks with the rest of the meat!

Sinclair's description of sausage-making is equally nauseating:

> There was never the least attention paid to what was cut up for sausage... There would be meat that had tumbled out on the floor, in the dirt and sawdust, where the workers had tramped and spit uncounted billions of consumption [tuberculosis] germs... There would be meat stored in great piles in rooms, and thousands of rats would race about on it. These rats were nuisances, and the packers would put poisoned bread out for them; they would die and then rats, bread, and meat would go into the hoppers together. This is no fairy tale and no joke; the meat would be shoveled into carts, and the man who did the shoveling would not trouble to lift out a rat even when he saw one.[394]

Slaughtering animals and processing meat are inherently dirty jobs, no matter how much care is taken.

The cow moves along a narrow conveyor, where the "knocker" stuns or kills the animal by firing a retractable bolt into its forehead. The "shackler" wraps a chain around a hind leg and the animal is hoisted onto an overhead conveyor belt. The "sticker" slits the throat—aiming for the carotid artery and jugular vein—and the animal is bled. The horns, hocks (lower legs) and udder are hacked off. The head is skinned and removed, and eventually picked clean for ingredients for ground beef and hot dogs. The hide is cut down the middle, rolled up over the carcass and peeled away.

The carcass is then eviscerated—the gastrointestinal tract, bladder, lungs, heart, and other organs scooped out. The carcass is sawed in half, the tail removed and excess fat trimmed away. The sides are decontaminated—as well as possible—by cutting away feces and other filth, steam vacuuming, hot water rinsing, and applying organic acids. The sides are chilled for one to two days before they are finally deboned and cut into pieces ready for sale.[395,396]

There are any number of opportunities for *E. coli* O157:H7 to contaminate meat in slaughterhouses, which can operate at speeds of up to 400 cows per hour. Hides are often caked with manure, which can fall onto meat when the hide is ripped off. Knives can puncture intestines when they are pulled out of the carcass, spilling feces onto meat. And, improperly cleaned knives can transfer feces from one hunk of meat to another.

Since the first known *E. coli* O157:H7 outbreak, which struck about 50 adults and children who ate McDonald's hamburgers in Michigan and Oregon in 1982, the presence of foodborne pathogens has risen dramatically. According to a 1996 USDA study of pathogens in ground beef, half contained *Clostridium perfringens*, a third contained *Staphylococcus aureas*, and about 10 percent contained *Listeria monocytogenes* and *Salmonella*. All told, three-fourths of the meat contained bacteria spread mainly through feces.[397] Up to 40 percent of cows are infected with *E. coli* O157:H7.[398]

Prior to the 1970s, however, these and other bacteria were almost unheard of. They seem to be an unintended consequence of modern industrialized meat production. Ironically, at the same time these new bacteria were on the rise, the U.S. government was easing the rules governing inspection of slaughterhouses and meat processing plants.

The government and corporate buzzword of the late 1970s was deregulation. If only federal bureaucrats would get off the backs of businesses and allow the free market to be truly free, so the argument went and continues, corporations would run more efficiently, competition would drive down prices, and everyone from consumers to stockholders would benefit.

The wave began in 1978, when President Carter deregulated the airline industry. Trucking, railroad, and oil soon followed. President Reagan picked up where Carter left off, deregulating the savings and loan, natural gas, and cable television industries.

Deregulation hit the meat industry in 1983, when Reagan—having appointed several meat industry executives to top USDA positions—created the Streamlined Inspection System, or SIS. The meat industry wanted to accommodate the new technologies that allowed slaughterlines to move faster by reducing government inspection of every carcass, which they regarded as a bottleneck. The roots of this scheme trace to an obscure internal memo written by a high-ranking USDA official in 1981: "Special interest groups supporting the meat and poultry industry have won and now have the ear of Washington. They paid their dues and are now in the driver's seat."[399,400]

Washington listened. The Reagan administration cut the number of USDA inspectors working in meat plants, and allowed animals to be slaughtered and processed at greater speeds. In the meat industry speed is the enemy of safety and quality.

Within just a few years after SIS was dreamt up, foodborne pathogens became a serious public health problem. The National Research Council told the USDA in 1985 to improve its inspection system in order to prevent *Salmonella, Campylobacter*, and other emerging pathogens from entering the food supply.[401] SIS did the opposite, allowing slaughterlines to operate up to 40 percent faster and limiting government inspection.

Under the new system, employees of private companies—not USDA inspectors who work for taxpayers—became responsible for detecting feces, vomit, scabs, abscesses, organ remnants, machine grease, and other filth on meat.[402] The natural result: more of this stuff made its way into the food supply.

Gail Eisnitz, a mild-mannered but tenacious sleuth whose book *Slaughterhouse* is a modern-day *Jungle*, gruesomely chronicles the utter failure of SIS. The numerous eyewitness accounts Eisnitz obtained bring you right down to the kill-floor.

A former worker at poultry giant Perdue Farms told Congress:

> After they are hung, sometimes the chickens fall off into the drain that runs down the middle of the line. This is where roaches, intestines, diseased parts, fecal contamination and blood are washed down. Workers get sick to their stomachs into the drain. The Perdue supervisors told us to take the fallen chickens out of the drain and send them back down the line... Chickens keep getting removed from the condemn barrel and slipped past USDA. Gall birds [chickens with ruptured gall bladders] keep going out despite green pus in their intestines.

Another worker reported: "Every day, I saw black chicken, green chicken, chicken that stank, chicken with feces on it. Chicken like this is supposed to be thrown away, but instead it would be sent down the line to be processed."

Said another: "In the department where chicken bones were ground up and processed into chicken franks and bologna...often there were maggots on them. The bones were never cleaned off so the maggots were ground up with everything else and remained in the final product."

Under SIS, USDA inspectors had to examine up to 30 chicken carcasses per minute, double their normal workload. Automation makes these high speeds possible. Machines stun, decapitate, and eviscerate chickens, which are scalded in hot water and pummeled with defeathering contraptions that, in the process, pound feces and other filth into the birds. In many plants, carcasses are then dipped into chemical baths intended to kill bacteria but, in the end, amount to what is known in the industry as "fecal soup."

It is little wonder that shortly after SIS was implemented in poultry plants, up to 98 percent of chickens were infected with *Campylobacter* and up to three-fourths with *Salmonella*.[403]

As if SIS had not been a colossal failure in poultry plants, it was then tried on an experimental basis in five cattle slaughterhouses that produced one-fifth of the U.S. beef supply, and which supplied fast-food chains including McDonald's and Jack-in-the-Box. The facilities were Excel plants in Friona and Plainview, Texas; a National Beef plant in Liberal, Kansas; and ConAgra plants in Grand Island, Nebraska, and Greeley—the same facility where the 2002 recall occurred.

The results were as disgusting as those in the chicken plants, as company employees—not government inspectors—were responsible for deciding what was too filthy to be sold to the public.

All manner of wretchedness was reported by USDA inspectors, who could do little more than watch. Cows with pneumonia, cows "stuffed with regurgitated food that was oozing out," and cows with peritonitis, a bloody, mucus-like fluid in their bellies, were sent to slaughter. Plants produced meat with "disease symptoms that previously would have forced it to be condemned, or, at most, approved for dog food." And, because of the failure to keep the facility clean, "rats were all over the coolers at night, running on top of meat and gnawing at it."

Meat from vomit-filled cow heads known as "puke heads" was used in ground beef, cold cuts, and hot dogs. Cows clogged with urine—"water bellies"—entered the food chain: "There is the equivalent of buckets of urine in their briskets, shank, and bellies. It just floods out when the cow is slaughtered."[404] "Streamlined 'wholesome' also included many more cattle penises attached to the inner sides of meat that goes into steaks."[405]

Over time, SIS came to be known as the "streamlined *infection* system." Some USDA inspectors who raised concerns were suspended, harassed, or physically attacked. One was suspended for shutting down a slaughterline because the beef was moving too quickly for him to inspect it.[406] Carcasses dangling from conveyor belts sped by at rates of up to 325 per hour.

In 1990, several years into the cattle experiment, the National Academy of Sciences reported that *none* of the USDA's inspection systems were "designed to detect or eliminate microbial or chemical hazards," and that the SIS itself "was not intended to provide greater public health protection." The Academy said 15 years ago what union leader Gary Dahl is saying today: "Some inspectors believe that SIS deputizes industry to police itself and that industry is incapable of shouldering this responsibility because it cannot resist the temptation to cut corners to increase profits."[407]

Congress terminated SIS in June 1992, shortly after exposés by *Mother Jones* and *PrimeTime Live* sparked a USDA investigation. *Mother Jones* quoted a worker at ConAgra's Grand Island plant as saying: "We've seen feces on the table, but the line is moving so fast that the meat goes right through to 'edible'."[408]

Six months later a disaster struck that, in case there was any doubt, confirmed that inspection of slaughterhouses and meat processing plants needed to be stepped up, not reduced. In December 1992 and January 1993, more than 700 adults and children in Washington, Idaho, Nevada, and California fell ill from eating hamburgers from Jack-in-the-Box fast-food restaurants contaminated with *E. coli* O157:H7. Two hundred people were hospitalized and four children under the age of seven died.

Health officials repeatedly told Jack-in-the-Box to cook beef to 155° F to kill any possible *E. coli*, a fact that company President Bob Nugent denied to Congress. "To say that they were not notified is pure baloney," a Washington state health official said at the time, adding, "If the meat had been cooked at 155°, it might not have killed anybody."[409]

Ironically, a Jack-in-the-Box spokesperson had this to say about the Streamlined Inspection System six months earlier: "If streamlining was creating a problem, there are two or three places we would catch it before it would get into the restaurant." Jack-in-the-Box received meat produced from three of five SIS plants,[410] though the exact source of the *E. coli* was never identified.

Fallout from the Jack-in-the-Box tragedy led to another industry-induced adventure in meat inspection that was promoted by the Clinton Administration. A new acronym was born: HACCP (pronounced "hassip")—the Hazard Analysis and Critical Control Point system. Meat companies began writing plans to reduce bacterial contamination and other filth, and started testing meat for *E. coli* (though only in its generic form, not specifically for O157:H7). Along with that, the USDA began conducting *Salmonella* tests in meat plants.

Like SIS, however, the central feature of HACCP is handing more authority to company employees and taking power away from USDA inspectors. Companies, for example, can literally decide where USDA inspectors are permitted to stand along processing lines. And USDA inspectors' ability to ensure that fecal-smeared and other contaminated meat is yanked out of production has been severely limited.

Instead of scrutinizing meat, USDA inspectors now spend much if not most of their time looking over company paperwork. Making sure that companies follow their hygiene plans has taken precedence over everything else, and the USDA does not even have the authority to reject company plans that are dangerously inadequate.

A recent survey of USDA inspectors by the Government Accountability Project and Public Citizen puts HACCP's shortcomings into sharp focus.

The Jungle 2000 reports that 81 percent of inspectors said they could not effectively enforce the law under HACCP. Two-thirds said they took no action when they saw contamination, such as feces, vomit, and metal shards. Threats and coercion are not uncommon. Two-fifths of inspectors surveyed said they had been threatened with lawsuits, and one-fifth said they'd been told not to document company violations.

The inspectors' individual accounts are sickening:

- "Feces is tolerated. Sores and scabs are tolerated as long as they're small enough to put in a frying pan."

- "Kidney [and] sex glands in young chickens [were] allowed in wieners."

- "If you can dilute feces, then it'll work."[411]

HACCP was sold to Congress, consumer groups, and even the USDA inspectors' union as a way to bring modern science into meat plants, where the theoretically less sophisticated "poke and sniff" method of finding contamination had been used for decades. Progress was needed but HACCP has marched backward, to the point where it's become little more than an industry honor system. Or, as inspectors call it, "Have a Cup of Coffee and Pray."

Before HACCP could even be implemented, however, an event occurred that marked a turning point for the meat industry, government regulators, and consumers alike.

In August 1997 a large but obscure meat producer named Hudson Foods, headquartered in the Ozark Mountains town of Rogers, Arkansas, recalled 25 million pounds of ground beef for fear of possible *E. coli* O157:H7 contamination. At the time it was by far the largest meat recall in U.S. history, and it remains the largest recall of ground beef. Sixteen people in Colorado and Kentucky fell ill; no deaths were reported.

Commercially, Burger King was hit the hardest. All Hudson hamburgers were dumped, and about a fourth of Burger Kings in the U.S. ran low or completely ran out of burgers. Some patrons took pause: "In the back of your mind," said a customer in Omaha, "you're always wondering, 'Have they sent all the bad meat back?'"

Boston Market experienced a major disruption, too, as nearly half of its restaurants went a spell without meatloaf. Retail giants Safeway and Wal-Mart also jerked Hudson meat out of circulation.[412,413]

USDA officials smelled something fishy from the beginning. Hudson recalled 20,000 pounds on August 12, but that grew to 40,000, then to 1.2 million, and finally to 25 million pounds within a week. The delay immediately raised red flags at the USDA.[414] Hudson had brushes with the USDA one year earlier, when the company recalled 145,000 pounds of chicken, and two years earlier when it recalled three million pounds of turkey—in both cases because of bone splinters in the meat.

Serving as USDA secretary under President Clinton at the time was Dan Glickman, a former Congressman from Kansas cattle country. Glickman had a public relations nightmare on his hands. While he had close connections to the agriculture industry, he also had to promote some changes to the system.

As a result of the Hudson recall, the USDA reasserted itself. In December 1997, two Hudson employees and the company itself were charged in federal court with conspiring to hide the extent of the possible *E. coli* contamination. The charges were the first of their kind ever known to be filed. One of Glickman's top deputies said, "We want everyone to understand that the health and safety of the public are more important than the corporate bottom line."[415]

At the trial, held two years later in Lincoln, Nebraska, a federal judge and jury cleared Hudson and the two former employees, Michael Gregory and Brent Wolke. By this point, however, Hudson was no more. The company had been sold to Tyson/IBP, a former competitor that ultimately phased the Hudson brand out of existence.

The USDA used the Hudson recall as an opportunity to seek more authority to reject contaminated products and crack down on companies that produce food unfit for human consumption. Just two weeks after the recall, Glickman asked Congress for the power to fine companies that violate safety laws, order recalls, shut down dirty meat plants more quickly, and require companies to tell the USDA when substandard meat is produced.

The government can order recalls of unsafe toys, cars, pesticides, and infant formula, but recalls of tainted meat are voluntary—left to the discretion of meat companies. And, inexplicably, while the USDA can fine people who sell cats without a license, abuse circus elephants, sell potatoes that are too small, and keep poor records on watermelons, the agency cannot fine companies that sell meat contaminated with *E. coli*, *Listeria*, and other potentially fatal bacteria.

"At a certain point, it becomes fairly evident who's being protected here," Glickman told Congress.[416] The proposal received some weighty support, from the likes of Sens. Tom Daschle, Tom Harkin, Ted Kennedy, and Pat Leahy. "Today," Harkin said, "a food safety outbreak can be tantamount to a plague."[417]

Just as in 1994 and 1995, however, when similar reforms were proposed following the Jack-in-the-Box disaster, the ability to truly regulate the meat industry was stymied. Standing in the way were the National Cattlemen's Beef Association, National Food Processors Association, Grocery Manufacturers Association, and other powerful food industry groups that have given millions of dollars to the campaigns of key members of Congress.

Instead of cracking down on companies that produce filthy meat, Congress, under the food industry's heavy influence, went in the opposite direction. In September 1997, one month after the Hudson recall, Rep. Greg Ganske introduced the "Hamburger Safety Act," ordering the FDA to legalize irradiated red meat.

Ganske, a Republican plastic surgeon from Iowa, had just received $30,000 for his 1996 re-election campaign from a Who's Who of pro-irradiation companies and groups: Cargill, Philip Morris/Kraft, National Cattlemen's Beef Association, Grocery Manufacturers of America, National Food Processors Association, and the American Medical Association.[418] (Ganske's claim to fame was unseating 36-year incumbent Democrat Neal Smith in 1994 by driving around in a beat-up 1958 DeSoto with a sign on the roof lampooning Smith's longevity, "'58 Nealmobile - WHY is it still running?")

Ganske's ally in the Senate was Republican Mitch McConnell of Kentucky, a powerful member of the Agriculture Committee. McConnell, too, had collected large donations from agriculture interests for his 1996 reelection campaign. Dozens of contributions from the livestock, poultry, dairy, food processing, agricultural services, and related industries totaled $370,000.[419] And McConnell supported legislation to weaken labeling of irradiated foods, which also passed in 1997.

The FDA promptly complied with Congress's mandate, approving irradiated beef in December 1997. Like nearly all prior applications, this one came not from a food company but an irradiation outfit, Isomedix (see Chapter 7).

Just as the FDA and USDA thought they were getting a handle on the *E. coli* problem, another harmful bacteria showed up.

One may not realize it, based on the company's quaint, down-home image, but Sara Lee is one of the largest food and consumer products companies in the world. With $18 billion in annual sales that span the globe, Chicago-based Sara Lee has more than 500 production and distribution facilities in 34 U.S. states and 50 countries. In addition to its namesake, its many popular brands include Pillsbury, Ball Park, Hillshire Farms, Jimmy Dean, Chock Full o'Nuts, and Chase & Sanborn.

It's a company that doesn't make many big mistakes. Something did go wrong, however, at Sara Lee's hot dog and cold cut factory in Zeeland, Michigan, near Grand Rapids, in 1998. *Listeria monocytogenes* contaminated the company's largest meat facility, which produces up to one million pounds of meat per day and operates under the name Bil Mar Foods.

Plant managers knew about the problem but didn't do anything to fix it until 15 people died, six miscarriages occurred, and some 100 other people fell ill in 22 states.

Listeria are among the most dangerous foodborne pathogens, killing one-fifth of people afflicted—about 500 of 2,500 infected people per year. A so-called "cold-loving" bacteria, it can live in cheese, ice cream, raw vegetables, and all types of raw meat, including poultry, fish, and sausage. *Listeria* thrives in moist conditions like drains and condensation from machinery, so the key to preventing *Listeria* contamination in meat plants is good sanitation, as well as environmental testing. Unfortunately, under HACCP, USDA inspectors no longer do preproduction inspections to make sure that surfaces are dry and clean. The corporation is supposed to make sure that its safety plan addresses these types of hazards.

At its most mild, *Listeria* can cause diarrhea, nausea, and vomiting. At its worst it can cause meningitis and encephalitis. Pregnant women can suffer miscarriages and stillbirths. Especially vulnerable people include infants, the elderly, the frail, and people with chronic diseases or weakened immune systems.

Thirty-five million pounds of hot dogs, turkey breast, corned beef, and other meat products sold under the Ball Park, Grillmaster, Hygrade, and other labels were recalled nationwide in what stands as the largest meat recall in U.S. history. Though the first illnesses were reported in August 1998, the recall did not begin until December.

Bil Mar was among the first meat plants in the country to operate under HACCP. The outbreak illustrates the system's core problem: giving profit-driven corporations more power to inspect themselves and less to federal inspectors, who work for the consumers.

USDA inspectors cited the plant 112 times during the first half of 1998. Workers dropped knives on dirty floors and used them without cleaning them. Old pieces of meat were found in equipment that ostensibly had been cleaned. Turkey carcasses headed for hot dogs and cold cuts were smeared with feces. Food was littered with rust, pieces of plastic, metal shavings, and other trash.

In April 1998, eight months before the recall, a Bil Mar customer returned 218 cases of turkey breast after it tested positive for *Listeria*. Bil Mar might have known about the problem beforehand but it had stopped testing for the bacteria the previous November. This decision was made shortly after the USDA designated Bil Mar one of the dirtiest meat plants in the Midwest and briefly shut it down. A worker told a USDA inspector that it was "OK for the plant to sell product they thought had *Listeria* in it as long as they didn't know for sure."

Tests on environmental conditions that can give rise to *Listeria* contamination were still being conducted, but they were kept in a special file "that was to be withheld from the USDA." These tests, some of which were coming back positive, led one Bil Mar employee to say "with virtual certainty" that dirty products were being shipped out of the plant, and that upper management knew about the problem.

A week after the recall, a Bil Mar employee told co-workers: "You all know too much. This could sink Sara Lee, and loose lips sink ships."

All of this came out during a USDA investigation that concluded that Bil Mar "knew or should have known" that the meat was fouled by *Listeria*.

Despite the USDA's findings, and despite statements from Bil Mar employees who said the *Listeria* problem was well known within the company, federal prosecutors decided against filing felony charges against Sara Lee. The company pleaded guilty in June 2001 to one misdemeanor count of selling tainted meat, paid a $200,000 fine and donated $3 million to Michigan State University for food safety research.[420,421,422]

Sara Lee also reached a number of settlements with families of people killed or sickened in the outbreak. One of them is Melanie Moul, whose daughter, Hope, died 10 minutes after she was born on December 29, 1998. Moul, of Sewickly, Pennsylvania, near Pittsburgh, came down with flu-like symptoms about a month after eating contaminated hot dogs. An autopsy confirmed that Hope was infected with *Listeria*. "It was a horrible night," Moul said, "and a horrible experience."[423]

One year after the Sara Lee/Bil Mar recall, the federal government released the first of several reports finding serious flaws with the USDA's meat inspection system. In December 1999, the General Accounting Office (GAO), the investigative arm of Congress, determined that USDA inspectors weren't trained well enough to enforce the agency's new system, HACCP.

Under HACCP, many USDA inspectors didn't know how dirty a meat plant had to be in order to file violations or require a company to improve its hygiene programs. And, many inspectors didn't know whether they could use certain bacteria tests conducted by companies as a rationale to issue violations or shut down plants.[424]

These ambiguities struck at the heart of the ConAgra recall, which occurred more than two years after the GAO report. USDA inspectors assigned to the Greeley plant knew ConAgra's internal tests were turning up positive for *E. coli*, but because they didn't know whether they could use these results to act against the company, they didn't.

Seven months later, in June 2000, the USDA's in-house investigators found that HACCP "had reduced its oversight beyond what was prudent and necessary for the protection of the consumer." In particular, investigators faulted the USDA for not requiring meat companies to turn over their bacteria test results, including tests for *E. coli* and *Listeria*. When USDA inspectors did find hygiene problems, they frequently did nothing about it. It was also found that many meat facilities did not have adequate hygiene plans in place at all.[425]

Another disaster struck six months later. In December 2000, Cargill recalled 16.7 million pounds of ready-to-eat turkey and chicken sold under several labels, including Boar's Head, Plantation, Riverside, and Honeysuckle. About 30 people living in 10 states were infected with *Listeria*. Four people died and three miscarriages were reported.

Cargill, based in Minneapolis, is the largest privately held company in the U.S. While it has a reputation for being highly concerned about food safety, it is also widely known for holding its cards close to the vest.

Similar to the Sara Lee/Bil Mar outbreak, Cargill knew it had a *Listeria* problem but didn't tell USDA inspectors about it. In-house testing revealed a generic type of *Listeria*, and the company detected the potentially deadly *Listeria monocytogenes* strain in some products. The outbreaks at Cargill fell through a huge loophole. The USDA has a "zero-tolerance" policy on *Listeria* in sealed packages, but the products that tested positive weren't in sealed packages.

Though people started getting sick in July, Cargill didn't recall any meat until December, when investigators from the U.S. Centers for Disease Control confronted the company with evidence linking blood from sickened consumers to the *Listeria* found in Cargill's plant. Shockingly, meat recalls are voluntary. The government has no ability to require a meat company to recall a contaminated product.

How much respect does the meat industry have for the government? A Cargill spokesperson said that even if the company did tell USDA inspectors about the *Listeria* problem, he presumed they wouldn't have told the company to fix it.[426]

For reasons that remain unclear, perhaps because of Cargill's ability to do damage control, the recall did not generate nearly as much media attention as other major outbreaks—even some that did not cause any deaths.

A year after the Cargill recall yet another federal government report criticized HACCP. The system's essential feature—giving meat companies more authority to inspect their own operations—wasn't working. Company employees were not properly trained to determine whether diseased or contaminated carcasses should be rejected—a task USDA inspectors once performed. Inexplicably, USDA officials said they would not require company employees to receive such training.

Additionally, the GAO found a dramatic increase in fecal contamination of carcasses in 11 chicken plants. Violations at one facility increased by more than 500 percent. Slaughterline speeds had increased from 20 to 80 carcasses per minute, making the job of detecting contamination much more difficult.[427]

Eight months later, during the ConAgra recall in July 2002, the GAO released its most damning report yet, which described a meat inspection system seemingly flawed beyond repair. The USDA was failing to ensure that companies' hygiene plans were designed to prevent contamination—the very center of HACCP. Once again the GAO found that USDA inspectors were not adequately trained.

Perhaps most disturbing, the USDA inspectors frequently did nothing when they observed hygiene problems. One facility was cited 154 times in a single year for allowing feces on carcasses, yet the USDA took no action.

The GAO grimly concluded that "consumers may be unnecessarily exposed to unsafe foods."[428]

There is, of course, never a good time for a massive recall of potentially contaminated meat. Having one shortly after a government report criticizes the nation's meat inspection system is particularly tragic and embarrassing.

In October 2002, three months after the ConAgra recall, Pilgrim's Pride recalled 27.4 million pounds of fresh and ready-to-eat turkey and chicken products feared contaminated with *Listeria*. The meat was produced at a facility in Franconia Township, Pennsylvania, near Philadelphia, that operates under the name Wampler Foods. Founded in 1946 in Pittsburg, Texas as a one-man chicken feed store, Pilgrim's Pride is now the second-largest poultry company in the U.S., with $2.6 billion in annual sales.

The recall was the third-largest in U.S. history. The outbreak was held responsible for seven deaths (including an infant), three miscarriages and more than 50 illnesses in eight Northeast and Midwest states. More than 25 deaths and 130 illnesses were attributed to a *Listeria* outbreak during the summer and fall of 2002, though the cause of most of them could not be determined.

Though no illnesses were reported, about two million pounds of the meat entered the federal school lunch program, which may have been the impetus that led the USDA to lift the irradiated food ban seven months later.

Subsequent inquiries confirmed the worst fears harbored by watchdogs about allowing food companies to inspect themselves, and about permitting former meat industry executives to take over the USDA's upper ranks.

Emerging as a key figure in the Wampler fiasco was Vince Erthal, a USDA inspector who alerted agency higher-ups about serious problems at the Wampler plant nearly a year before the recall. Not only were Erthal's requests for an official USDA investigation of the plant consistently rejected, the agency turned the tables after the affair became public and accused him of falling down on the job.

Erthal, who worked at the plant for two years, called the conditions there "horrendous." He told Congressional investigators: "Live flies and cockroaches in processing departments during operations, dead flies observed on exposed product, repeated condensation dripping on product, dried meat particles from previous days' operation, algae growth on walls and ceilings, rusty equipment, and foreign matter in raw materials."

Poultry parts that fell into a barrel labeled "inedible" were retrieved from this "*Listeria* soup" and returned to the production line. Foods dropped onto the floor were put back on the line without being washed.

"My first day at Wampler, I just couldn't believe it," Erthal told *60 Minutes II*. "I've been to approximately 150 different plants throughout this country as an inspector, and I have never seen a plant as bad as that. [It was] by far the worst."[429]

Erthal says his USDA superiors discouraged him from filing reports on these and other filthy conditions at the plant.

The Wampler outbreak exposed a weakness in an inspection system often characterized as "don't ask, don't tell"—or worse, "don't look, don't know." In a laughable loophole, the USDA randomly tests processed meat for *Listeria*, but not processing facilities and equipment. Many companies, including Wampler, voluntarily do such tests but are not required to share results with USDA inspectors.

Similar to Sara Lee/Bil Mar, Wampler was doing its own tests on environmental conditions that can give rise to *Listeria*, and some were coming back positive. Also like Sara Lee/Bil Mar, Wampler failed to take the next step and run specific tests for *Listeria monocytogenes*. Unlike this earlier recall, however, USDA officials knew about the positive results at Wampler four months before the recall but did nothing to fix the problems, Congressional investigators learned.

What's more, Wampler employees were given advance notice of the USDA's *Listeria* tests on poultry, rendering the tests "rigged," according to Congressional investigators.[430,431]

These breakdowns likely explain why the source of the dirty meat wasn't discovered by the USDA, but by the U.S. Centers for Disease Control, which was investigating a *Listeria* poisoning outbreak in the Northeast.

Representative Henry Waxman led yet another Congressional inquiry: "If what I have been told is true, the USDA abdicated its duty to protect the consumer."[432]

Within a month of the outbreak, the USDA announced it would start testing facilities and equipment for *Listeria*, or force companies to turn over their own results. USDA officials acknowledged that the Wampler outbreak might not have been as severe had these tests been underway.[433] The new policy, however, was watered down from its original version, which would have called for violators to be fined. This was snipped out at the behest of the food industry, which pleaded its case directly to the Bush White House.[434]

Following these and other recalls over the past decade, many of the companies involved have used or explored irradiation:

- Colorado Boxed Beef, which recalled 359,000 pounds of beef after an *E. coli* scare in November 1998, sells irradiated hamburger patties under the "New Generation" label at 800 Publix grocery stores in the Southeast.

- Omaha Steaks, which recalled 22,000 pounds of ground beef patties in October 2000 because of a possible *E. coli* contamination, now sells only irradiated hamburgers. The company announced the change one month after the recall.

- Schwan's, which recalled large quantities of ice cream products in 1995 after a *Salmonella* outbreak sickened from 3,000 to 200,000 people, sells only irradiated hamburgers through its home-delivery service. (Irradiation cannot be used on dairy products.)

- Rochester Meat, which recalled 30,000 pounds of ground beef in September 2000 because of a possible *E. coli* contamination, has sold irradiated beef. Rochester also owns Huisken Meats, which was among the first U.S. companies to sell irradiated hamburgers. Huisken's meat is irradiated at Texas A&M University, home to former USDA officials and long-time irradiation advocates Elsa and Peter Murano (see Chapter 6).

- IBP, which bought the Hudson Foods facility responsible for the 1997 recall, has sold irradiated beef. IBP also purchased Thorn Apple Valley after the Southfield, Michigan-based company recalled 30 million pounds of hot dogs and deli meat in January 1999. IBP has issued several recalls of its own, including a half-million pounds of ground beef in August 2001. IBP was since purchased by Tyson Foods, which has also issued recalls in recent years and expressed an interest in irradiation.

- Excel, which recalled 190,000 pounds of ground beef and pork in June 2001, has sold irradiated beef and considered installing its own irradiation machines. Excel, a division of Cargill, owns Emmpak Foods, which recalled 3.4 million pounds of ground beef in 2002 after more than 50 people in seven states fell ill from *E. coli* O157:H7. Emmpak briefly sold irradiated ground beef before it was acquired by Excel.

- Carneco Foods, which recalled 131,000 pounds of ground beef in July 2002, has irradiated some of its beef products.

Clearly, with so many recalls taking place, and with so many companies discussing irradiation as a solution, something is fundamentally wrong with the way that meat—particularly ground beef—is produced in this country.

First, the meat industry has become extremely concentrated over the past 30 years. Enormous multinational corporations that own or control millions of animals face intense pressure from stockholders and competitors to cut corners, while simultaneously trying to maintain hygienic conditions in huge, ungainly slaughterhouses and processing plants:

- The top four beef-packing companies—Tyson, Swift/ConAgra, Cargill/Excel, and Farmland National Beef—control 83 percent of the U.S. market, up from 72 percent in 1990;

- The top five pork-packing companies—Smithfield (which recently acquired Farmland Foods), Tyson/IBP, Swift/ConAgra, Cargill/Excel, and Hormel—control 59 percent of the U.S. market, up from 40 percent in 1990;

- The top four chicken-producing companies—Tyson/IBP, Gold Kist, Pilgrim's Pride, and ConAgra—control 50 percent of the U.S. market, up from 44 percent in 1990; and

- The top four turkey-producing companies—Hormel (Jennie-O), ConAgra (Butterball), Cargill, and Pilgrim's Pride—control 45 percent of the U.S. market, up from 33 percent in 1990.[435]

Second, cattle are crammed into vast feed-lots better described as "factory farms," where shared food and water sources spread bacteria and disease; in trucks and railroad cars, where feces smudge from one cow onto the next; and in slaughterhouses, where sloppy handling practices spread filth everywhere. In processing plants, one infected cow can contaminate eight tons of ground beef. In one instance, a single batch of ground beef was traced to slaughterhouses in six states and 443 cows.

In addition, the use of antibiotics has increased dramatically since the 1950s. No longer given only to sick animals, these drugs are now applied routinely for their mysterious ability to speed growth and reduce an animal's need for food and water. These "sub-therapeutic" doses are also used to ease the incredibly unhealthy and stressful conditions of modern feed-lots. Many antibiotic-resistant bacteria have emerged.

Further, cows are commonly fed corn to fatten them up for slaughter. These low-fiber foods change the chemical and microbial conditions in cattle guts, promoting the growth of pathogens. Feeding cows hay, which is high in fiber, can reduce *E. coli* O157:H7.[436]

Finally, relentless advertising has significantly increased consumers' preference for highly processed foods. The more food is chopped, commingled, formed, and otherwise handled from the farm to the fork, the more opportunities there are for contamination to occur.[437]

What's To Be Done?

Just as the main reasons for foodborne disease are well known, so are many solutions.

Currently, the USDA cannot order a company to recall products known or suspected to be contaminated. The agency can only make recommendations. Days can pass before a recall occurs, permitting hazardous food to reach market. Proposals to give recall authority to the USDA have been introduced in Congress for years but have been defeated by senators and representatives who receive large campaign contributions from agriculture interests.

Bacteria testing could be improved. Unbeknownst to most consumers, most meat actually leaves processing plants and reaches stores and restaurants before test results are returned, allowing potentially contaminated meat to be consumed. Quicker tests are available and are being used in Europe. Further, companies are not required to release all test results to the USDA, and tests are not required for many common foodborne bacteria, such as *Campylobacter*, *Clostridium perfringens*, and *Shigella*. And, tests for *E. coli* O157:H7 are conducted sparsely on live cows, hogs, turkeys, and chickens.

Reformers have called for giving the USDA power to fine companies that maintain dirty facilities, and giving agency inspectors the authorities they had before HACCP took effect. Tracing tainted meat as far back as the animal's birth would help clean up feed-lots, transportation systems, and slaughterhouses. Setting caps on slaughterline speeds would allow inspections to be more thorough and reduce the pressure on workers that leads to mistakes, as well as sanitation shortcuts that spread contamination. Better worker training is also needed. Ensuring the quality and safety of livestock feed would reduce illness and bacterial contamination.

Instead of these and many other sensible ideas that make food safer, the industry seems more inclined to focus on irradiation. From the industry's perspective, irradiation might represent the most logical next step.

The industry is entrenched in a system where accountants make decisions about how animals are raised, slaughtered, and processed. Corporations treat cows, pigs, chickens, and other food animals like so many widgets—not living beings that will go on to be consumed by living beings, but just another product that is made, distributed, advertised, and sold. This mentality might be the best approach when it comes to the bottom line, but it has created a system that is growing increasingly incompatible with producing safe, wholesome food, especially in light of the absence of strict regulations and the lack of enforcement of current regulations.

Chapter 12

The Future: Going Global

Fran Jell was an unlikely participant in the 10-month occupation of a food irradiation facility being constructed on the east coast of Australia, in Narangba, 40 km north of Brisbane. She and her husband, Frank Jell, have been married for 43 years and had looked forward to living in the country, running their small building commissioning company, and enjoying their grandchildren.

They retired to Narangba, a peaceful rural town, and Jell, who has a soft spot for marsupials like possums and gliders, became a volunteer caretaker for injured and orphaned animals. The Jells' home, immaculately kept, is in the center of a large garden where they have planted native species of flowering trees and abundant flowers.

The Jells were shocked when they found in July 1999 that the food irradiation company Steritech had already presented its plans for an irradiation facility to the local Council during the preceding April. The plant would be located less than a kilometer from the Jells' house. There was no time to mount an effective campaign.

The Council approved the facility one month later, in August—the same month that Australia lifted its 10-year ban on irradiation, bending the rules so that the facility could be located in the Jells' Shire, a nuclear-free zone.

The local citizenry was outraged. Not only had the public been told that the new facility would not handle food, they had been assured it would be non-nuclear, when in reality it was to be fueled by cobalt-60. And even though the facility would be located in an endangered wetland area that flows into Moreton Bay, no environmental impact study was conducted.

Jell is not someone who "rolls over" easily. Raised in the outback, and sent to a town boarding school hundreds of miles away, as most outback children were in times past, Jell is a very independent person who believes in holding her elected representatives accountable. So, when activists from nearby

Brisbane began arriving in Narangba for strategy meetings, Jell was ready to work in coalition to fight back. After all, "as the crow flies," her home was 500 meters from the plant.

Robin Taubenfeld, an anti-nuclear activist from Brisbane, had caught wind of the plant and was outraged that the Council found "no significant risk" from the radioactive cobalt. The authorities were not even planning to write a disaster plan. (Eventually the community forced officials to acknowledge that the plant needed a disaster plan, and the state and local governments were sent into a flurry of confusion as to who was responsible for what.)

Taubenfeld, an American, grew up in Dallas, Texas, the daughter of a diplomat and a college professor. After going to school at Swarthmore College, she moved to Japan where she taught English for several years, eventually emigrating to Australia. She is a full-time community activist.

Jell and Taubenfeld were joined by Anna Barnes, an energetic Tasmanian and talented organizer, and a host of other activists, in making the protest camp a success. A range of organizations became involved including the East Narangba Community Action Group, Everyone for a Nuclear Free Future (ENuFF), Friends of the Earth (FOE), and the Stop Food Irradiation Alliance.

They started protesting at the site June 6, 2002, the day after the earthwork began. That day, 11 protesters linked arms and blocked several trucks carrying dirt for the facility's foundation from entering the facility. Work stopped and tension mounted as the company pushed to resume construction. One young woman locked herself to a Bobcat work machine; arrests soon followed.

Over the next two weeks, dozens of people were removed from the site; seven were arrested on various charges. Among them, besides Taubenfeld, were Queensland Greens spokesperson Drew Hutton and Greg Brown of the Refugee Action Collective. Some of those arrested were fined. Meanwhile, a fence was built around the Steritech site and authorities moved the protesters to the state-owned land across the street.

Fran Jell says, "Never in my life have I witnessed such violence as I have from police towards the community." In the end, about 30 people were charged with criminal offenses, including one man who was fined $120 for tooting his horn to say goodbye to protesters—an "unlawful use of a warning device."

The *Sunday Mail* reported on July 7 that threats had been made against protesters. Five days later someone threw a supposed bomb into the camp that did not explode. On the other hand, the company claimed that protesters had caused hundreds of thousands of dollars of damage.

In the interim, the protesters settled into their "camp." On August 7 more than 200 people blocked heavy equipment from entering the site as part of a seven-day picket. A Steritech employee is alleged to have punched a protester in the face, one of several such reported assaults, many of them against women.

The ugliness continued into January 2003, when police sent dogs to attack the protesters. One protester had his nose broken and bloodied by an officer and others were injured. In February, Queensland officials filed an eviction order against the twice-arrested Taubenfeld, who the government charged was the "organizer and representative of all those in occupation of the camp site."

However, even though the camp was often on edge, the protesters had made it a relatively comfortable place for those who lived there full time, and the large numbers of weekend visitors. Meals were cooked in the solar-powered kitchen, a welcome center offered visitors information, a garden provided fresh vegetables, music was played and songs were sung around the nightly campfires, and a festive atmosphere often reigned.

In a scene that's been compared to *Mad Max*, protesters built a 12-foot-tall "Deception Castle" with colored flags as signs for protection of the area's bushland ecosystem. They built eight-foot-tall "Nuclear-Free Knights" in shiny, stainless steel armor made of recycled metal salvaged from the property.

Although the State Supreme Court threw out the eviction order and required state officials to pay all legal fees, approximately 100 police officers stormed the site on March 6, 2003, with horses, trail bikes, dogs, paddy wagons, barricades, shields, and batons. Much to their surprise, they found three lone campers maintaining the campfire, because an eavesdropping protester overheard officers discussing the action the night before, allowing nearly all of the protesters to get out early. The protestors were evicted and the camp was shut down.

The local action at the protest camp has morphed into a national campaign against food irradiation in Australia. Taubenfeld is coordinating the effort along with many of the activists and volunteers who have been involved since the protest camp, in addition to many new people. These activists are engaging in outreach to consumers and organizing a legislative campaign that requires truthful labeling. Most Australians, as is common of many people all over the world, will not buy food that is irradiated.

Taubenfeld says of the transition to a full-scale campaign, "It was time for us to move on from putting energy into the camp to developing a full-scale campaign against food irradiation. The issue is broader than the danger of nuclear materials—it's about the safety of our food and the survival of Australian agriculture."

Those are sentiments that Andre Leu shares. As chair of the Organic Federation of Australia and vice-president of the Australian Lychee Growers Association, Leu is someone who knows agriculture. Andre, a slim, well-spoken man in cowboy boots, is one of the pioneers of the exotic tropical fruit industry and now grows lychees in Queensland, Australia. He is a frequent world traveler, who has been involved in negotiating several trade protocol agreements with the Australian government at the state and federal levels. One of the goals of these protocol agreements is to prevent invasive pests and diseases from being introduced into the importing country.

Another has been the use of light food-grade oils as a protocol for importing Rambutans, a strange-looking oval fruit with bright red skin covered with short fleshy hairs, into Japan.

Leu says, "These oils have replaced the use of toxic methyl bromide to disinfest fruits of external insect pests. Another method that is used to rid fruit trees of insect pests is weekly spraying of protein bait on a few leaves of a fruit tree. It is important that fruit be pest free so that fruit from Queensland, Australia can be traded in fruit fly-free areas."

Leu is worried about the current push to use irradiation as a quarantine protocol. He says, "Irradiation will add extra costs to Australia's horticultural exports, which are very expensive on the world market because we pay our farm laborers a livable wage. It is going to give large corporations a monopoly on the export of Australian products and further concentrate farming income with agribusiness—all at the expense of the family farm."

His concerns are justified. Around the globe, multinational corporations such as Philip Morris, Kraft, Delmonte, Con-Agra, Tyson, and other transnational corporations are planning to use irradiation to increase their global reach.

Why?

Irradiation is one tool that can be used to increase global food trade because it kills invasive insects on fruits and vegetables, doubles or triples the shelf life of food, and it masks the contamination on factory-farm produced meat. This means that agribusiness can more aggressively pursue its plan to move food production to countries where labor costs are lower and pesky environmental regulations do not interfere with maximizing profits. In short, irradiation could play an important role in global food trade, which is at the center of multinational food corporations' strategy for growing profits.

In the U.S. and other developed countries, these companies have used their enormous political muscle to eliminate the regulations that set a floor for prices and historically have kept an oversupply of farm products from flooding the market. Farmers have been urged to embrace the marketplace, accept the free trade of commodities and other food products across borders, and to surrender protective farm programs. The result has been the devastation of family farming.

The effects are already widespread. In the U.S. every month, as a result of changes in national and international farm policy, 1,200 small farms fail.[438]

George Naylor, a farmer in Iowa, knows firsthand how these policies hurt farmers. Naylor is president of the National Family Farm Coalition (NFFC), an organization founded in 1986 to represent and empower family farms and rural groups whose members face the deepening economic recession in rural communities. The NFFC works to reduce the corporate control of agriculture and to promote a more socially just farm and food policy.

Naylor is an activist at heart. In his own community he is a member of the Iowa Citizens for Community Improvement, a 30-year-old organization that works on issues ranging from agriculture to housing and utilities to Latino organizing. Naylor talks to farmers every day in Iowa, and as president of NFFC he has the opportunity to meet and discuss issues with farmers from around the world.

Naylor, who grows 470 acres of corn and soybeans near Churdan, Iowa, with his wife Peggy and their two sons, has been actively involved in farm policy issues since shortly after he began farming in 1976. He considers himself an environmentalist as well as a farmer.

Naylor says, "Giant corporations like Cargill and ConAgra have pushed for so-called market-oriented approaches to agriculture policy. Current U.S. agriculture policy and various trade agreements have adopted this philosophy, resulting in the curse of low prices, which then spreads around the world."

He goes on to say, "This rapid globalization of agricultural commodity markets, and the resulting low prices paid to farmers, has resulted in a crisis that threatens the survival of farm families worldwide. But, it has benefited agribusiness immensely, especially industrialized livestock producers who buy cheap grain for their confined animal feeding operations. This has allowed the spread of factory farms here and is fueling them in many developing countries."

Kathy Ozer, executive director of NFFC, explains that because farmers from around the world are being pitted against each other, NFFC believes it is critical to have an international alliance for the purpose of strategizing and coordinating on farm policies. It is also vital to understand how U.S. farm policy and trade work together to benefit transnational corporations.

Ozer should know. She has been working on farm policy for 15 years, and few people in Washington, DC know as much about trade and agriculture policy. She is a virtual walking encyclopedia on the past three U.S. farm bills and negotiations around trade.

Ozer explains the genesis of the global coalition to which her organization belongs, "NFFC's membership is on a national level, yet our activities are international through our participation in Via Campesina—an international coalition of farmers and peasants. From the late 1980s farmers in the U.S. have been working with farmer allies in Europe—first in response to ongoing trade negotiations in Geneva and later leading up to the World Trade Organization (WTO) meetings in Seattle in 1999. Seattle was an important time in the growth of Via Campesina and the involvement of NFFC leaders in this important international effort to link farmers and peasants across borders and regions. Alongside other important meetings, rallies, teach-ins, and events going on in Seattle, Via Campesina met daily to further the analysis and develop plans to work together."

"Via Campesina, has grown tremendously and has representation from around the globe. Its member groups—like NFFC—have continued to work closely together on international agriculture and trade issues. Via Campesina is also very supportive of NFFC's work on U.S. farm policy because it recognizes how what happens here—like the collapse of grain prices—affects the world market and the ability of farmers around the world to survive and feed their domestic populations. Via Campesina understands that it is important to be a strong countervailing force to the multinational corporations that are influencing agricultural policies worldwide."

The multinational food companies have been instrumental in creating a series of global trade pacts that increased international commodity flows and mandated changes in farm programs. These agreements have created an international market where agricultural products are sold far below the cost of production, and they have required nations to remove many of the protections that safeguard domestic markets. This has been achieved through the adoption of policies that force open borders and allow large corporate players to buy cheap food products and to sell them across international borders wherever they can make the most profit.

Ozer goes on to say, "In the U.S., the 1996 Freedom to Farm Act eliminated farm programs that stabilized production and price of many commodities. This radical legislation came to be called by farmers the Freedom to Fail Act. It created incentives to bring more acreage into production for commodity crops like grain, thus benefiting corporations like Cargill and ConAgra."

Dennis Olsen, an expert on these issues with the Institute for Agriculture and Trade Policy explains it this way, "U.S. farmers were told that the 1996 Freedom to Farm bill was going to get government out of the way. They were told they were the most efficient farmers in the world and that they could export their way to prosperity. But, as a result of deregulation, prices for commodities eventually collapsed by as much as 40 percent."

Olsen explains, "The international grain cartels can go on the world market and buy feed grains like soy and corn at 30 to 40 percent below what it costs to produce the crop. For instance, Cargill can then provide their industrialized animal production operations this cheap feed. This has driven many family-owned farms out of business."

Olsen, who is originally from Montana, has seen firsthand what is happening to family farmers. Shortly after he graduated from college, he worked on agriculture and coal-mining issues for the Illinois South Project, which is now called the Illinois Stewardship Alliance. One of his duties was staffing a hotline on farm foreclosures and farm credit issues. He saw firsthand how farmers and rural communities were suffering.

His experience in Illinois influenced him profoundly and he spent several years working first for the Dakota Resource Council, and later at the Northern Plains Resource Council on agriculture and trade issues. Among the issues that these grassroots community-based organizations work on are family farming, ranching, and fair trade.

Olsen says, "Food irradiation could be a big benefit to the giant meat companies like Cargill and Tyson Foods. The first stage of their strategy was to gain control of the meat industry in the U.S., which they have done. But, now they are moving into other countries like Brazil, where it's even cheaper to raise cattle, hogs, chickens."

"Companies don't have to send live animals to the U.S. or other markets," Olsen says. "They can move their processing plants where labor is cheap and they don't have to bother with pesky environmental regulations, and ship it to its final destination."

This approach is based on the "free trade" dogma, although one could argue that there is nothing "free" about it. Within it, all countries adopt the same economic model. The goal is to remove geographic and cultural differences that might reduce the efficiency of corporate operations. The national laws and regulations of democratic nations designed to protect the country's citizens and environment are viewed as impediments to corporate profits. The establishment of the WTO in 1995 continues to be one way that the "free trade" model is being advanced. It requires each member country to conform its laws, regulations, and administrative procedures to the agreements that it enforces, which range from agriculture to intellectual property rights.

The International Forum on Globalization describes this unaccountable international institution:

> The specific role of the WTO is to set homogenized global rules for all countries—one size fits all—and to specifically challenge national environmental and social laws viewed as obstacles to corporate free trade. Given that it was granted draconian enforcement powers, the WTO can now impose harsh punishments on democratic nations that stray from its rules. A past president of the WTO, Renato Ruggiero put it bluntly in 1998: The WTO will be "the new constitution for a global economy."[439]

Under the current trade regime, the WTO is the final authority. It can require nations to change their laws and standards to accommodate its decisions made in secret proceedings by trade officials—or else be subject to severe economic sanctions. The WTO has a tribunal system that uses sanctions as a punishment to countries that do not follow its rules regarding "trade barriers." These so-called trade barriers are often the protective laws and regulations that countries enact through a democratic process to protect citizens and natural resources.

The WTO's rules on agriculture, currently being renegotiated, are called the Agreement on Agriculture (AOA). These rules are based on the idea that food should be treated like any other good or commodity. It does not recognize that farming and agriculture are different than manufacturing other goods for the marketplace. Food is a necessity of life. The economic supply, demand, and price modeling that are used to describe how widgets are produced does not explain how food is grown. Pigs are not pipe, steers are not stoves, and frying pullets are not frying pans. Manufacturers can respond quickly to changes in market supplies to reduce costs and stabilize prices. Farmers, on the other hand, cannot easily manipulate the supply of agricultural products once their crops are in the ground or their calves are born.

This failed philosophy has resulted in many nations moving toward losing the ability to produce food for the citizens within their own borders—a notion known as food security. Developing nations are often forced by international finance institutions like the World Bank to develop export economies based on industrialized agriculture. This means that the independent peasant farmers who were once able to provide food for their families and communities are forced to grow crops for export to wealthy developed nations.

The World Bank and other development banks work hand-in-hand with institutions like the WTO to pressure developing nations to offer incentives to giant corporations for growing export commodities. The idea is that some countries are well positioned to grow a crop and so they should concentrate on growing it, rather than feeding their population. Instead, they will purchase the foods from other countries that have a "competitive advantage," (an economist-coined term,) for growing some other crop. Of course, it is an advantage for giant food corporations that are looking for the cheapest place to grow the food items they need. This is the antithesis of growing food for local consumption, and the advancement of this philosophy could be devastating for peasant farmers around the world.

Today, almost half of the world's population grows food for their families and communities. They grow staples and a mix of diverse crops. They have developed their own seed varieties, fertilizers, and pest management. They live in communities where the concept of the commons is strong, resulting in shared seeds, water, and labor. This system has worked since the beginning of time. Unfortunately this kind of local self-sufficiency is scorned by multinational corporations, and the institutions they influence.[440]

"Irradiation, if widely adopted, will facilitate this type of food production," says Jayson Cainglet, a Filipino activist working to stop irradiation and save family farming in the Philippines. "Irradiation is designed to cover up inherent problems in production methods that agribusiness employs, but small-scale farms do not rely on these technologies."[441]

For more than 15 years, Cainglet has represented peasant groups in the Philippines and worked with non-governmental organizations that support their interests. Most recently his focus has been on trade and agriculture.

As someone who grew up in the Philippines, Cainglet is an unusual activist. In college he became aware of the reasons for the tremendous disparity between the rich and poor in his country. The Philippines suffers from major economic stratification. Since college, he has devoted himself to creating a new social order. He says that he is inspired when he sees people from different countries and backgrounds working together to create a new vision.

Cainglet has been instrumental in stopping the construction of an irradiation plant in the Philippines that was being promoted by SureBeam before the company's bankruptcy. Before its demise, SureBeam had been negotiating with two local agribusinesses to build an irradiation facility near Manila that would have cost at least $5 million. SureBeam was also negotiating with Tomas Osmena, the mayor of the city of Cebu, on the scenic island of the same name.

Unfortunately, plans for the irradiation facility were not on hiatus for long. The Philippine Nuclear Research Institute (PNRI) is actively promoting food irradiation and plans for an irradiation facility are back on the front burner. But activists are ready to oppose any plans to build a plant in the country. Cainglet says, "Only agribusiness in the Philippines would benefit from the adoption of irradiation as a quarantine measure for exporting exotic fruits. Small-scale farmers would likely be severely hit by this technology."

Cainglet also actively follows trade issues and is often in Geneva, where the WTO is located. He says that a facility in the Philippines would allow the irradiation of not only mangoes, but also papayas, bananas, and pineapples, directly increasing international trade and destabilizing local, domestic food security. Cainglet goes on to say that the Sanitary and Phytosanitary Agreement (SPS), which is enforced by the WTO, is an important component of the corporate model of agriculture.

Among the SPS Agreement's stated goals is protecting the health of human, animal, and plant life from the risks of pests or disease. Consequently, it covers numerous rules, including those related to meat inspection and the spread of pests.

This SPS Agreement helps facilitate "harmonization," a term in the trade vernacular used to describe the industry's effort to replace national standards and regulations with a single global system. The Agreement also requires member countries to accept the SPS measures of other countries as equivalent, even if they are different, if the exporting country can prove to the importing country that its measures reach the importing country's level of protection.

One example of how these rules are playing out is the way meat is inspected. As was described in Chapter 11, the U.S. has been in the process of deregulating its meat inspection system with disastrous results. Unfortunately, the HACCP system is being foisted on the world. When USDA developed HACCP for domestic beef, it required that its trading partners do the same. In some cases, countries exporting to the U.S. have even weaker laws governing inspection, but the USDA considers them "equivalent." For instance, Brazil has a completely privatized meat inspection system, but it can import meat into the U.S.[442]

To facilitate harmonization and equivalency, the agreement names specific international standards that are presumed to be WTO-legal, such as those established by the International Plant Protection Convention in Geneva and the Codex Alimentarius Commission in Rome. Codex Alimentarius (Latin for "food law") was established in 1963 by the World Health Organization and the U.N. Food and Agriculture Organization to promote world food trade through internationally accepted standards.[443]

It sets standards on behalf of 168 nations. In July 2003, Codex weakened the international food irradiation rules to allow any food to be irradiated at any dose. The decision was made over the objections of more than 10 countries. As alluded to above, these standards are enforceable through the WTO, which means that member nations with laws stricter than the new Codex could have their laws challenged.[444]

The International Plant Protection Convention (IPPC) is an international treaty for plant protection to prevent the spread and introduction of pests to plants and plant products, and to promote appropriate measures for controlling them. It was adopted in November 1952 and has been amended several times since then. It has adopted a guideline for the use of irradiation for pest risk management that allows ionizing radiation from different sources to be used. It says that irradiation can be applied as part of packing operations, to bulk unpackaged commodities, and at centralized locations, such as ports of entry.[445] This measure, which was heavily lobbied for by the International Atomic Energy Agency and other proponents of irradiation, has helped facilitate the push for irradiation of fruits and vegetables.

Codex and the IPPC are two institutions whose rules help facilitate the goals of the WTO. Their regulations, which are global in nature, help large agribusiness interests who want to increase their profits and their control of markets. However, the WTO is not the only instrument for accomplishing this agenda. There are also numerous bilateral agreements and multilateral agreements that promote the interests of giant agriculture.

Trade Treaties

The North American Free Trade Agreement (NAFTA), a trade pact among the U.S., Canada, and Mexico, is an example of a multilateral agreement. Created by making false guarantees, farmers were promised they could export their way to lasting economic success and consumers were promised lower food prices. The promised benefits never materialized: farm income has declined, and consumer prices have risen while some agribusinesses—which lobbied hard for NAFTA and now are avidly promoting its expansion—have seen record profits.[446]

Ironically between 1994 and 2001, during the time that the WTO and NAFTA were supposed to bring new export opportunities to U.S. agriculture, the total contribution of U.S. agriculture to the U.S. economy declined by five percent, a $4 billion decline.[447]

Katie Edwards, executive director of the Dade County Farm Bureau, explains the effect of NAFTA on Florida farmers:

> In fact, for many in the agriculture industry in Miami-Dade County, NAFTA has been nothing short of an unmitigated disaster and come to symbolize devastation within the agriculture industry in general... Florida had a net loss of 35,511 jobs as a direct consequence of NAFTA, a large percentage of which came from the agriculture industry. Florida lost over 1,000 small- and medium-sized farms since NAFTA was implemented...

> Miami-Dade's tomato and pepper farmers were hardest hit. NAFTA drove more than two-thirds of Florida's tomato farmers out of business and the same predicament is now facing our pepper growers. As the Dade County Farm Bureau has said repeatedly, Florida's farmers must contend with higher costs for land and labor than their Mexican counterparts. There is no way our farmers can compete with selling below production costs.[448]

Since NAFTA passed in 1996, wheat farmers, ranchers, vegetable, flower, and fruit growers, chicken producers, and other farmers in the U.S. have suffered declining commodity prices and farm income while a flood of NAFTA imports outpaced U.S. exports to Canada and Mexico. But it was not farmers in Mexico or Canada who benefited from the misery experienced by U.S. farmers. For instance, millions of peasant farmers throughout Mexico have lost a significant source of income and been forced from their small corn farms. Some of these farmers became farm laborers working in squalid conditions for poverty wages on large plantations growing crops for export to the U.S. Others moved to Mexico's cities where unemployment is high, and the quality of life for the poor is difficult.[449]

The major beneficiaries of NAFTA are transnational corporations. The trade agreement gives them immense power over the signatory governments because it grants foreign corporations the ability to challenge local, state, and federal laws in a closed-door trade court. Corporations have taken advantage of this provision. For instance, while massive job losses and millions of small farmers have been ruined in all three countries, profits and the global reach of large corporations continue to grow. Tyson is the largest poultry producer in the world and since its acquisition of the giant meat company IBP, it is now the world's largest red meat producer. Tyson is quickly gaining market share in Mexico, along with other meat producers like Cargill. Both of these companies have considered irradiation as an option.

Mexico is home to several irradiation facilities and 64 different foods can be irradiated, including dehydrated products such as chile peppers and spices. In 2000, Ion Beam Applications, a Belgian company, and MDS Nordion, a Canadian company, opened a new facility in Tepeji, 60 kilometers from Mexico City. This $7 million facility, NGS Enterprises, uses radioactive isotopes to irradiate a range of food items.[450]

Another company, Phytosan, has begun construction on what will be the largest irradiation facility in the world, to be located in Matehuala. They plan to irradiate guava, star fruit, grapefruit, oranges, and mangoes. They are also planning to build a facility in Guadalajara. This company is a joint venture between future customers through their growers associations supported by the Mexican secretary of Agriculture for exports to the U.S and for free trade zones in northern Mexico. The company was formed in response to pressure from the USDA to use irradiation treatments for fruits and vegetables that are hosts to fruit flies and seed weevils.

NAFTA is just one of a host of trade agreements that transnational corporations in the food industry lobbied for, in order to increase their stranglehold on food production. Trade agreements that would expand NAFTA to other countries in the Western Hemisphere are being considered. The Central American Free Trade Agreement (CAFTA) is an agreement among the U.S., the Dominican Republic, and the Central American nations of Costa Rica, El Salvador, Guatemala, Honduras, and Nicaragua. It was ratified by the U.S. Congress in the summer of 2005, and went into effect in El Salvador, Guatemala, Honduras, and Nicaragua in the first half of 2006. As this book goes to press, trade agreements with Peru and Colombia are also being considered. Like NAFTA, major food corporations have lobbied for CAFTA, and are currently pushing for Congress to support the agreements with Peru and Colombia.

Multinational corporations see this as an incentive to move their operations overseas where they can process commodities or grow livestock, or produce fruit and vegetables for export back to the U.S. and other developed countries. Irradiation is one of the technologies that is being advanced to facilitate this strategy.

The U.S. government is heavily under the influence of these multinational corporations that will benefit from opening borders for trade and is a big proponent of using irradiation to promote global food trade. In 2002, in preparation for harmonization, the USDA ruled that irradiation could be used in place of chemical or heat treatments to kill pests.

In June 2003, the USDA hosted a conference on agricultural science and technology in Sacramento, California, inviting ministers of agriculture, environment, and trade from 180 nations. The stated goal of the conference was that it would promote agricultural technologies to feed the world's 800 million starving people, and irradiation was one of the highlighted technologies. Sure-Beam, which had not yet gone bankrupt, spent $50,000 to host the opening ceremony of the Corporate Exposition, which took place simultaneously with the conference.

A month later, USDA Under-secretary for Food Safety, Elsa Murano, in a press release publicizing her keynote address at the First World Congress on Food Irradiation, quoted Pasisan Loaharanu, former head of the International Atomic Energy Agency's food irradiation program. He said, "The Congress is expected to lead to a wider acceptance and application of food irradiation as a measure to facilitate food trade worldwide."[451]

The U.S. Department of Agriculture's Animal and Plant Inspection (APHIS) is also a proponent of using irradiation to boost trade. Arnold Foudin, a special assistant to the director at APHIS said at the "Food Irradiation 2001" conference in Washington, DC, in February 2001, "The main mission of APHIS used to be keeping non-native species out of this country. Today our mantra is to help facilitate trade."[452]

Unfortunately, APHIS is not very forthcoming about its promotion of irradiation and its role in free trade. When the authors of this book attempted to interview Foudin, we were told that he no longer works on food irradiation. Our request to interview a staff person who works on irradiation was denied and we were told by a public affairs specialist to send a list of questions. Unsurprisingly, the insipid responses to our questions did not provide any new insights into the agency's role in promotion of irradiation.[453]

In 2001, Foudin was much less hesitant to speak about food irradiation and global food trade. In his speech to "Food Irradiation 2001" he went on to say that irradiation is "absolutely necessary" to further the goals of free trade. He explained that the U.S. does not have enough inspectors to physically inspect all of the agricultural products coming into this country and that irradiation will solve this problem.

Irradiating Brazil

Foudin also mentioned that Brazil was planning to build new food irradiation facilities. The fruit will be irradiated and then exported on 747s. He said that the goal is to make Brazil "the tropical fruit basket of the world."

And it is true that the irradiation industry has had its eye on Brazil. The country is already a major world exporter of fruits and vegetables, and irradiation could increase the shelf life of produce, kill the invasive species that prevent countries from accepting its produce, and destroy bacteria on meat. Proponents of irradiation say that with the use of irradiation Brazil could become a food production powerhouse, with four growing seasons and a land-mass approximating the size of the U.S.

According to the *International Trade Statistics 2004* of the World Trade Organization, Brazil's total agriculture exports to the world were $24.2 billion for 2003 (latest available), ranking it fourth behind the EU, U.S., and Canada. That's up from $9.8 billion in 1990.[454]

Land ownership patterns favor large industrialized agriculture, which seeks to utilize irradiation to increase profitability. As in many developing countries, Brazil has an extremely concentrated structure of land tenure, which enables corporations to move in and control large amounts of acreage. According to Brazil's 1996 Agricultural Census, one percent of landowners control 45 percent of farm land.[455]

Land in Brazil is cheap in comparison to the industrialized world. The prospect of acquiring large parcels of land is attracting corporations from across the world that want to grow lucrative cash crops for export. As companies have moved in and bought up land for industrialized agriculture productions, they have also reached into the fertile, but delicate Amazon region.

Labor is also cheap in Brazil, which has the most permissive irradiation laws in the world. Any food can be irradiated at any dose of radiation, for any reason. Until SureBeam's demise, the company was targeting Brazil as a hot spot for the irradiation business. They were working with a Brazilian company, Tech Ion Industrial Brazil, to build 21 facilities around the country. They did build a large plant in Rio de Janeiro that only operated for six months – closing its doors when SureBeam imploded.

Despite the setbacks, Brazil remains a target for the irradiation industry, and a few irradiation facilities continue to operate in the country. Some factions in the Brazilian government continue to see irradiation as a necessary tool for food production, especially for produce because of post-harvest losses for lack of transportation infrastructure.

In the future, Brazil hopes to greatly expand its export markets for both produce and meat. The adoption of irradiation could make factory farming more attractive to food corporations. Hog producers like the U.S. giant Smithfield are already moving into Brazil.

So is agribusiness giant Cargill, which has acquired a majority share of Seara Alimentos, a Brazilian-branded poultry and pork processor with nine processing plants in the country.[456] (In the U.S., Cargill subsidiary Excel, which has had major recalls for contaminated meat, has been a proponent of irradiation and was irradiating meat for grocery stores like Kroger and Wegman's at the SureBeam facility in Iowa, before it closed.)

In Brazil, citizen organizations are beginning to be concerned about irradiation because it is also likely to be used on domestically consumed food. The consumer group, Instituto de Defesa do Consumidor (Institute for the Defense of the Consumer), is conducting an education campaign on the issue. The organization conducted an online poll on irradiation in March 2005, which found that 86 percent of the people did not know what irradiation is and that 98 percent said that it should be labeled. They will be pushing for the labeling of any irradiated food product in Brazil.

Other organizations are concerned about the unintended consequences if irradiation, including increasing the influence and ability of foreign multinationals to gain a foothold in Brazil. Also, the very sensitive environment in regions of Brazil could be imperiled, such as the expansion of agriculture into what was once rainforest or savannah. Water resources could also be impacted by the increased need for new dams and water diversions for irrigation.

Several Latin American countries are also exploring irradiation because proponents have been doing outreach and the U.S. government has been promoting irradiation widely. Argentina has three irradiation facilities. One opened in 2000 in Salta especially for the 13 foods that are cleared for irradiation. Chile is home to one irradiator, and it has legalized 20 food products for irradiation, including potatoes, papaya, wheat, chicken, onions, rice, fish products, and spices.

Irradiation Around the World

On the other side of the globe, Thailand is home to four irradiation facilities, three of which use the radioactive isotope cobalt-60. SureBeam, before its bankruptcy, was working with Thai Electron Pasteurized Company, Ltd. to build a facility near Bangkok. If built, the facility would process around 200 million pounds of fruit, flowers, vegetables, and seafood. Funding is being sought to complete the project without the involvement of SureBeam.

Currently, Thailand has approved 23 foods for irradiation, including "exotic" fruits. Until recently, fruit imports into the U.S. had to be treated with chemicals or heat to remove pests that, if released into the United States, would threaten domestic agriculture. Since the USDA's Animal and Plant Inspection Service (APHIS) now allows irradiation in place of chemical or heat treatments for imported fruits and vegetables, it is likely that Thai exports of exotic fruits to the U.S. will greatly increase.

SureBeam also targeted Vietnam for an irradiation facility that would have been built near Ho Chi Minh City. Vietnam allows irradiation of eight foods; the most significant is fish. The Vietnamese fish market equals 4.6 billion pounds annually. The introduction of an irradiation facility in Vietnam would facilitate trade to importing countries by extending the shelf lives of fish products, especially shrimp, which is produced in unsustainable fish farms built along the coast. Introducing this irradiation would have adverse effects on coastal communities that have already been devastated by these "factory fish farms."

All told, at least 30 countries have irradiation facilities and are irradiating food commercially.[457] These nations, and many others have passed legislation legalizing irradiation. Their health agencies have approved a list of foods that can be irradiated within their borders, and they have indicated strong support for irradiation.

How did irradiation become so widely accepted?

Irradiation Clout

A little investigating unveils a simple answer. In 1984, as a result of cooperation among IAEA, the World Health Organization (WHO), and the Food and Agriculture Organization (FAO), an international body was established to advance irradiation. The International Consultative Group on Food Irradiation (ICGFI) was established after these three institutions invited UN member states to cooperate in an "independent body composed of government-designated experts" in the promotion of food irradiation. Forty-four nations indicated an interest in joining the effort, including countries like Iraq and Syria. FAO, IAEA, and WHO, through the Joint FAO/IAEA Division of Nuclear Techniques in Food and Agriculture based in Vienna, serve as its Secretariat.[458]

ICGFI, through its annual meetings, outreach to Member States, and other promotional efforts became one of the most effective propagandists for irradiation. The group funded and operated its own programs, and helped and encouraged countries to legalize irradiation through their national legislatures and regulatory agencies.

ICGFI materials discuss how trade barriers are overcome by irradiation:

> Food imports and exports are important to the health and economy of nations and people, yet trade barriers caused by pests, diseases and food safety issues continually threaten or inhibit trade. Several technologies work to remove trade barriers. Irradiation is one such technology that could assist in the improvement of trade.

The document also discusses the requirements for nations to accept irradiated food products from exporting nations.

> A government can deny entry of any product into its territory. However, under the provision of the Agreement on the Application of Sanitary and Phytosanitary Measures (SPS), being enforced by the World Trade Organization (WTO), such a government (if a member of WTO) may be requested to furnish scientifically-based justification for regulations that are stricter than the only recognized international standards for food, which are the guidelines, and recommendations of the Codex Alimentarius Commission (food safety), the International Plant Protection Convention (IPPC) (plant protection and quarantine), and the International Office of Epizootics (animal health and quarantine). With the existence of the Codex General Standard for Irradiated Foods, which recognizes the safety and effectiveness of food irradiation, and the endorsement of irradiation as a quarantine treatment of fresh agricultural produce by regional plant protection organizations operating within IPPC, irradiated food treated according to the principle of the Codex Standard can no longer be denied entry into countries on scientific grounds.[459]

However, despite ICGFI's success, the group decided at its October 2003 meeting to disband in May 2004 because it had helped "establish the safety of irradiated foods." At the time this decision was made, SureBeam had become the number one promoter of irradiation around the world, and in one sense it had taken over much of ICGFI's initiative by working with numerous countries to plan irradiation facilities. The international irradiation industry did not seem to know that SureBeam was in trouble. It went belly-up soon after in June of 2004.

IFGFI said in its final statement that in view of its success in collaborating "with the Joint FAO/WHO/Codex Alimentarius Commission (Codex) and the International Plant Protection Convention (IPPC) in the finalization of international standards related to irradiation, there was no further justification for the continuation of ICGFI beyond the expiration of its mandate in May 2004."

It went on to say:

> Further activities related to the application of irradiation for sanitary and phytosanitary purposes will be carried out by the Joint FAO/IAEA Division of Nuclear Techniques in Food and Agriculture and where appropriate, in collaboration with WHO, Codex, the IPPC and other international organizations. Examples of such activities include the sponsoring of visiting scientists, the convening of ad hoc groups of experts to provide independent and authoritative advice, and research projects supported through the FAO/IAEA technical cooperation program and other assistance programs of the agencies involved.[460]

In 2004, a new trade association, the International Irradiation Association (iiA) was formed to represent the irradiation industry. It replaced the Association of International Industrial Irradiators. A letter from the board of directors of iiA explains its history and mission:

> During 2004 the board dissolved the AIII and transfer its assets to the new International Irradiation Association (iiA). This decision was taken due to inherent problems associated with the administration of the old Association. Finally in October 2004 an association manager was recruited to help fulfil the aims of the organisation. This is currently a part-time role but it is hoped that as membership grows the board will be able to appoint a full-time manager...The new organisation was officially launched in November 2004 with membership open from January 2005. A list of current members is available...and it includes irradiation service providers, suppliers of irradiation facilities and equipment, consultants, suppliers of items such as dosimeters and users of the irradiation services. The membership includes companies with an interest in

Electron Beam, Gamma, and X-Ray technology, and has geographical coverage including Europe, North America, South America, Africa, Asia and Australia.[461]

The association is taking a very active role in promoting irradiation. It has taken over organizing the biennial International Meeting of Radiation Processors and will also assume the NGO status that AIII held at the IAEA.[462]

The IAEA continues to support irradiation around the world. At the International Meeting on Radiation Processing 2006, in Kuala Lumpur, Malaysia, Ramamoorthy Natesan, the head of the Division of Physical and Chemical Sciences at IAEA, discussed the agency's support for irradiation. IAEA is promoting irradiation activities in Moldova, Iran, Pakistan, Syria, Vietnam, the Philippines, Tunisia, Saudi Arabia, Poland, and Egypt. It has established a new Regional Project for Eastern and Central European countries on "Quality Control Methods and Procedures for Radiation Technology." They had a meeting in Warsaw, Poland in February 2005, which was attended by representatives from Albania, Armenia, Azerbaijan, Belarus, Denmark, Germany, the Czech Republic, Bulgaria, Hungary, Italy, Kazakhstan, Lithuania, Moldavia, Poland, Romania, Russia, Serbia, Montenegro, Spain, Switzerland, Turkey, and the Ukraine.[463]

IAEA's Technical Cooperation (TC) Department is an organization within the UN system that helps transfer nuclear technologies to countries throughout the world. It disburses more than $70 million worth of equipment, services, and training per year in approximately 100 countries, and irradiation is one of the technologies it is promoting. TC has 190 staff members and it works with technical officers from other departments within IAEA and in member states. It also collaborates with the World Bank and other similar institutions. Currently, TC is sponsoring four irradiation projects, located in Beijing, China; Bangkok, Thailand; Jarinu, Brazil; and Guatemala City, Guatemala.[464]

It is no surprise that TC is concentrating on these countries, which all desire to increase their export markets. China is of particular interest. The IAEA has supported the Chinese government in developing the commercial application of food irradiation. While it is difficult to obtain statistics, China appears to have become the largest irradiator in the world. China has 78 irradiators, several of them new, with 50 irradiating food. The other facilities irradiate medical supplies and construction materials. In 2005, 130,000 tons of food were irradiated, primarily garlic. Food irradiation has been promoted on China Central TV and local TV stations.[465]

Thirty national regulatory standards have been established for irradiation since the 1980s.[466]

David Brubaker, an expert on China, has an impressive list of degrees after his name, including a Ph.D. from the University of Southern Illinois and a Master of Science from the University of London, Imperial College of Science, Technology and Medicine. He worked for agribusiness from 1982 to 1997, and currently is working as a consultant to the People's Republic of China.

Although he hopes to be wrong, he makes dire predictions: "Given present trends, I believe that in ten years (or less) we'll have two types of meat: 90 percent will be cheap meat from places like China and 10 percent boutique meat for niche markets. The latter will be home grown. In fact, increased regulation of factory farms in the U.S. has helped to grow the Chinese industry. By 2015, China will account for over 60 percent of world pork production—up from current production at 50 percent. Worldwide meat consumption will continue to grow, with China being the largest market. U.S. consumption will remain steady."

He goes on to say, "The large-scale importation of meat has not yet begun. When it does, meat will be transported similar to other goods such as fresh-cut flowers. Look for massive U.S.-China agribusiness partnerships to meet the growing demand for meat. This will also occur in other developing countries."

Certainly, if Brubaker's predictions are true, irradiation could play a role in facilitating the global trade of meat. At the same time, as long as the IAEA, WHO, FAO, and other domestic institutions like the FDA and USDA devote resources to the global promotion of irradiation, the construction of irradiation infrastructure may continue. This is especially true if some of the large agribusiness interests decide to invest in it in a significant way.

Europeans Fight Back

Fortunately, a strong citizens' movement is keeping irradiation from making the inroads that its proponents hope for. One of the most important deterrents for the commercialization of irradiation occurred in Europe, as the result of citizen activism and cross-border cooperation. It demonstrates that as long as citizens are vigilant, organize citizen opposition, and participate in the political process, doomsday scenarios can be averted.

In the European Union (EU), each member state has its own set of rules governing the foods that are permitted to be irradiated within its borders. In February 1999, the European Commission, which plays the role in the EU of kicking off new policy initiatives, introduced framework directive 1999/2/CE that would have expanded the list of foods that could be irradiated and sold throughout the Union. The original list of products that can be sold everywhere in the EU included spices, dried aromatic herbs, and vegetable seasonings.

Public Citizen had become alarmed about the situation in Europe because SureBeam was known to be looking for opportunities to promote irradiation in Europe and there are several irradiation companies in Europe lobbying for liberalization of irradiation rules. Public Citizen contacted the Food Commission in the UK, an organization that had been one of the leaders in fighting irradiation in the 1980s, and informed them about the situation.

A campaign was quickly organized by people at the Food Commission in the UK, the Movimento dei Consumatori in Italy, Active Consumers Denmark, the Swedish Consumer Coalition, and EuroCoop. They quickly gathered information from the U.S. about SureBeam and the ongoing campaign on irradiation. They started conducting outreach, providing education to consumers, policymakers, and the media, and lobbied members of Parliament.

This band of dedicated people recognized that if Europe, a huge market, accepted irradiation it would quickly accelerate its acceptance and spur the commercialization of the technology. But, if they were able to stop the directive from moving forward, or slow it down, it would help impede irradiation throughout the world.

As a result of the campaign, in December 2002, the European Parliament opposed expanding the original list of foods approved to be irradiated. In addition, the European Parliament agreed to depend on its own research indicating the health safety of irradiated foods, rather than that of the World Health Organization (WHO). This decision could be revisited at a later time.

However, the decision made by the European Parliament did succeed in impeding the expansion of food irradiation facilities in Europe. It also has curbed the excitement for irradiation in some food-exporting countries. Meanwhile, the coalition in Europe has expanded, with new coalition partners in Spain, the Netherlands, Finland, Belgium, Austria, and Poland.

The coalition has been instrumental in organizing demonstrations at seven food irradiation facilities in France in the spring of 2005 and 2006. Every year it plans activities in November for the "Global Action Week Against Food Irradiation." Activities are currently being planned for 2007.

Food & Water Watch is an active member of the coalition, and recently delivered to every member of the European Parliament a letter signed by 30 organizations. It voiced concerns about the increase in unlabeled irradiated food in Europe and recommended increased inspections to curtail it.

The coalition against irradiation in France has grown to 15 member organizations. It is coordinated by Véronique Gallais of Action Consommation. It plays an important role in the international movement because many food irradiation companies are located in France. In the spring of 2007, the coalition hosted a forum on irradiation that included scientists and activists concerned about the trend towards irradiation.

The jury is still out on irradiation's role in globalized food trade. The campaigns around the world to label irradiated food, to stop facilities from being built, and to educate consumers and policymakers about the dangers are impeding its advancement. There is every indication that with the new awareness of irradiation, corporations and governments will not be able to advance the technology without resistance. An exciting development in the citizen struggle to stop irradiation is the international strategizing and information transfer that happens via the Internet. While corporate globalization is destructive, global cooperation among citizen groups is acting as a check on corporate power.

Visionary activist Maude Barlow, who is chairperson of the Council of Canadians, the largest citizens organization in Canada, put it this way, "The world is poised to make crucial decisions about the kind of food system we are going to pass on to our children and grandchildren. Are major transnational corporations going to gain control of food production and use technologies like irradiation to increase their profitability? Are we going to allow family farmers from around the world to be driven from their land and replaced by factory farms? If we are silent and do nothing, this will be the course. But, if we organize across borders, we educate and agitate, if we refuse to be defeated, we can create a just and sustainable food system."

Epilogue

Down the Line

Adopt the pace of nature; her secret is patience.
  – Emerson

It's no wonder that most Americans reacted apathetically when news hit that mad cow disease finally landed on our shores. Over the last several years, we've been forced to wade through such an onslaught of threats in the headlines that it's produced a numbing effect on our psyche: war, terror alerts, school shootings, natural disasters, computer viruses, and the possibility of chemical attacks that sent everyone running for duct tape and bottled water. Relatively speaking, one mad cow in Washington state seemed to be the least of our concerns.

But mad cow disease, which is aptly named for its devastating effect on the animal's brain and nervous system, should be an invitation to all of us to think about the "why" and "how" of this latest food safety concern. It fits neatly into a package of threats against our food supply along with other scary names like *E. coli*, *Salmonella*, and *Listeria*. So, what's causing this barrage of attacks from evil germs and bacteria on everything from green onions to hamburgers to chicken sandwiches?

The Global Proliferation of Big Agribusiness

While we're focused on the sporadic, but increasingly common, food safety threats in our nation, we're missing the bigger picture. Every germ and bacteria that poisons our food are symptoms of a disease that is creeping into our food system. It's called corporate agriculture. What's worse than the bacteria sickening us is the fact that most of the population is woefully unaware of how our food culture has changed in the last 50 years. In fact, in the span of relatively few generations, the way we produce, distribute, and buy food has changed dramatically.

On average, your food now travels more than 2,000 miles from field to table, which is as much as 25 percent farther than in 1980, according to the Worldwatch Institute. The consequences of "cheap" food mean that regulation and sanitation get lost in the process.

Our food industry holds in its ranks some of the most powerful players on the political battlefield. As corporations buy out family farmers in record numbers, a new infrastructure is radically changing the way our food supply operates. From the time food leaves the field and ends up on your fork, it's had a wild adventure that rivals NBC's hit reality show *Fear Factor*. What you put in your mouth has been in places you wouldn't be able to imagine. There's a reason why massive slaughterhouses don't have windows. Some say that if we could replace every concrete wall in a slaughterhouse with a glass wall, our current "factory farming" model would come crashing down in a day. No consumer, regardless of iron-stomach boasts, would bite into a hamburger if he or she knew how it was processed.

Which is why the food industry is pushing irradiation. Instead of making sure that food is clean to begin with, some companies want to irradiate it at the end of the line. They seem ignorant of decades' worth of other expedient solutions that have brought our agriculture system to ruin. Feeding ground-up cows back to cows, pumping livestock with antibiotics and growth hormones, standardizing rather than diversifying crops, relying almost solely on chemical pesticides and fertilizers. It's unsustainability on top of unsustainability.

Our industrialized agriculture system, with maximizing production its only goal, has set off an epidemic of bacterial contamination. Overusing antibiotics has spawned an army of mutant "super-bugs." Feeding grain to cattle instead of grass, which they have evolved to eat, hampers their ability to fight infection. Filthy, cramped factory farms not only serve as havens for bacteria, but stress inflicted upon livestock compromises their immune systems.

Irradiation is no solution. And consumers know it—they are pushing back and saying "no." They're saying no to protect their children from eating irradiated meat at school, they're saying no to irradiated foods in grocery stores, and they're saying no in the stock market because most investors don't consider irradiation a sound idea.

Though it seems like it's been with us forever, the whole notion of a fully industrialized agriculture system dates only to the 1950s. Most crops are now grown—and some are being genetically engineered to coexist—with pesticides, fertilizers, and herbicides derived from petroleum and toxic chemicals. Cattle are raised, slaughtered, and processed in unmanageably huge facilities that are impossible to keep clean. Seafood is either mined by trawlers that dredge up everything within their grasp, or raised in polluted ponds on factory-style fish farms.

The pursuit of profits made imperative by the structure of the market and competition, instead of nutrition, has caused severe health problems unique to the developed world. Combine eating, one of humankind's most primal urges, with expanding discretionary income and you get "diseases of affluence."

Overdosing on fat, sugar, and salt, tens of millions of Americans are being stricken with cancer, heart disease, diabetes, obesity, high blood pressure, and other life-threatening conditions. The number of "extremely obese" U.S. adults—at least 100 pounds overweight—has quadrupled since the 1980s to about 4 million. About 300,000 Americans die each year from eating too much; that's almost as many as die from smoking.

Thanks to pandering advertising and habit-forming ingredients, adults aren't the only ones getting fat. Twenty percent of children in the U.S. are overweight—about five per classroom. Since 1980, the number of overweight and extremely obese kids has increased by 50 and 100 percent, respectively. With little or no regard to nutrition, the industry has ingeniously hooked children on food loaded with fat and sugar—and on huge portions.

A bedfellow of Westerners' fast-food, couch-potato lifestyles is an obsession with getting other people to do their grunt work. There isn't time to make dinner, mow the grass, do laundry, wash the car—even look after the children. Advertisers have beautifully exploited this myth, reminding us day after day that our busy lifestyles leave us no time to do anything ourselves. This is one of the marketing industry's greatest triumphs: the busier they say we are, the busier we think we are, so the more we think we need their products and services.

There's no time to chop lettuce, peel potatoes, or slice melon. So we buy pre-cut portions sold in bulky plastic containers that persist for centuries in landfills. We're even too busy to spread peanut butter with a knife. Researchers at Oklahoma State University thought this was a big problem, so they spent five years experimenting with 5,000 pounds of peanut butter to come up with "P.B. Slices." Encased in plastic like pre-fab cheese, they go well with another revolutionary time-saver, "IronKids Crustless Bread." Meanwhile, mom and dad can enjoy macaroni-and-cheese sticks, which come in microwaveable cardboard boxes. Grocery stores are aggressively pushing these highly profitable "home meal replacements," which the industry apparently doesn't even consider to be meals.

This cycle is difficult to penetrate—the corporate players are content with their profit margins and consumers have less time to prepare meals, as wages stagnate and two or more incomes are required to sustain a family. Today's economy leaves most families struggling to feed the next generation—quantity trumps quality on tight budgets. But every once in awhile, something jams up the vicious cycle, grinds it to a halt, and forces every shopper to think about his or her food. Throw a mad cow in the mix and for a couple of weeks, the usually complacent customer will become curious about where his beef comes from. Perhaps that curiosity could spark a slow awakening to a corrupt food system that pits consumers, family farmers, animals, and the environment as losers.

Consumers do have power, we just need to use it. As Worldwatch founder Lester Brown says, a remedy is within our reach, but the burden will fall on family planners, not farmers and fishers.

"There is no identifiable technology waiting in the wings," Brown says, "that will lead to a quantum jump in food production comparable to those that came from earlier technological gains, such as the discovery of fertilizer or the hybridization of corn."⁴⁶⁷

In India, Navdanya (Nine Seeds), an organization dedicated to sustainability, has created "Freedom Zones" in 3,000 villages. There are no genetically engineered crops, chemicals, hybrid seeds, or corporate meddling. With more than 20 seed banks, Navdanya serves more than 10,000 farmers and has rescued literally thousands of varieties of vegetables, rice, pulses, millet, and oilseeds.

In Zimbabwe, urban farmers have found markets for indigenous vegetables such as lady's finger (okra), horned cucumber, spider flower, and bottle gourd. In Italy, 300 companies serving organic food in school cafeterias have started up since 2000, when school districts began passing laws discouraging unnaturally grown produce.

This is the "food democracy" movement—"the growing number of farmers, consumers, chefs, and food businesses resisting the temptation to eat blindly and instead eating deliberately," says Worldwatch. A hole has been ripped in our society that the movement seeks to mend: "Changing our diets is about adding something back to our lives that has been lost—our connection to food and the people who produce it."⁴⁶⁸

Food democracy is shaping up to be the first universal sociopolitical movement of the 21ˢᵗ century. Consumers around the world, particularly in the West, are beginning to see "conventional" agriculture for what it truly is. They are educating themselves like never before about diet and nutrition, the well-documented hazards of unnatural pesticides and fertilizers, the health and environmental benefits of organic farming, the effects of globalization and other economic trends that put profits before people, and the dangers of irradiation, genetic engineering, and other technological time bombs.

The days when consumers had very little impact on the food production system are over. This is no longer just a movement of graying hippies whose influence in the economic and political marketplace extended no further than keeping mom-and-pop health food stores in business. Hundreds of natural food supermarkets, almost unheard of a generation ago, have opened in all regions of the U.S.

Of all the facets of the food democracy movement, organic farming and all-natural production are the centerpieces. Far beyond their stylish appeal to what is becoming a more affluent customer base, organic products are starting to make more economic sense than unnatural products. Organic sales rose from $1 billion in 1990 to $15 billion in 2004, and they're expected to reach $32 billion by 2009. Though impressive, it's less than one percent of the conventional food market, making the potential for growth huge. Organic sales are expanding by about 20 percent per year, compared to just two or three percent for unnatural.

In the U.S., community supported agriculture (CSA) programs have become extremely successful. A CSA is a subscription vegetable program. This program allows its members to get fresh, local, and in-season vegetables, herbs, and flowers, straight from a farmer's garden, each week throughout the growing season. The family becomes a "shareholder" in the farm and assumes some of the farmer's risk. Usually the produce is grown organically. Sometimes farmers add meat, cheese, or fruit to the farm.

Some CSAs encourage their members to work on the farm and visit it. Often people participate not only to get good food, but to show their children how food is produced. Like CSAs, farmers' markets are also thriving.

Soaring demand has not only made organic food more affordable and available, it tastes good and is often more nutritious. There are all-natural and sustainable alternatives for virtually every unnatural product you can find at the grocery store: artificial hormone-free milk, fair-trade coffee, eggs from free-range chickens, beef from pasture-fed cattle, bird-friendly rainforest crops, and wild-caught seafood, to name just a few.

Spreading the Word

GRACE is one place to go for educational materials about the problems of factory farming and for help in finding the alternatives to corporate meat and dairy products. The organization launched a project called "Sustainable Table" to help make consumers aware of the problems related to industrialized animal production and to help them find solutions. Check it out at http://www.gracelinks.org.

Sustainable Table offers an introduction to issues surrounding today's agricultural system and what is happening with our food, in particular, the meat supply. Its goal is to help you understand the issues, offer suggestions on what you can do, direct you to more in-depth information, and introduce you to the exciting and hugely popular sustainable food movement exploding around the world. Check it out at http://www.sustainabletable.org/.

Sustainable Table hosts the Eat Well Guide, which is a wonderful free directory of sustainably raised meat, poultry, dairy, and eggs from stores, farms, and restaurants in your area. Enter your zip code to find products in the United States and Canada that are healthful, humane, better for the environment, and support family farms. Visit it at http://www.eatwellguide.org.

Sustainable Table has also created an educational campaign based on the award-winning, critically acclaimed spoofs of "The Matrix," "The Meatrix" and its recently released sequels, "The Meatrix II: Revolting," and "The Meatrix II ½." These flash animations have been seen by millions of people, many of whom were unaware of the how meat and dairy products are produced. They can be seen at http://www.TheMeatrix.com.

The day may come when "organic food" will be redundant, and it once again will simply be known as food, which by nature is produced sustainably. What we call "conventional" today might be known tomorrow as "unnatural" or even "poisonous." But to reach that point, widespread political action will be necessary.

Fortunately, around the world there is a growing movement of consumers, family farmers, and food activists who are working to change the food production system. The campaign to stop food irradiation is but one example of how activists are stopping industry and its allies in government from putting corporate profits above people's health. Become a food activist today.

For up-to-date information on irradiation and other food, water, and marine issues, check out the Food & Water Watch Web site at http://foodand waterwatch.org and see how you can become engaged in creating a sustainable future.

Appendix A

Charting a Path

A Chronology of Food Irradiation and Nuclear Technology

1895: Wilhelm Konrad Röntgen of Germany discovers X-rays.

1896: Antoine-Henri Becquerel of France discovers the radioactive properties of uranium.

1896: F. Minsch of Germany proposes using radiation to preserve food by killing microorganisms that cause spoilage.

1898: Marie and Pierre Curie of Poland and France, respectively, discover the radioactive properties of radium and coin the term "radioactive."

1904: Samuel C. Prescott of the Massachusetts Institute of Technology publishes studies on the ability of radiation to kill bacteria.

1905: Patents to irradiate food are issued in England and the United States.

1916: G.A. Runner of the U.S. Department of Agriculture uses X-rays to kill the tobacco beetle in tobacco leaves. Thirteen years later, the American Tobacco Co. begins using X-rays but technical problems soon end the project.

1916: Irradiating strawberries to kill spoilage fungus is studied in Sweden.

1921: Benjamin Schwartz of the U.S. Department of Agriculture obtains a patent to use X-rays to kill the *Trichinella spiralis* bacteria in pork.

1923: Studies in which irradiated foods are fed to test animals begin.

1930: A patent to irradiate canned foods is issued to O. Wüst in France.

1943: Massachusetts Institute of Technology Professor Bernard E. Proctor, working under a U.S. Army contract, demonstrates the "preservation" of ground beef with X-rays.

1948: The U.S. Army's Medical Nutrition Laboratory in Denver begins feeding irradiated foods to rats.

1950: The U.S. Atomic Energy Commission (AEC) begins a comprehensive food irradiation research program.

1953: The U.S. Army begins a comprehensive food irradiation research program.

Dec. 8, 1953: President Dwight Eisenhower unveils his "Atoms for Peace" program to the United Nations.

1954: The AEC begins giving nuclear waste to the Army Quartermaster Corps for its food irradiation lab in Dugway, Utah.

1955: Nine members of a Mennonite Church in Colorado—most of whom are conscientious objectors—begin eating irradiated foods as part of an experiment at the Army's nutrition lab in Denver.

1957: Spices, reportedly used in sausages, are irradiated in West Germany.

1958: Irradiation is banned in West Germany.

Sept. 6, 1958: Congress passes the Food Additives Amendment to the Food, Drug and Cosmetic Act, which defines irradiation as a "food additive," which must be subjected to an extensive battery of toxicity tests before irradiated foods can be approved for human consumption.

1958: The Soviet Union becomes the first country to officially legalize food irradiation when it approved irradiation of potatoes to delay sprouting.

May 28, 1959: The World Health Organization (WHO) signs an agreement extending to the International Atomic Energy Agency (IAEA) the primary responsibility for developing atomic energy for "peaceful purposes throughout the world."

1959: The Soviet Union approves irradiation of grains to kill insects.

Nov. 9, 1960: Canada legalizes irradiation of potatoes to inhibit sprouting.

1961-62: Experimental irradiation facilities are built at the University of California-Davis, the University of Florida, Massachusetts Institute of Technology, and the University of Washington.

Oct. 23-30, 1961: Officials with the IAEA, WHO, and Food and Agriculture Organization (FAO) meet in Brussels. Research revealing blood abnormalities in rats that ate irradiated foods, among other problems, leads one scientist to warn: "These effects should not be overlooked. [They] may be one link in the chain of events leading to cancer."

Jan. 1963: The U.S. Army opens a food irradiation research center at its laboratory in Natick, Massachusetts.

Feb. 8, 1963: The FDA approves the Army's petition to irradiate bacon to achieve sterilization, marking the first such approval in the world.

Aug. 15, 1963: The FDA approves a petition to irradiate wheat and wheat products submitted by Lloyd Brownell of the University of Michigan.

1964: The first pilot irradiation facility on record was opened in the Soviet Union at the Dzerzhinskii Base for Moscow Fruit and Vegetable Procurement.

April 21-28, 1964: Meeting in Rome, officials with the FAO, IAEA, and WHO agree to "influence legislation in various countries" to "facilitate international acceptance of the process."

June 30, 1964: The FDA approves the Army's petition to irradiate potatoes.

Sept. 1964: The U.S. Department of the Interior opens the Marine Products Development Irradiator in Gloucester, Massachusetts, for the purposes of irradiating seafood with cobalt-60.

1965: The U.S. Army surgeon general declares irradiated foods "wholesome."

May 23, 1967: FDA toxicologist Jacqueline Verrett says: "Since irradiated food and its unknown components will be added to the ever-growing pool of chemicals in the human environment, the possibilities of potentiation of toxic effects, already formidable, become even more so." (Potentiation is the ability of one chemical to increase the effect of another chemical.)

Aug. 4, 1967: The AEC withdraws its FDA petition to irradiate strawberries, lemons, and oranges after rats fed irradiated fruit develop "significant numbers of tumors."

Aug. 23, 1968: FDA officials rescind the Army's bacon permit after reviewing previously unreleased Army documents showing that lab animals fed irradiated foods die younger, suffer more reproductive problems, and develop more malignant tumors than animals fed normal food.

Spring 1969: University of Pittsburgh radiation chemistry Professor Jack Schubert, working under an AEC grant, publishes a 32-page article in the *Bulletin of the World Health Organization* detailing numerous "mutagenic and cytotoxic agents" in irradiated food and food components.

April 8-12, 1969: Meeting in Geneva, officials with the FAO, IAEA, and WHO dismiss Schubert's findings.

1970: The International Project in the Field of Food Irradiation is established by the FAO, IAEA, and WHO in Karlsruhe, West Germany, at the government's nutrition laboratory. This major research facility lays the groundwork for irradiation approvals in the U.S. and Europe.

1970: The U.S. Army recommends disbanding its food irradiation program, but the program continues upon the urging of certain members of Congress.

1972: NASA begins feeding irradiated foods to American astronauts.

1973: Japan begins the industrial-scale irradiation of potatoes. The facility, in Sapporo, today is the longest-operating irradiation facility in the world.

Aug. 31-Sept. 7, 1976: At a meeting in Geneva chaired by FDA toxicology director Hubert Blumenthal, officials with the FAO, IAEA, and WHO recommend further research on the potential toxicity of radiolytic products formed in irradiated food.

Oct. 1977: A private company hired by the U.S. Army to conduct food irradiation research is dismissed from the project for its shoddy work.

Nov. 28-Dec. 1, 1977: Meeting in Wageningen, the Netherlands, officials with the FAO, IAEA, and WHO state: "It is obviously important for the relevant national regulations governing food irradiation to be harmonized."

Sept. 29, 1978: The U.S. General Accounting Office criticizes the Army's 25-year, $51 million investment in researching food irradiation.

1979: Statewide bans on irradiated food are passed in Maine, New Jersey, and New York.

Sept. 9, 1979: FDA toxicology director Hubert Blumenthal calls for the creation of the FDA's Irradiated Food Committee: "There has been little in the way of positive regulatory response."

1980: The Army's failed food irradiation research program is transferred to the U.S. Department of Agriculture.

July 1980: Based on little more than a theoretical calculation of the number and nature of new chemicals formed in irradiated foods, the FDA's Irradiated Foods Committee concludes that no new tests are needed for food irradiated at low levels, or for foods that comprise a very small percentage of the typical American's diet, such as spices.

Nov. 1980: A joint FAO/IAEA/WHO panel concludes that any food can be irradiated at up to 10 kiloGray (the equivalent of 330 million chest X-rays) and still be safe for human consumption.

April 9, 1982: A second internal FDA committee, the Irradiated Foods Task Group, concludes that only seven of the 409 research studies it reviewed support the safety of irradiated food and were adequately conducted.

March 9, 1983: Margaret Heckler, a former Congress member whose district included the Army's food irradiation lab in Natick, Massachusetts, becomes secretary of the Department of Health and Human Services, giving her control of the FDA's food irradiation program.

July 5, 1983: The FDA grants a petition from Radiation Technology to legalize the irradiation of a wide variety of spices and vegetable seasonings—including garlic powder, ginger, oregano, paprika, and basil—to kill microorganisms.

June 19, 1984: The FDA grants a petition from Radiation Technology to expand on its 1983 ruling by legalizing the irradiation of spices and vegetable seasonings to kill insects.

Oct. 3, 1984: Canada legalizes irradiation of herbs, spices, and vegetable seasonings to kill microorganisms and insects.

1985: The U.S. Department of Energy proposes building six irradiation facilities using cesium-137, a highly-radioactive waste from the production of nuclear bombs.

April 18, 1985: The FDA grants a petition from Radiation Technology to expand the list of spices and vegetable seasonings that can be irradiated.

July 22, 1985: The FDA grants a petition from Radiation Technology to legalize the irradiation of pork to kill the *Trichinella spiralis* bacteria.

April 18, 1986: The FDA, acting on its own accord, approves its "Omnibus Rule," legalizing the irradiation of fruit and vegetables to delay ripening and kill insects, and tripling the maximum dose for spices to kill microorganisms.

Feb. 23, 1987: The FDA rejects citizen requests for a public hearing to challenge the Omnibus Rule.

June 19, 1987: Rep. Henry Waxman, chair of a House Energy and Commerce subcommittee, holds a hearing on a bill that would have banned the irradiation of fruit, vegetables, and pork, and called for research into the health and environmental effects of irradiation. The bill dies in committee, and no congressional hearings on food irradiation have been held since.

Oct. 11, 1988: Martin Welt, founder of Radiation Technology, Inc., is sentenced to two years in federal prison for conspiracy and lying to the Nuclear Regulatory Commission. He serves eight months.

Dec. 30, 1988: The FDA again rejects citizen requests for a public hearing to challenge the Omnibus Rule.

May 2, 1990: The FDA grants a petition from Radiation Technology to irradiate poultry to kill microorganisms.

Jan. 1992: Vindicator (presently called Food Technology Service) opens the first facility in the U.S. specifically devoted to irradiate food, located in Mulberry, Florida, near Tampa. The plant uses radioactive cobalt-60.

March 1992: Independent grocery store Carrot Top, in the Chicago suburb of Northbrook, makes headlines by stocking irradiated strawberries, oranges, and grapefruit.

June 10, 1997: The U.S. Department of Agriculture, acting on its own accord, legalizes the shipment of irradiated tropical fruit from Hawaii to the continental United States.

Aug. 1997: Among respondents to a CBS News Poll, 73 percent say they oppose irradiated food and 77 percent say they will not eat it.

Sept. 1997: A joint FAO/IAEA/WHO panel concludes that any food can be irradiated at any dose and still be safe for human consumption.

Dec. 3, 1997: The FDA grants a petition from Isomedix to irradiate beef, lamb, and horse meat to kill microorganisms and extend shelf life. The FDA also rejects citizen requests for a public hearing to challenge the legalization of poultry irradiation.

Aug. 3, 1999: Australia and New Zealand lift their 10-year-old ban on irradiated foods.

Jan. 5, 2000: The National Food Processors Association submits an FDA petition to legalize the irradiation of "ready-to-eat" foods, such as luncheon meat, frozen dinners, baby food, and condiments.

Feb. 2000: SureBeam opens an electron-beam food irradiation facility, designed to treat meat, in Sioux City, Iowa. U.S. Sen. Tom Harkin and Rep. Tom Latham attend the grand opening.

May 2000: Irradiated ground beef goes on public sale for the first time in the U.S. in Iowa, Minnesota, North Dakota, South Dakota, and Wisconsin. The beef was irradiated by a linear accelerator owned by the Titan Corp. of San

Diego, which originally developed the technology for the "Star Wars" missile defense program.

July 21, 2000: The FDA grants a petition from Edward Josephson, former director of the Army's failed food irradiation research program, to legalize the irradiation of fresh shell eggs.

July 31, 2000: A partnership of SureBeam and Hawaii Pride begin shipping irradiated papayas from Hawaii to the continental United States.

Oct. 30, 2000: The FDA grants a petition from Caudill Seed Co. to legalize the irradiation of sprouting seeds to kill microorganisms.

Nov. 29, 2000: The FDA grants a petition from California Day-Fresh Foods to legalize the irradiation of fruit and vegetable juice to kill microorganisms (with ultraviolet radiation).

Oct. 2001: SureBeam opens an electron-beam food irradiation facility, designed to treat meat, in the Chicago suburb of Glendale Heights.

Feb. 2002: The fast-food chain Dairy Queen begins test-marketing irradiated hamburgers in Minnesota and South Dakota. The sales expand to the Northeast and Southwest U.S. in 2003.

Feb. 2002: Kroger, the second-largest grocer in the U.S., begins the test-marketing of irradiated ground beef in Peoria, Illinois. Sales expand to California, Colorado, and Georgia in 2003.

June 6, 2002: Protests begin at the construction site of a cobalt-60 irradiation plant in Narangba, Australia, near Brisbane.

Aug. 2002: SureBeam opens an electron-beam food irradiation facility in the Los Angeles suburb of Vernon.

Sept. 2002: Publix, an 800-store grocery chain in the Southeast, begins selling "New Generation" frozen hamburgers produced by Colorado Boxed Beef and irradiated with cobalt-60 by Food Technology Service.

Oct. 23, 2002: The U.S. Department of Agriculture, acting on its own accord, legalizes the importation of irradiated fruit and vegetables.

Nov. 6, 2002: The Berkeley (California) Unified School District becomes the first school district in the U.S. to ban irradiated foods.

Dec. 18, 2002: Citing health concerns, the European Parliament votes against expanding the list of foods that can be irradiated in the 15-nation European Union beyond herbs, spices, and vegetable seasonings.

May 29, 2003: The U.S. Department of Agriculture lifts its ban on irradiated food in the National School Lunch Program, which serves 27 million economically disadvantaged children nationwide. Irradiated ground beef is the first food to be proposed for inclusion in the program.

June 26, 2003: The U.S. Department of Agriculture, acting on its own accord, legalizes the shipment of irradiated sweet potatoes from Hawaii to the continental United States.

July 7, 2003: The Codex Alimentarius Commission, a United Nations affiliate that establishes food safety standards on behalf of more than 160 nations, rules that any food can be irradiated at any dose. The ruling is enforceable through the World Trade Organization.

July 2003: A cobalt-60 irradiation facility opens in Narangba, Australia, near Brisbane. It opens over the objections of hundreds of protesters, including several hunger strikers who state, "We'd rather starve than eat irradiated food."

Sept. 9, 2003: The Los Angeles Unified School District bans irradiated foods in its 677 schools.

Oct. 3, 2003: A cobalt-60 irradiation facility opens in Milford Township, Pennsylvania, about an hour's drive north of Philadelphia. The facility is operated by the Clemens Family Corporation, which owns Hatfield Quality Meats, the fifth-largest pork producer in the U.S. Local residents and government officials lost a lengthy battle against the facility, having appealed to county and federal courts, the Nuclear Regulatory Commission, and members of the U.S. Congress.

Nov. 23-29, 2003: The first annual International Anti-Food Irradiation Week is held, with protests, news conferences, and other events in Brazil, Italy, the Philippines, and the U.S. In Milford Square, Pennsylvania, 300 people hold a rally and traditional Lena'pe Nation ceremony to protest the opening of a cobalt-60 irradiator.

Jan. 12, 2004: SureBeam announces filing for Chapter 7 bankruptcy and closes its irradiation facilities in California, Illinois, and Iowa.

April 29, 2004: The San Francisco Board of Education bans irradiated foods in its 116 schools.

May 20, 2004: The District of Columbia Board of Education bans irradiated foods in its 167 schools.

June 30, 2004: President George W. Bush signs the Child Nutrition Act, which requires irradiated foods served in schools to be labeled and encourages schools to serve non-irradiated alternatives.

Sept. 3, 2004: The Seattle School Board passes a resolution discouraging the use of irradiated foods.

Sept. 16, 2004: California Gov. Arnold Schwarzenegger vetoes a bill that would have required public disclosure and parental notification before irradiated foods could be served in the state's schools.

Nov. 21-27, 2004: The second annual International Anti-Food Irradiation Week is held, with protests, news conferences, and other events in Australia, Canada, Denmark, Italy, the Philippines, and the U.S.

Dec. 23, 2004: The FDA increases by 50 percent the maximum dose that can be used to irradiate food, which could cause food to become radioactive. The FDA calls any potential radioactivity "trivially low."

Jan. 3, 2005: Elsa Murano leaves her position as under-secretary of Food Safety at the U.S. Department of Agriculture to become vice chancellor and dean of Agriculture and Life Sciences at Texas A&M University. A long-time irradiation promoter, Murano largely fails to advance the cause during her three years at the USDA.

March 5, 2005: Protests are held at seven food irradiation facilities in France.

June 2005: Fort Worth, Texas investor David Corbin reportedly reopens the dormant SureBeam irradiation facility in Sioux City, Iowa, under the name Sadex Corp. Corbin, a former SureBeam investor, says he is irradiating animal feed and hopes to add beef, pork, and turkey.

Nov. 21-28, 2005: The third annual International Anti-Food Irradiation Week is held, with protests, news conferences, and other events in Australia, Brazil, Canada, the Philippines, and the U.S.

Jan. 24, 2006: EarthJustice of Hawaii wins its request for a public hearing to challenge a cobalt-60 irradiation facility proposed to be built near the Honolulu International Airport along the Pacific coast. Hawaii residents oppose the facility because of concerns about airplane crashes, tsunamis, and hurricanes.

Feb. 26 - March 3, 2006: At the 14th International Meeting on Radiation Processing in Kuala Lumpur, Malaysia, the International Atomic Energy Agency promotes its irradiation activities throughout the world, including in Moldova, Iran, Pakistan, Syria, Vietnam, the Philippines, Tunisia, Saudi Arabia, Poland, and Egypt. The IAEA also announces a new irradiation initiative in Eastern and Central Europe.

March 2006: Food Irradiation Watch releases its "Irradiation-Free Food Guide," Australia's first-ever guide to eating irradiation-free food. About 20,000 copies have been distributed throughout the country.

Aug. 16, 2006: The FDA grants a petition from the National Fisheries Institute and the Louisiana Department of Agriculture and Forestry to legalize the irradiation of molluscan shellfish, including oysters, clams, and mussels.

Feb. 1, 2007: Hawaii residents tell the U.S. Nuclear Regulatory Commission that a proposed cobalt-60 irradiator near the Honolulu International Airport should not be built, because of concerns over aviation accidents, terrorist attacks, and the health risks associated with eating irradiated foods.

Appendix B

Taking It to the Shelves

Grocery stores that sold irradiated ground beef, 2000-2004[469]

Most stores have now discontinued selling irradiated ground beef.
(All beef was irradiated by SureBeam Corp. of San Diego, CA, unless otherwise noted.)

Chain	# stores[470]	Locations
Southeast		
Harris Teeter[471]	140	FL, GA, NC, SC, TN, VA
Lowes	105	NC, VA
Publix[472]	720	AL, FL, GA, SC
Winn-Dixie	1,060	AL, FL, GA, IN, KY, LA, MS, NC, OH, SC, TN, VA
Northeast/Mid-Atlantic		
Clemens Family Markets	19	PA
Farm Fresh	37	VA
Giant Food	189	DC, DE, MD, NJ, VA
Martin's	unknown	MD, PA, VA, WV
Pathmark	140	DE, NJ, NY, PA
Price Chopper	102	CT, MA, NH, NY, PA, VT
Safeway	136	DE, DC, MD, VA
Stop & Shop	335	CT, MA, NJ, NY, RI
Shop 'n Save/Hannaford	117	MA, ME, NH, NY, VT
ShopRite	200	CT, DE, NJ, NY, PA
Surefine Markets	31	MD, PA
Wegmans[473]	60	NY, PA, NJ
Weis	163	MD, NJ, NY, PA, VA, WV

Midwest		
Copps	22	WI
Dierbergs	20	MO (St. Louis area)
Giant Eagle	200	PA, OH, WV, MD
Hy-Vee	200	IL, IA, KS, MN, MO, NE, SD, WI
Jewel-Osco	200	IA, IL, IN, WI
Lunds/Byerly's	19	MN
Pick 'n Save	80	WI
Piggly Wiggly/Dick's	101	WI, IL
Schnucks	102	MO (St. Louis area)
Kroger	12	Peoria, IL

West		
Albertson's	unknown	CA

Nationwide		
Omaha Steaks	N/A	Mail Order
Schwan's	N/A	Home Delivery

Who's Who

Irradiation Facilities in the U.S.*

(Company headquarters are the same as facility locations unless otherwise noted with "HQ.")

CFC Logistics (closed its irradiation facility in April 2005)*
(HQ: Hatfield, PA)
Quakertown, Milford Township, PA (cobalt-60)

Food Technology Service
Mulberry, FL (cobalt-60)

Hawaii Pride[474]
Hilo, HI (electron beam / X-ray)

Iowa State University
Ames, IA (electron beam)

Mitec Advanced Technologies
Cedar Rapids, IA (electron beam / X-ray)

Sterigenics International[475]
(HQ: Oakbrook, IL)
West Memphis, AR (cobalt-60)
Corona, CA (cobalt-60)
Gilroy, CA (cobalt-60)
Hayward, CA (cobalt-60)
San Diego, CA (electron beam)
Tustin, CA (cobalt-60)
Gurnee, IL (cobalt-60)
Schaumburg, IL (cobalt-60 / electron beam / X-ray)
Gaithersburg, MD (electron beam)
Charlotte, NC (cobalt-60)
Haw River, NC (cobalt-60)
Bridgeport, NJ (electron beam / X-ray)
Rockaway, NJ (cobalt-60)
Salem, NJ (cobalt-60)
Westerville, OH (cobalt-60)
Fort Worth, TX (cobalt-60)

STERIS/Isomedix[476]
(HQ: Mentor, OH)
Ontario, CA (cobalt-60)
Libertyville, IL (cobalt-60 / electron beam)
Morton Grove, IL (cobalt-60)
Northborough, MA (cobalt-60)
Whippany, NJ (cobalt-60)
Chester, NY (cobalt-60)
Groveport, OH (cobalt-60)
Vega Alta, PR (cobalt-60)
Spartanburg, SC (cobalt-60)
El Paso, TX (cobalt-60)
Sandy, UT (cobalt-60)

SureBeam Corp. (bankrupt)*
(HQ: San Diego, CA)
Vernon, CA (electron beam)**
Glendale Heights, IL (electron beam)**
Sioux City, IA (electron beam)**

Texas A&M University [477]
College Station, TX (electron beam)

Companies Providing Irradiation Equipment or Services, or Conducting Research

Accelerator Technology
Bryan, TX

Alpha Omega Technology
Cedar Knolls, NJ

Gray*Star
Mt. Arlington, NJ

REVISS Services/Puridec
Vernon Hills, IL

* From company Web sites, press accounts, Securities and Exchange Commission filings and authors' data.

** Not operating since SureBeam filed for bankruptcy in January 2004.

Appendix D

Deception, Disfigurement, and Death

Irradiation Facility Accidents Throughout the World

June 1974: A worker receives a near-fatal dose of radiation from cobalt-60 at an Isomedix facility in Parsippanny, New Jersey. Two years later a fire near the storage pool causes the cobalt-60 rods to corrode and leak.

May 1975: A worker is exposed to radiation at a cobalt-60 facility in Italy when he climbs onto a conveyor belt and enters the irradiation chamber. He dies 12 days later.

Sept. 1982: A worker receives a massive radiation dose at a cobalt-60 irradiation facility in Norway while trying to fix a jammed conveyor belt. He dies 13 days later.

June 1986: Executives of International Nutronics are charged in federal court with covering up a 1982 radioactive spill at their cobalt-60 irradiation facility in Dover, New Jersey. After the spill, workers were ordered to falsify their exposure to radioactivity, and to carry contaminated water in buckets and pour it into the public sewer system.

June 1988: Radioactive cesium-137 leaks into a storage pool at a Radiation Sterilizers irradiation plant near Atlanta, Georgia. Contaminated water splashes onto thousands of milk cartons and other containers that are shipped to market. The U.S. Energy Department spends four years and more than $40 million to clean up the site.

Oct. 1988: Martin Welt, president of Radiation Technology, is sentenced to two years in federal prison for conspiracy and making false statements to the NRC. The company's license had been suspended after more than 30 NRC violations at its cobalt-60 irradiation facility in Rockaway, New Jersey. In 1977, a worker there received a near-fatal dose of radiation when a system failure exposes him to cobalt-60.

Feb. 1989: Three workers are injured—one fatally—when they enter the radiation chamber at a cobalt-60 irradiation facility in El Salvador.

June 1990: A worker at a cobalt-60 irradiation facility in Israel dies 36 days after he enters the radiation chamber is was exposed for one minute.

Oct. 1991: A worker at a cobalt-60 irradiation facility in Belarus dies 113 days after he entered the radiation chamber and was exposed for one minute.

1991: A Maryland worker ignores safety warnings and receives a 5,000-rad dose from a three-million electron-volt linear accelerator. He loses four fingers.

1992: A mishap at a 15 million electron-volt linear accelerator in Hanoi cost the facility's research director a hand and several fingers.

Accidents Involving Radioactive Materials Removed From Facilities

1987: In Goiania, Brazil, a cesium-137 teletherapy source is removed from its housing and broken up. Fifty-four people are hospitalized following radiation exposure and four die. Contamination of the environment is extensive.

1992: In China, a cobalt-60 source is lost and picked up by a man. Three persons in his family die of overexposure.

1998: In Istanbul, Turkey, two cobalt-60 sources in their shipping containers are sold as scrap metal. Ten people are treated for acute radiation syndrome. Several months following the discovery of the event one of the two sources is still missing.

Sources

González, Abel J. "Strengthening the Safety of Radiation Sources & the Security of Radioactive Materials: Timely Action." *IAEA Bulletin*, 41(3):2-16, 1999.

"Accelerator safety: Self-study." Los Alamos National Laboratory, LA-UR-99-5089, April 1999.

"Fool irradiation: A potential unwanted byproduct of food irradiation?" Health Physics Society, McLean, VA, January 1999. "Inadequate Control of World's Radioactive Sources." International Atomic Energy Agency, June 24, 2002.

Proposal for a Council Directive on the Control of High Activity Sealed Radioactive Sources. Commission of the European Communities, Brussels, 18 March 2002, COM (2002) 130 final.

"Review of events at large pool-type irradiators." U.S. Nuclear Regulatory Commission, Office for Analysis and Evaluation of Operational Data, NUREG-1345, March 1989.

Appendix E

FDA in the Act

Food Irradiation Approvals by the U.S. Food and Drug Administration[478]

Food	Approval Date	Applicant	Dose (kiloGray)
Bacon[479]	Feb. 8, 1963	U.S. Army	5.6
Wheat and wheat flour	Aug. 15, 1963	Lloyd Brownell, Univ. of Mich.	0.5
White potatoes	June 30, 1964	U.S. Army	0.1
Spices and vegetable seasonings	July 5, 1983	Radiation Technology, Inc.	10
Garlic, onion powder, and dried spices	June 19, 1984	Radiation Technology, Inc.	10
Additional spices and vegetable seasonings	April 18, 1985	Radiation Technology, Inc.	10
Dry or dehydrated enzyme preparations	June 30, 1985	Radiation Technology, Inc.	10
Pork	July 22, 1985	Radiation Technology, Inc.	1
Fruit and vegetables	April 18, 1986	Food and Drug Administration	1
Tropical fruit from Hawaii	July 10, 1997	APHIS [480]	0.25

Beef, lamb, and horse meat	Dec. 3, 1997	Isomedix, Inc.	4.5 / 7 [481]
Poultry	May 2, 1990	Radiation Technology, Inc. [482]	3
Eggs	July 21, 2000	Edward Josephson [483]	3
Sprouting seeds	Oct. 30, 2000	Caudill Seed Co.	8
Pet food	April 10, 2001	Sterigenics [484]	50
Imported fruit and vegetables	Oct. 23, 2002	APHIS	various
Sweet potatoes from Hawaii	June 26, 2003	APHIS	0.4
Molluscan shellfish (e.g., oysters, clams)	Aug. 16, 2005	multiple [485]	5.5

Food Irradiation Applications Pending at the FDA

Food	Application Date	Applicant	Dose (kiloGray)
Increase radiation dose for poultry	Dec. 21, 1999	APHIS	4.5 / 7 [4]
Undefined "meat products"	Dec. 22, 1999	FSIS [486]	4.5
Processed (ready-to-eat) foods	Jan. 5, 2000	Food Products Assoc.[487]	4.5 / 10 [488]
Crustacean shellish (e.g., shrimp, lobsters)	Feb. 6, 2001	National Fisheries Institute	unknown
Vitamins	May 8, 2003	STERIS/ Isomedix	30

Planet Irradiation

Countries that Have Legalized Irradiated Foods

Argentina	Israel
Australia	Japan
Austria	Libya
Bangladesh	Luxembourg
Belgium	Mexico
Brazil	The Netherlands
Canada	New Zealand
Chile	Norway
China	Pakistan
Costa Rica	The Philippines
Croatia	Poland
Cuba	Portugal
Czech Republic	Russia
Demark	South Africa
Egypt	South Korea
Finland	Spain
France	Sweden
Germany	Syria
Ghana	Thailand
Greece	Turkey
Hungary	Ukraine
India	United Kingdom
Indonesia	Uruguay
Iran	United States
Ireland	Vietnam

Source: International Atomic Energy Agency, Vienna

Appendix G

Bad Bugs

Foodborne Pathogens and Illnesses

Bacteria	U.S. illnesses per year	U.S. deaths per year	Food Sources	Symptoms
Bacillus cereus	27,360	0	meat, milk, vegetables, fish, sauces, salads	diarrhea, abdominal cramps, nausea
Campylobacter spp.	1,963,141	99	raw chicken, raw milk	bloody diarrhea, abdominal pain, fever, death
Clostridium botulinum	58	4	canned vegetables, fish, chicken, deli meat, lobster	breathing problems, vertigo, lassitude, weakness
Clostridium perfringens	248,520	7	prepared foods, meat and meat products, gravy	abdominal cramps, vomiting, HUS,[489] death
Escherichia coli 0157:H7	62,458	52	ground beef, raw milk	bloody diarrhea, vomiting, death
Listeria monocytogenes	2,493	499	ice cream, smoked fish, raw meats of all types, soft cheeses	meningitis, bacteria in the blood, death
Salmonella spp.	1,342,532	556	beef, poultry, eggs, dairy, fish, shrimp, sauces, salad dressing	nausea, vomiting, cramps, fever, headache, death

Shigella spp.	89,648	14	deli salads, poultry, raw vegetables, dairy	abdominal pain, diarrhea, fever, vomiting
Staphylo-coccus	185,060	2	beef, poultry, eggs, deli salads, cream desserts, dairy, sand-wich fillings	nausea, vomit-ing, abdominal cramping, prostration
Streptococ-cus	50,920	0	milk, eggs, sausage, cheese, rice pudding, lobster, shrimp	malaise, vomi-ting, tonsillitis, fever, chills, headache
Vibrio spp.	5,218	31	shellfish, esp. oysters, shrimp, crabs, raw fish	diarrhea, vomit-ing, prostration, death
Yersinia enterocoli-tica	86,731	2	ice cream, lamb, pork, oysters, shrimp, chicken, fish	diarrhea, severe abdominal pain, meningitis

Parasites	U.S. illnesses per year	U.S. deaths per year	Food Sources	Symptoms
Crypto-sporidium parvum	30,000	7	water contami-nated by human or ani-mal feces	severe diarrhea, abdominal cramps, weight loss
Cyclospora cayetanen-sis	14,638	0	food and water containing feces from an infected person	explosive bowel movements, fever, fatigue
Giardia lamblia	200,000	1	water contami-nated by hu-man or animal feces	diarrhea, stom-ach cramps, fatigue, weight loss

Toxoplasma gondii	112,500	375	raw or very rare meat, cat feces	flu-like symptoms, birth defects, blindness, death
Trichinella spiralis	52	0	pork, wild game, often spread by garbage-eating animals	abdominal pain, fever, muscle pain, pneumonia, death

Viruses	U.S. illnesses per year	U.S. deaths per year	Food Sources	Symptoms
Hepatitis A	4,170	4	food and water containing feces from an infected person	fever, malaise, anorexia, jaundice
Norwalk-like	9,200,000	124	food and water containing feces from an infected person	nausea, vomiting, abdominal pain, death

Prion	U.S. illnesses per year	U.S. deaths per year	Food Sources	Symptoms
variant Creutzfeldt-Jakob Disease	3,800 [490]	153 [491]	cattle brains, spinal cord, eyes, small intestine, certain ganglia (neurons)	Loss of mental and physical abilities, blindness, death

Unknown Causes	U.S. illnesses per year	U.S. deaths per year	Food Sources	Symptoms
No identifiable pathogen	62,000,000	3,400	?	?

Sources

Jones, Julie Miller. *Food Safety*. St. Paul, MN: Eagan Press, 1995.

Mead, Paul S., et al. "Food-Related Illness and Death in the United States." *Emerging Infectious Diseases*, 5(5):607-625, September-October 1999. (Authors' note: This is the most recent national data available.)

Redman, Nina E. *Food Safety: A Reference Handbook*. Santa Barbara, CA: ABC-CLIO, 2000.

Bibliography

Baldwin, Roger. *Wandering Through Milford Township: A Glimpse at its Past and Present*. Milford Township Supervisors, 1984.

Boyer, Paul. *By the Bomb's Early Light: American Thought and Culture at the Dawn of the Atomic Age*. New York: Pantheon Books, 1985.

Brown, Lester. *Tough Choices: Facing the Challenge of Food Scarcity*. The Worldwatch Environmental Alert Series. New York: W.W. Norton & Company, 1996.

Brown, Lester. *Who Will Feed China?: Wake-Up Call for a Small Planet*. The Worldwatch Environmental Alert Series. New York: W.W. Norton & Company, 1995.

Campbell, John W. *The Atomic Story*. New York: Henry Holt and Company, 1947.

Caufield, Catherine. *Multiple Exposures: Chronicles of the Radiation Age*. New York: Harper & Row, 1989.

Churnus, Ira. *Eisenhower's Atoms for Peace*. College Station: Texas A&M University Press, 2002.

Commoner, Barry. *Science and Survival*. New York: Viking Press, 1966.

Curie, Eve. *Madame Curie*. London: William Heinemann Ltd., 1938.

Darden, Richard and P.J. Richardson. *Corporate Giants: Personal Stories of Faith and Finance*. Grand Rapids, MI: Fleming H. Revell, 2002.

Diehl, J.F. *Safety of Irradiated Foods*. New York and Basel: Marcel Dekker Inc., 1990.

Dietz, David. *Atomic Energy in the Coming Age*. New York: Dodd, Mead & Company, 1945.

Drexler, Madeline. *Secret Agents: The Menace of Emerging Infections*. New York: Penguin Books, 2002.

Eisnitz, Gail A. *Slaughterhouse: The Shocking Story of Greed, Neglect, and Inhumane Treatment Inside the U.S. Meat Industry*. Amherst: Prometheus Books, 1997.

Elias, P.S. and A.J. Cohen (Eds.). *Recent Advances in Food Irradiation*. Amsterdam: Elsevier Biomedical Press, 1983.

Fermi, Laura. *Atoms for the World*. Chicago: The University of Chicago Press, 1957.

Fischer, David. *History of the International Atomic Energy Agency: The First Forty Years*. Vienna: International Atomic Energy Agency, 1997.

Ford, Barbara. *Future Food: Alternative Protein for the Year 2000*. New York: William Morrow and Company, 1978.

Ford, Brian J. *The Future of Food*. New York: Thames & Hudson, 2000.

Fox, Brian A. and Allan G. Cameron. *Food Science, Nutrition and Health* (Sixth Edition). London: Edward Arnold (Hodder Headline Group), 1995.

Fox, Nichols. *Spoiled: Why Our Food is Making Us Sick and What We Can Do About It*. New York: Penguin Books, 1998.

Gaull, Gerald E. and Ray A. Goldberg. *New Technologies and the Future of Food and Nutrition*. New York: John Wiley & Sons, 1991.

Gibbs, Dr. Gary. *The Food that Would Last Forever: Understanding the Dangers of Food Irradiation*. Golden City Park, NJ: Avery Publishing Group, 1993.

Gofman, John W. *Radiation and Human Health: A Comprehensive Investigation of the Evidence Relating Low-Level Radiation to Cancer and Other Diseases*. San Francisco: Sierra Club Books, 1981.

Gould, Robert F. (Ed.) *Radiation Preservation of Foods*. Washington, DC: American Chemical Society, Advances in Chemistry Series 65, 1967.

Green, Harold P. and Alan Rosenthal. *Government of the Atom: The Integration of Powers*. New York: Atherton Press, 1963.

Halwell, Brian. *Eat Here: Reclaiming Homegrown Pleasures in a Global Supermarket*. A Worldwatch Book. New York: W.W. Norton & Company, 2004.

Halwell, Brian. *Home Grown: The Case for Local Food in a Global Market.* Worldwatch Paper 163, Worldwatch Institute, Washington, DC, November 2002.

Herman, Patrick and Richard Kuper. *Food for Thought: Towards a Future Food for Farming.* London: Pluto Press, 2003.

Institute of Medicine, National Academies. *Escherichia Coli 0157:H7 in Ground Beef. Review of a Draft Risk Assessment.* Washington, DC, 2002.

International Forum on Globalization, *Does Globalization Help the Poor? A Special Report*, August 2001.

Institute of Medicine, National Research Council. *Scientific Criteria to Ensure Safe Food.* Washington, DC: The National Academies Press, 2003.

Jones, Julie Miller. *Food Safety.* St. Paul, MN: Eagan Press, 1992.

Josephson, Edward S. and Martin S. Peterson. *Preservation of Food by Ionizing Radiation.* Boca Raton, FL: CDC Press, 1982.

Kramish, Arnold. *The Peaceful Atom in Foreign Policy.* New York and Evanston: Harper & Row, 1963.

Leon, Warren and Caroline Smith DeWaal with the Center for Science in the Public Interest. *Is Our Food Safe? A Consumer's Guide to Protecting Your Health and the Environment.* New York: Three Rivers Press, 2002.

McNealy, Terry A. *Bucks County: An Illustrated History.* Doylestown, PA: Bucks County Historical Society, 2002.

Metzger, H. Peter. *The Atomic Establishment.* New York: Simon and Schuster, 1972.

Midkiff, Ken. *The Meat You Eat: How Corporate Farming Has Endangered America's Food Supply.* New York: St. Martin's Press, 2004.

Molins, Ricardo A. *Food Irradiation: Principles and Applications.* New York: John Wiley & Sons Inc., 2001.

Murano, Elsa A. (Ed.). *Food Irradiation: A Sourcebook.* Ames, IA: Iowa State University Press, 1995.

Murray, David. R. *Biology of Food Irradiation.* Taunton, Somerset, England: Research Studies Press Ltd., 1990.

Nestle, Marion. *Food Politics: How the Food Industry Influences Nutrition and Health.* Berkeley, CA: University of California Press, 2003.

Nestle, Marion. *Safe Food: Bacteria, Biotechnology, and Bioterrorism.* Berkeley, CA: University of California Press, 2003.

Neuzil, Mark and William Kovarik. *Mass Media & Environmental Conflict.* Thousand Oaks, CA: Sage Publications, 1996.

Pence, Gregory E. (Ed.) *The Ethics of Food: A Reader for the 21ˢᵗ Century.* Lanham, MD: Rowman & Littlefield Publishers, 2002.

Pflaum, Rosalynd. *Grand Obsession: Madame Curie and Her World.* New York: Doubleday, 1989.

Postel, Sandra. *Dividing the Waters: Food Security, Ecosystem Health, and the New Politics of Scarcity.* Worldwatch Paper 132, Worldwatch Institute, Washington, DC, September 1996.

Potter, Robert D. *The Atomic Revolution.* New York: Robert M. McBride & Company, 1946.

Redman, Nina E. *Food Safety: A Reference Handbook.* Santa Barbara, CA: ABC-CLIO, Inc., 2000.

Rifkin, Jeremy. *Beyond Beef: The Rise and Fall of the Cattle Culture.* New York: Dutton, 1992.

Rodengen, Jeffrey L. and Richard F. Hubbard. *The Legend of the Titan Corporation.* Fort Lauderdale, FL: Write Stuff Enterprises, Inc., 2002.

Satin, Morton. *Food Irradiation: A Guidebook.* Boca Raton, FL: CRC Press, 1996.

Seaborg, Glenn T. *Nuclear Milestones.* Self-published, (no publication date).

Seaborg, Glenn. T. *Peaceful Uses of Nuclear Energy: Speeches by Glenn T. Seaborg.* Oak Ridge, TN: U.S. Atomic Energy Commission, Division of Technical Information, 1970.

Seaborg, Glenn. T. and William R. Corliss. *Man and Atom: Building a New World Through Nuclear Technology.* New York: E.P. Dutton & Co., 1971.

Seaborg, Glenn T. with Eric Seaborg. *Adventures in the Atomic Age: From Watts to Washington.* New York: Farrar, Straus and Giroux, 2001.

Sinclair, Upton. *The Jungle.* New York: Barnes and Noble Classics, 2003.

Starke, Linda (Ed.). *State of the World 2004: A Worldwatch Institute Report on Progress Toward a Sustainable Society*. New York: W.W. Norton & Company, 2004.

Starke, Linda (Ed.), *Vital Signs 2003: The Trends that Are Shaping Our Future*. Worldwatch Institute in Cooperation with the United Nations Environmental Programme. New York: W.W. Norton & Company, 2003.

Strathern, Paul. *The Big Idea: Curie and Radioactivity*. New York: Doubleday, 1997.

Stull, Donald D. and Michael J. Broadway. *Slaughterhouse Blues: The Meat and Poultry Industry in North America*. Southbank, Victoria, Australia: Thomson Wadsworth, 2004.

Webb, Tony, Tim Lang, and Kathleen Tucker. *Food Irradiation: Who Wants It?* Rochester, VT: Thorsons Publishers, Inc., 1987.

Wallach Lori and Patrick Woodall, *WTO: Whose Trade Organization?* New York: The New Press, 2004.

Woodbury, David O. *Atoms for Peace*. New York: Dodd, Mead & Company, 1955.

Yam, Philip. *The Pathological Protein: Mad Cow, Chronic Wasting Disease, and Other Deadly Prion Diseases*. New York: Copernicus Books, 2003.

Acknowledgements

The authors wish to thank Food & Water Watch staff Patricia Lovera, Tony Corbo, Erin Greenfield, Brendan Hoffman, Patrick Woodall, and Felicia Nestor for their assistance with this project. Without their help, this book could not have been written. Also we wish to thank former Food & Water Watch staff Audrey Hill and Andrianna Natsoulas, who were instrumental in providing information for this project.

Mary Ricci, Food & Water Watch board member, and Erica Hartman, former Communications director at Food & Water Watch, deserve special thanks for the editing the manuscript.

We also wish to thank the following individuals and organizations:

Peter Jenkins, formerly of the Center for Food Safety;

Diane Hatz, Sustainable Table;

Kathy Ozer and George Naylor, National Family Farm Coalition;

Joan Claybrook, Dr. Sidney Wolfe, and Lori Wallach, Public Citizen;

Dennis Olsen and Dr. David Wallinga, Institute for Agriculture and Trade Policy;

Dr. Samuel S. Epstein, Cancer Prevention Coalition;

John Kelly, former New Jersey Assembly Member, and aide Michael Perrone;

Leigh Hauter, farmer and writer;

Andrea Helm, researcher;

Kathleen Tucker and Bob Alvarez, Health and Energy Institute;

Paul Fehribach, Illinois Food Safety Coalition;

Tracy Lerman and Monique Mikhail, formerly of Public Citizen.

Resources

Animal Welfare Institute
P.O. Box 3650
Washington, DC 20027
(703) 836-4300
www.awionline.org
awi@awionline.org

Center for Food Safety
National Headquarters
660 Pennsylvania Avenue, SE
Suite 302
Washington DC, 2003
(202) 547-9359
www.centerforfoodsafety.org
office@centerforfoodsafety.org

Center for A Livable Future
615 N Wolfe Street E2150
Baltimore, MD 21205
(410) 502-7578
www.jhsph.edu/clf
clf@jhsph.edu

Community Food Security Coalition
P.O. Box 209
Venice, CA 90294
(310) 822-5410
www.foodsecurity.org
Maya@foodsecurity.org

Consumers Union
101 Truman Avenue
Yonkers, NY 10703-1057
(914) 378-2000
www.consumerreports.org
www.consumersunion.org

Council of Canadians
700-170 Laurier Avenue
West Ottawa, ON, K1P 5V5
Canada
(613) 233-2773
www.canadians.org
inquiries@canadians.org

Eat Well Guide
Sustainable Table
215 Lexington Avenue
Suite 1001
New York, NY 10016
(212) 726-9161
www.eatwellguide.org
info@sustainabletable.org

The European Food Irradiation Campaign
Véronique Gallais
www.irradiation.info
vgallais@no-log.org

Farm Aid
11 Ward Street
Suite 200
Somerville, MA 02143
(617) 354-2922
www.farmaid.org
info@farmaid.org

Food & Water Watch
1616 P Street, NW
Suite 300
Washington, DC 20036
(202) 683-2500
www.foodandwaterwatch.org
foodandwater@fwwatch.org

Food Irradiation Watch
PO Box 5829
West End,
Brisbane QLD, 4101
Australia
www.foodirradiationinfo.org
foodirradiationwatch@yahoo.com.au

FoodRoutes
31 East Durham Street
Philadelphia, PA 19119
(814) 349-6000
www.foodroutes.org
info@foodroutes.org

FoodRoutes Farm to College Program
31 East Durham Street
Philadelphia, PA 19119
(570) 658-2265
www.foodroutes.org/farmtocollege.jsp
kristen@foodsecurity.org

Glynwood Center
P.O. Box 157
Cold Spring, NY 10516
(845) 265-3338
www.glynwood.org

GRACE
215 Lexington Avenue
Suite 1001
New York, NY 10016
(212) 726-9161
www.gracelinks.org
info@gracelinks.org

Government Accountability Project
1612 K Street
Suite 1100
Washington, DC 20006
(202) 408-0034
www.whistleblower.org
gapdc@whistleblower.org

Institute for Agriculture and Trade Policy
2105 First Avenue South
Minneapolis, MN 55404
(612) 870-0453
www.iatp.org
iatp@iatp.org

The Meatrix
c/o Sustainable Table
215 Lexington Avenue
Suite 1001
New York, NY 10016
(212) 726-9161
www.themeatrix.com
leo@themeatrix.com

National Campaign for Sustainable Agriculture
P.O. Box 396
Pine Bush, NY 12566
(845) 361-5201
www.sustainableagriculture.net
campaign@sustainableagriculture.net

National Family Farm Coalition
110 Maryland Avenue, NE
Suite 307
Washington, DC 20002
(202) 543-5675
www.nffc.net
nffc@nffc.net

Organic Consumers Association
6771 South Silver Hill Drive
Finland, MN 55603
(218) 266-4164
www.organicconsumers.org

Public Citizen
1600 20th Street, NW
Washington, DC 20009
(202) 588-1000
www.citizen.org
hrg1@citizen.org

Sierra Club
Sierra Club National Headquarters
85 Second Street, 2nd Floor
San Francisco, CA 94105
(415) 977-5500
www.sierraclub.org
information@sierraclub.org

The Small Planet Institute
25 Mt. Auburn Street
Suite 203
Cambridge, MA 02138
(617) 441-6300, x115
www.smallplanet.org
jess@smallplanet.org

Slow Food USA National Office
20 Jay Street
Suite 313
Brooklyn, NY 11201
(718) 260-8000
 www.slowfoodusa.org
info@slowfoodusa.org

Socially Responsible Agricultural Project
P.O. Box 687
McCall, ID
(208) 315-4836
www.sraproject.org

Sustainable Table
215 Lexington Avenue
Suite 1001
New York, NY 10016
(212) 726-9161
www.sustainabletable.org
info@sustainabletable.org

Endnotes

[1] Gofman, John W. *Radiation and Human Health: A Comprehensive Investigation of the Evidence Relating Low-Level Radiation to Cancer and Other Diseases*. San Francisco: Sierra Club Books, 1981.

[2] Bhaskaram, C. and G. Sadasivan. "Effects of Feeding Irradiated Wheat to Malnourished Children." *The American Journal of Clinical Nutrition*, No. 28, pp. 130-135, 1975.

[3] Vijayalaxmi. "Cytogenetic Studies in Monkeys Fed Irradiated Wheat." *Toxicology* 9:181-184, 1978.

[4] Vijayalaxmi and K.V. Rao. "Dominant Lethal Mutations in Rats Fed on Irradiated Wheat." *International Journal of Radiation Biology*, 29:93-98, 1976.

[5] Vijayalaxmi and G. Sadasivan. "Chromosomal Aberrations in Rats Fed Irradiated Wheat." *International Journal of Radiation Biology*, 27:135-142, 1975.

[6] Vijayalaxmi. "Cytogenic Studies in Rats Fed Irradiated Wheat." *International Journal of Radiation Biology*, 27:283-285, 1975.

[7] Vijayalaxmi." Genetic Effects of Feeding Irradiated Wheat to Mice." *Canadian Journal of Genetics and Cytology*, 18:231-238, 1976.

[8] Anderson, D., et al. "Irradiated Laboratory Animal Diets: Dominant Lethal Studies in the Mouse." *Mutation Research*, 80:333-345, 1981.

[9] Bugyaki, L., et al. "Do Irradiated Foodstuffs Have a Radiomimetic Effect? II. Trials with Mice Fed Wheat Meal Irradiated at 5 Mrad." *Atompraxis*, 14:112-118, 1968.

[10] Moutschen-Dahmen, M., et al. "Pre-implantation Death of Mouse Eggs Caused by Irradiated Food." *International Journal of Radiation Biology*, 18:201-216, 1970.

[11] Johnston-Arthur T., M. Brena-Valle, K. Turanitz, R. Hruby, and G. Stehlik. "Mutagenicity of Irradiated Food in the Host Mediated Assay System." *Studia Biophysica* (Berlin), 50:137-141, 1975.

[12] Renner, H.W. "Chromosome Studies on Bone Marrow Cells of Chinese Hamsters Fed a Radiosterilized Diet." *Toxicology*, 8:213-222, 1977.

[13] Vijayalaxmi and S.G. Srikantia. "Review of the Studies on the Wholesomeness of Irradiated Wheat, Conducted at the National Institute of Nutrition, India." *International Journal of Radiation Application and Instrumentation, Part C*, 34(6):941-952.

[14] "Safety Evaluation of 35 Kinds of Irradiated Human Foods." *Chinese Medical Journal*, 100(9):715-718, 1987.

[15] Jaarma, Maire. "Studies of Chemical and Enzymatical Changes in Potato Tubers and Some Higher Plants Caused by Ionizing Radiation, Including Studies on the Wholesomeness of □ (Gamma)-Irradiated Potato Tubers and Effects on Some Carbohydrates *In Vitro*." Biochemical Institute, University of Stockholm, 1967.

[16] Levy, Lester M., et al. "An assessment of the possible toxic effects to human beings of short-term consumption of food sterilized with gamma rays." U.S. Army Medical Nutrition Laboratory, Fitzsimons Army Hospital, Denver. Report No. 203, March 1957.

[17] Plough, I.C., et al. "An evaluation in human begins of the acceptability, digestibility and toxicity of pork sterilized by gamma radiation and stored at room temperature." U.S. Army Medical Nutrition Laboratory, Fitzsimons Army Hospital, Denver. Report No. 204, May 1957.

[18] Bierman, E.D., et al. "Short-term human feeding studies of foods sterilized by gamma radiation and stored at room temperature." U.S. Army Medical Nutrition Laboratory, Fitzsimons Army Hospital, Denver. Report No. 224, July 1958.

[19] Shaw, M.W. and E. Hayes. "Effects of Irradiated Sucrose on the Chromosomes of Human Lymphocytes *In Vitro*." *Nature*, 211:1254-1255, 1966.

[20] Kesavan, P.C. and M.S. Swaminathan. "Cytotoxic and radiomimetic activity of irradiated culture medium on human leukocytes." *Current Science*, 16:403-404, 1966.

[21] Barna, Joseph. "Compilation of Bioassay Data on the Wholesomeness of Irradiated Food Items." *Acta Alimentaria*, 8:205-315, 1979.

[22] *Bad Taste: The Disturbing Truth About the World Health Organization's Endorsement of Food Irradiation*. Public Citizen, Washington, DC, and Global Resource Action Center for the Environment, New York, NY, October 2002.

[23] Metta, V.C., et al. "Vitamin K deficiency in rats induced by feeding of irradiated beef." *Journal of Nutrition*, 69:18-21, 1959.

[24] Mellette, S.J. and L.A. Leone. "Influence of age, sex, strain of rat and fat soluble vitamins on hemorrhagic syndromes in rats fed irradiated beef." *Federation Proceedings*, 19:1045-1048, 1960.

[25] Poling, C.E., et al. "Growth, Reproduction, Survival and Histopathology of Rats Fed Beef Irradiated with Electrons." *Food Research*, 20:193-214, 1955.

[26] Anderson, D., et al. "Irradiated Laboratory Animal Diets: Dominant Lethal Studies in the Mouse." *Mutation Research*, 80:333-345, 1981.

[27] Moutschen-Dahmen, M., et al. "Pre-implantation Death of Mouse Eggs Caused by Irradiated Food." *International Journal of Radiation Biology*, 18:201-216, 1970.

[28] Reichelt, D., et al. "Long-term animal feeding study for testing the wholesomeness of an irradiated diet with a high content of free radicals." Federal Research Institute for Food Preservation, Institute for Radiation Technology, Karlsruhe, Germany, 1972.

[29] DaCosta, E. and S.M. Levenson. "Effect of diet exposed to capacitron irradiation on the growth and fertility of the albino rat." U.S. Army Medical Nutrition Laboratory, Fitzsimons Army Hospital, Denver. Report No. 89, 1951. Cited in Kraybill, H.F. and T.E. Huber. "The wholesomeness of irradiated food and its military implications." Paper to be presented at 63rd Annual Convention, Association of Military Surgeons, United States of America, Hotel Statler, Washington, DC, Nov. 12-14, 1956.

[30] Bugyaki, L., et al. "Do irradiated foodstuffs have a radiomimetic effect? II. Trials with mice fed wheat meal irradiated at 5 Mrad." *Atompraxis* 14:112-118, 1968.

[31] Bugyaki, et al., op. cit.

[32] Vijayalaxmi. "Cytogenetic Studies in Monkeys Fed Irradiated Wheat." *Toxicology* 9:181-184, 1978.

[33] Löfroth, G., et al. "Biological Effects of Irradiated Food. II: Chemical and Biological Studies of Compounds Distilled from Irradiated Food." *Arkiv för Zoologi*, 18:529-547, 1966.

[34] Vijayalaxmi." Genetic Effects of Feeding Irradiated Wheat to Mice." *Canadian Journal of Genetics and Cytology*, 18:231-238, 1976.

[35] Vijayalaxmi and G. Sadasivan. "Chromosomal Aberrations in Rats Fed Irradiated Wheat." *International Journal of Radiation Biology*, 27:135-142, 1975.

[36] Renner, H.W. "Chromosome Studies on Bone Marrow Cells of Chinese Hamsters Fed a Radiosterilized Diet." *Toxicology*, 8:213-222, 1977.

[37] Scarascia-Mugnozza, G.T., et al. "On genetic effects produced by irradiated food and food components." Organisation for Economic Co-operation and Development, European Nuclear Energy Agency, Steering Committee for Nuclear Energy, Study Group on Food Irradiation, SEN/IR(65)15, Nov. 8, 1965.

[38] De, A.K., et al. "Biochemical Effects of Irradiated Sucrose Solutions in the Rat." *Radiation Research*, 37:202-215, 1969.

[39] *Federal Register*, Vol. 69, pp. 76844-76847, Dec. 23, 2004.

[40] Easterly, C. E., et al. "Assessment of Petition to Increase the Maximum X-Ray Energy to 7.5 MeV from the Value of 5.0 MeV for the Treatment of Food by Ionizing Radiation."

ORNL-2003-1, Oak Ridge National Laboratory, Life Sciences Division, Oak Ridge, TN, 2003.

[41] Brynjolfsson, Ari. "Natural and Induced Radioactivity in Food." Proceedings of the International Conference on Future Nuclear Systems. *Global '99: Nuclear Technology—Bridging the Millennia.* Aug. 29-Sept. 3, 1999, Jackson Hole, WY.

[42] *Natural and Induced Radioactivity in Food.* International Atomic Energy Agency, Vienna, IAEA-TECDOC-1287, April 2002.

[43] Wakeford, C.A., et al. "Induction and Detection of Radioactivity in Foodstuffs Irradiated with 10 MeV Electrons and X-Rays." *Radiation Physics and Chemistry*, 38(1):29-38, 1991.

[44] Swaminathan, M.S., et al. "Mutations: Incidence in *Drosophila melanogaster* Reared on Irradiated Medium." *Science*, 141:637-638, 1963.

[45] Rinehart, R.R. and F.J. Ratty. "Mutation in *Drosophila melanogaster* Cultured on Irradiated Whole Food or Food Components." *International Journal of Radiation Biology*, 12(4):347-354, 1967.

[46] Rinehart, R.R. and F.J. Ratty. "Mutation in *Drosophila melanogaster* Cultured on Irradiated Food." *Genetics*, 52(6):1119-1126, 1965.

[47] Parkash, Om. "Induction of Sex-linked Recessive Lethals and Visible Mutations by Feeding X-irradiated DNA to *Drosophila melanogaster.*" *Nature*, 205:312-313, 1965.

[48] Parkash, Om. "Mutagenic effect of irradiated DNA in *Drosophila melanogaster.*" *Nature*, 214:611-612, 1967.

[49] Kesavan, P.C. and M.S. Swaminathan. "Mutagenic Effects of Irradiated Culture Media in *Drosophila melanogaster.*" *Indian Journal of Genetics & Plant Breeding*, 29:173-183, 1969.

[50] Parkash, Om. "On the Radiomimetic Effect of Irradiated Desoxyribonucleic Acid (DNA$_m$) on *Drosophila melanogaster.*" *Die Naturwissenschaften*, 6:142, 1965.

[51] Swaminathan, et al., op. cit.

[52] Aiyar, A.S. and V.S. Rao. "Studies on Mutagenicity of Irradiated Sugar Solutions in *Salmonella typhimurium.*" *Mutation Research*, 48:17-28, 1977.

[53] Stone, W.S., et al. "The Production of Mutations in *Staphylococcus aureus* by Irradiation of the Substrate." *Proceedings of the National Academy of Sciences*, 33:59-66, 1947.

[54] Wagner, R. P., et al. "The Effect of Irradiated Medium, Cyanide and Peroxide on the Mutations Rate in *Neurosopora.*" *Genetics*, 35:237-248, 1950.

[55] Chopra, V.L. "Lethal and Mutagenic Effects of Irradiated Medium on *Escherichia coli.*" *Mutation Research*, 8:25-33, 1969.

[56] Stone, W.S., et al. "The Role of Mutation and of Selection in the Frequency of Mutants Among Microorganisms Grown on Irradiated Substrate." *Proceedings of the National Academy of Sciences*, 34:142-149, 1948.

[57] Wyss, O., et al. "The Production of Mutations in *Staphylococcus aureus* by Chemical Treatment of the Substrate." *Journal of Bacteriology*, 54:767-772, 1947.

[58] Wyss, O., et al. "The Role of Peroxide in the Biological Effects of Irradiated Broth." *Journal of Bacteriology*, 56:51-57, 1948.

[59] Chopra, V.L. "The effects of irradiated culture medium on bacteria." *Microbial Genetics Bulletin*, 23:8-9, 1965.

[60] Aiyer, op. cit.

[61] Wagner, op. cit.

[62] Ehrenberg, L., et al. "Biological Effects of Irradiated Food. I: Effect on Lymphocyte Numbers in the Peripheral Blood of the Rat." *Arkiv för Zoologi*, 18:195-216, 1965.

[63] Spiher, A.T. "Food Irradiation: An FDA Report." *FDA Papers*, Oct. 1968.

[64] Donald B. Louria, Testimony before the House Committee on Energy and Commerce, Subcommittee on Health and the Environment, U.S. House of Representatives, June 19, 1987.

[65] Tritsch, George L. "Food Irradiation." *Nutrition*, 16:698-701, 2000.

[66] Chinn, H.I. "Evaluation of the health aspects of certain compounds found in irradiated beef." Federation of American Societies for Experimental Biology, Bethesda, MD. Prepared for U.S. Army Medical Research and Development Command. Contract No. DAMD-17-76-C-6055, August 1977.

[67] LeTellier, P.R. and W.W. Nawar. "2-alkylcyclobutanones from the Radiolysis of Triglycerides." *Lipids*, 7: 75-76, 1972.

[68] Delincée, H. and B. Pool-Zobel. "Genotoxic Properties of 2-dodecylcyclobutanone, a Compound Formed on Irradiation of Food Containing Fat." *Radiation Physics and Chemistry*, 52: 39-42, 1998.

[69] Delincée, H., et al. "Genotoxicity of 2-dodecylcyclobutanone." Food Irradiation: Fifth German Conference, Karlsruhe, Nov. 11-13, 1998.

[70] Delincée, H., et al. "Genotoxicity of 2-alkylcyclobutanones, Markers for an Irradiation Treatment in Fat-containing Food—Part I: Cyto- and Genotoxic Potential of 2- tetradecylcyclobutanone." *Radiation Physics and Chemistry*, 63:431-435, 2002.

[71] Burnouf, D., et al. Etude toxicologique transfrontalière destinée à évaluer le risque encouru lors de la consommation d'aliments gras ionisés - Toxikologische Untersuchung zur Risikobewertung beim Verzehr von bestrahlten fetthaltigen Lebensmitteln—Eine französisch-deutsche Studie im Grenzraum Oberrhein, Rapport final d'étude Interreg II, projet N° 3.171. BFE-R—02-02, Federal Research Centre for Nutrition, Karlsruhe, Germany, 2001.

[72] *Hidden Harm: How the FDA is Ignoring the Potential Dangers of Unique Chemicals in Irradiated Food*. Public Citizen and the Center for Food Safety, Washington, DC, December 2001.

[73] Ibid.

[74] Burnouf, op. cit.

[75] *What's in the Beef: Scientists Question the Safety of Irradiated Ground Beef*. Public Citizen and The Center for Food Safety, Washington, DC, November 2003.

[76] *A Broken Record: How the FDA Legalized—and Continues to Legalize—Food Irradiation without Testing It for Safety*. Public Citizen, Cancer Prevention Coalition, and Global Resource Action Center for the Environment, Washington, DC, October 2000.

[77] Ibid.

[78] Ibid.

[79] Ibid.

[80] Ibid.

[81] Smith, Kathie. "Irradiated Beef May Be Coming to Your Store." *Toledo Blade*, March 21, 2000.

[82] Long, John S. "Irradiated Food a Time Bomb or a Lifesaver?" *Cleveland Plain Dealer*, March 1, 2000.

[83] Ward, Mark. "Gamma Rays Zap Bacteria, Other Pathogens." *Milwaukee Journal Sentinel*, Nov. 24, 1995.

[84] Diehl 1969, op.cit.

[85] Gibbs, Gary. *The Food That Would Last Forever*. Garden City Park, NY: Avery Publishing Group, 1993.

[86] Maxie, E.C., et al. *Radiation Botany*, 405-411, 1964.

[87] Diehl, J.F. "Vitamin A in Irradiated Foodstuffs." *Zeitschrift fuer Lebensmittel-Untersuchung und Forschung*, 168:29-31, 1979.

[88] Janave, M. T. and P. Thomas. "Influence of Post-Harvest Storage of Potato Carotenoids." *Potato Research*, 22:365-369, 1979.

[89] FDA Memorandum from Kim M. Morehouse (Division of Product Manufacture and Use) to William Trotter (Division of Product Policy), April 11, 2000.

[90] Diehl, J.F. "Combined Effects of Irradiation, Storage and Cooking on the Vitamin E and Vitamin B_1 Levels of Foods." Presented at the 33rd Annual Meeting of the American Institute of Nutrition, 1969.

[91] Kilcast, D. "Effect of Radiation on Vitamins." *Food Chemistry*, 49:157-164, 1994.

[92] Ziporin, Z.Z., et al. U.S. Army Medical Nutrition Laboratory, April 1957.

[93] Stevenson, M.H. "Nutritional and Other Implications of Irradiating Meat." *Proceedings of the Nutrition Society*, 53: 317-325, 1994.

[94] Metta, V.C., et al. "Vitamin K Deficiency in Rats Induced By Feeding of Irradiated Beef." *Journal of Nutrition*, 69: 18-21, 1959.

[95] Diehl, J.H. "Combined Effects of Irradiation, Storage, and Cooking on the Vitamin E and B1 Levels of Foods." *Food Irradiation*, 10: 2-7, April 14, 1967.

[96] Jo, C. and D.U. Ahn. "Production of Volatile Compounds from Irradiated Oil Emulsion Containing Amino Acids or Proteins." *Journal of Food Science*, 65(4):612-616, 2000.

[97] Nam, K.C. and D.U. Ahn. "Effects of Ascorbic Acid and Antioxidants on the Color of Irradiated Ground Beef." *Journal of Food Science*, 68(5):1686-1690.

[98] Jo, C. and D.U. Ahn. "Volatiles and Oxidative Changes in Irradiated Pork Sausage with Different Fatty Acid Composition and Tocopherol Content." *Journal of Food Science*, 65(2):270-275, 2000.

[99] Ahn, D.U., D.G. Olson, et al. "Packaging and Irradiation Effects on Lipid Oxidation and Volatiles in Pork Patties." *Journal of Food Science*, 63(1):15-19, 1998.

[100] Ahn, D.U., D.G. Olson, et al. "Volatiles Production and Lipid Oxidation in Irradiated Cooked Sausage as Related to Packaging and Storage." *Journal of Food Science*, 64(2):226-299, 1999.

[101] Hicks, Sally. "Food Plant Under Fire." *St. Petersburg Times*, Nov. 25, 1990.

[102] Blackford, Darris C. "Intervention is Divine in Plate Vote; Minister, Prayer Sway Irradiation Decision." *Tampa Tribune*, Sept. 6, 1990.

[103] "Broadsides." Food & Water Inc., Montpelier, VT, http://www.broadsides.org/about.html, March 30, 2005.

[104] "Firm Betting Americans Will Accept Irradiated Foods." *Wisconsin State Journal*, June 5, 1991.

[105] McKenna, Peter. "Environmentalists Spy on New Food Plant." *Restaurant Business*, March 1, 1992.

[106] Donnelly, John. "First Shipments of Treated Strawberries Face Protests from Determined Opponents. Knight-Ridder via *Buffalo News*, Jan. 12, 1992.

[107] Booth, William. Food Irradiation Makes Florida Debut Amid Persistent Protests over Safety." *Washington Post*, Jan. 12, 1992.

[108] Donnelly, John. "Debate on Irradiated Food Centers on Small Florida Town." *Miami Herald*, July 2, 1991.

[109] Food Technology Service filings, U.S. Securities and Exchange Commission.

[110] "Food Technology Stock Rises." *The Ledger* (Lakeland, FL), Dec. 29, 2004.

[111] Reinan, John. "Zapped." *Tampa Tribune*, Feb. 21, 2000.

[112] U.S. Code of Federal Regulations, Title 21,§170.22.

[113] *Radiation Processing for Safe, Shelf-Stable and Ready-to-Eat Food.* Proceedings of a Final Research Co-ordination Meeting Held in Montreal, Canada, 10-14 July 2000. International Atomic Energy Agency, Vienna, IAEA-TECDOC-1337, January 2003.

[114] Bruhn, Christine M. "Consumer Attitudes and Market Response to Irradiated Food." *Journal of Food Protection*, 58(2):175-181, 1995.

[115] Editorial "Lettuce Irradiate." *Investor's Business Daily*, Dec. 19, 2006.

[116] Mudgett, Randy. "*E. coli* outbreaks prompt leaders to back irradiation." *Farm News* (Fort Dodge, IA), Dec. 20, 2006.

[117] Rowe, Jeff. "Grocers Worry Irradiation Will Take Life Out of Spices." Knight-Ridder Tribune News Service, via *Austin American-Statesman*, July 27, 1994.

[118] Josephson, Edward S. "An Historical Review of Food Irradiation." *Journal of Food Safety*, 5(4):161, 1983. Cited in Satin, Morton. *Food Irradiation: A Guidebook* (Second Edition). Boca Raton, FL: CRC Press, 1996, p. 23.

[119] Moeller, David R. "The Problem of Agricultural Concentration: The Case of the Tyson-IBP Merger." *Drake Journal of Agricultural Law*, 8:33-56, 2003.

[120] Groves, Martha. "Less-Than-Glowing Image Hampers Food Irradiation." *Los Angeles Times*, March 15, 1998.

[121] Moskowitz, Dara. Let Them Eat S—t." *City Pages* (Twin Cities), Feb. 25, 1998.

[122] Sugarman, Carol. "An End to Food Scares: Reconsidering Irradiation, with All Its Pros and Cons." *Washington Post*, Nov. 12, 1997.

[123] *Sterigenics International v. County of Orange*. In the Court of Appeal of the State of California, Fourth Appellate District, Division Three. Opinion G014938, July 31, 1996.

[124] Catherine Caufield, *Multiple Exposures; Chronicles of the Radiation Age* (New York: Harper & Row, 1989). pp. 3-21.

[125] Strathern, op. cit., pp. 33-39.

[126] "Highlights in Radiation Research—A Timeline." Low Dose Radiation Research Program, Washington State University Tri-Cities, Richland, WA.

[127] Caufield, op. cit.

[128] Caufield, op. cit., pp. 3-21.

[129] Caufield, op. cit., pp. 22-28.

[130] Strathern, op. cit., pp. 39-42.

[131] Pflaum, Rosalynd. *Grand Obsession: Madame Curie and Her World*. New York: Doubleday, 1989, pp. 59-60.

[132] "Curie and the Science of Radioactivity." American Institute of Physics, College Park, MD.

[133] Strathern, op. cit., pp. 43-77.

[134] Curie, Eve. *Madame Curie*. London: William Heinemann Ltd., 1938, pp. 150-173.

[135] Caufield, op. cit., pp. 22-28.

[136] Irvine, Martha. "Suffering Endures for 'Radium Girls' Who Painted Watches in the '20s." Associated Press, Oct. 4, 1998.

[137] Caufield, op. cit., pp. 43-45.

[138] "Guide to the Nobel Prizes." *Encyclopedia Britannica*.

[139] Potter, Robert D. *The Atomic Revolution*. New York: Robert M. McBride & Company, 1946, p 33.

[140] Metzger, H. Peter. *The Atomic Establishment*. New York: Simon and Schuster, 1972, p. 23.

[141] Potter, op. cit., p. 85.

[142] Caufield, op. cit., p. 64.

[143] Dietz, David. *Atomic Energy in the Coming Age*. New York: Dodd, Mead & Company, 1945, pp. 12-20.

[144] Potter, op. cit., pp. 103-108.

[145] "Atoms for Peace: Dwight D. Eisenhower's Address to the United Nations." Published for the National Archives and Record Administration by the National Archives Trust Fund Board, Washington, DC, 1990.

[146] Ibid., pp. 12-13.

[147] Campbell, op. cit., pp. 263-264.

[148] Metzger, op. cit., pp. 203-208.

[149] Cartwright, Vincent. "Dream of Atomic-Powered Flight." *Aviation Week*, March 1995, pp. 30-36.

[150] Metzger, op. cit., pp. 208-217.

[151] Boyer, Paul. *By the Bomb's Early Light: American Thought and Culture at the Dawn of the Atomic Age*. New York: Pantheon Books, 1985, pp. 295-298.

[152] *Peaceful Uses of Atomic Energy*. Report of the Panel on the Impact of the Peaceful Uses of Atomic Energy to the Joint Committee on Atomic Energy, U.S. Congress, January 1956.

[153] "Why Did the Savannah Fail?" *Atomic Energy Insights*, July 1995.

[154] Metzger, op. cit., pp. 199-237.

[155] Caufield, op. cit., pp. 148-150.

[156] Bretnor, Reginald. "Maybe Just a Little One." *Harper's*, August 1947, pp. 137-144.

[157] *Food Preservation by Irradiation*. U.S. Atomic Energy Commission, Division of Technical Information, Oak Ridge, TN, October 1964, reprinted April 1968.

[158] Kramish, Arnold. *The Peaceful Atom in Foreign Policy*. New York and Evanston: Harper & Row, 1963, pp. 132-138.

[159] *Memorial Tributes: Volume 5*. National Academy of Engineering. Washington, DC: National Academy Press, 1992.

[160] "National Food Irradiation Research Program: Hearings Before the Joint Committee on Atomic Energy, Congress of the United States." Jan. 14-15, 1960. Washington, DC: U.S. Government Printing Office, 1960, p. 150.

[161] Ibid, pp. 66-69.

[162] Ibid, p. 51.

[163] Ibid, pp. 21-27.

[164] Caufield, op. cit., p. 104.

[165] Caufield, op. cit., pp. 154-157.

[166] Metzger, op. cit., p. 111.

[167] Commoner, Barry. *Science and Survival*. New York: Viking Press, 1966.

[168] "Review of the Food Irradiation Program: Hearing Before the Subcommittee on Research, Development, and Radiation of the Joint Committee on Atomic Energy, Congress of the United States." Sept. 12, 1966. Washington, DC: U.S. Government Printing Office, 1967, pp. 28-30.

[169] Ibid., pp. 68-69.

[170] *Food Preservation by Irradiation*. U.S. Atomic Energy Commission, Division of Technical Information Extension, Oak Ridge, TN, April 1968.

[171] "Status of the Food Irradiation Program: Hearings Before the Subcommittee on Research, Development, and Radiation of the Joint Committee on Atomic Energy, Congress of the United States." July 18 & 30, 1968. Washington, DC: U.S. Government Printing Office, 1968, pp. 107-108.

[172] Metzger, op. cit., p. 15.

[173] U.S. Government Printing Office, 1968, op. cit., p. 100.

[174] Ibid., p. 59.

[175] Ibid., p. 100.

[176] Ibid., p. 108.

[177] Seaborg, Glenn. T. and William R. Corliss. *Man and Atom: Building a New World Through Nuclear Technology.* New York: E.P. Dutton & Co., 1971, p. 174.

[178] *Peaceful Uses of Nuclear Energy: A Collection of Speeches by Glenn T. Seaborg, Chairman, United States Atomic Energy Commission.* U.S. Atomic Energy Commission, Division of Technical Information Extension, Oak Ridge, TN, July 1970, pp. 121-156.

[179] Seaborg, Glenn. T. and William R. Corliss. op. cit, p. 194-196.

[180] "AEC Authorizing Legislation, Fiscal Year 1971: Hearings Before the Joint Committee on Atomic Energy, Congress of the United States." Feb. 3, 18 & 19, 1970. Washington, DC: U.S. Government Printing Office, 1970, pp. 180, 474, 479.

[181] "AEC Authorizing Legislation, Fiscal Year 1970: Hearings Before the Joint Committee on Atomic Energy, Congress of the United States." April 29-30, 1969. Washington, DC: Government Printing Office, 1970, p. 1692.

[182] Fischer, David. *History of the International Atomic Energy Agency: The First Forty Years.* International Atomic Energy Agency, Vienna, 1997, p. 35.

[183] Letter to the UN Secretary General: Exclude the Promotion of Nuclear Technology from the Mandate of the IAEA.

[184] "Agreement Between the International Atomic Energy Agency and the World Health Organization." Approved by the Twelfth Health Assembly, Geneva, May 28, 1959. Resolution WHA12.40.

[185] Preamble to the Constitution of the World Health Organization, as adopted by the International Health Conference, New York City, June 19-22, 1946.

[186] *Mental Health Aspects of the Peaceful Uses of Atomic Energy: Report of a Study Group.* Technical Report Series No. 151, World Health Organization, Geneva, 1958, pp. 5, 12, 31, 48.

[187] *Report of the Meeting on the Wholesomeness of Irradiated Foods.* Organized by the Food and Agriculture Organization, the World Health Organization, and the In-

ternational Atomic Energy Agency, Brussels, Oct. 23-30, 1961. Food and Agriculture Organization of the United Nations, Rome, 1962.

[188] *The Technical Basis for Legalization of Irradiated Food.* Report of a Joint FAO/IAEA/WHO Expert Committee, Rome, 21-28 April 1964. World Health Organization Technical Report Series No. 316. World Health Organization, Geneva, 1966.

[189] *Wholesomeness of Irradiated Food with Special Reference to Wheat, Potatoes, and Onions.* Report of a Joint FAO/IAEA/WHO Expert Committee, Geneva, 8-12 April 1969. World Health Organization Technical Report Series No. 451. World Health Organization, Geneva, 1970.

[190] Bugyaki, L., A.R. Deschreider, J. Moutschen, M. Moutschen-Dahmen, A. Thijs, and A. LaFontaine. "Do irradiated foodstuffs have a radiomimetic effect? Ii. Trials with mice fed wheat meal irradiated at 5 Mrad." *Atompraxis* 14:112-118, 1968.

[191] Ibid.

[192] Vijayalaxmi and K.V. Rao. "Dominant lethal mutations in rats fed on irradiated wheat." *International Journal of Radiation Biology*, 29:93-98.

[193] *Wholesomeness of Irradiated Food.* Report of a Joint FAO/IAEA/WHO Expert Committee, Geneva, Aug. 31-Sept. 7, 1976. World Health Organization Technical Report Series No. 604. World Health Organization, Geneva, 1977.

[194] Ibid.

[195] Ibid.

[196] J. Barna. Compilation of Bioassay Data on the Wholesomeness of Irradiated Food Items. Vol. 8. Acta Alimentaria 3. 205. 1979. This study is reported in Webb, Tony, Tim Lang, Kathleen Tucker. *Food Irradiation: Who Wants It?* Rochester, VT: Thorsons Publishers, Inc., 1987.

[197] *Wholesomeness of Irradiated Food.* Report of a Joint FAO/IAEA/WHO Expert Committee, Geneva, Oct. 27-Nov. 3, 1980. World Health Organization Technical Report Series No. 659. World Health Organization, Geneva, 1981.

[198] World Health Organization, 1977.

[199] *Safety Factors Influencing the Acceptance of Food Irradiation Technology.* Report of a Task Force Meeting on Public Information of Food Irradiation convened by the International Consultative Group on Food Irradiation and held in Cadarache, France, 18-21 April 1988. Vienna: International Atomic Energy Agency, 1989.

[200] *Marketing and Acceptance of Irradiated Foods.* Report of the Consultants' Meeting on the Marketing, Market Testing and Consumer Acceptance of Irradiated Foods,

Organized by the Joint FAO/IAEA Division of Isotope and Radiation Applications of Atomic Energy for Food and Agricultural Development, Sept. 27-Oct. 1, 1982. International Atomic Energy Agency, Vienna, 1983.

[201] Ralston Purina Co. Irradiation Sterilized Chicken: A Feeding Study in Rats. Contract No. 53-3K06-1-29,69, July 1982.

[202] D. W. Thayer. *Summary of Supporting Documents for Wholesomeness Studies of Precooked (Enzyme Activated) Chicken Products in Vacuum Sealed Containers Exposed to Doses of Ionizing Radiation Sufficient to Achieve "Commercial Sterility."* U.S. Department of Agriculture, Philadelphia, March 19, 1984. This study is reported in Webb, Tony, Tim Lang, Kathleen Tucker. *Food Irradiation: Who Wants It?* Rochester, VT: Thorsons Publishers, Inc., 1987.

[203] *Safety and Nutritional Adequacy of Irradiated Food.* World Health Organization, Geneva, 1994.

[204] *Review of Data on High Dose (10-70 kGy) Irradiation of Food.* Report of a Consultation, Karlsruhe, Germany, Aug. 29-Sept. 2, 1994. World Health Organization, Geneva, 1995.

[205] *High-Dose Irradiation: Wholesomeness of Food Irradiated with Doses Above 10 kGy.* Report of a Joint FAO/IAEA/WHO Study Group, Geneva, Sept. 15-20, 1997. World Health Organization, Geneva, 1999.

[206] *Bad Taste: The Disturbing Truth About the World Health Organization's Endorsement of Food Irradiation.* Public Citizen and Global Resource Action Center for the Environment, Washington, DC, October 2002.

[207] "Beneficial Uses of Defense Nuclear Materials Byproducts: Hearing Before the Procurement and Military Nuclear Systems Subcommittee of the Committee on Armed Services, House of Representatives." March 5, 1981. Washington, DC: U.S. Government Printing Office, 1981.

[208] Review of Proposed Criteria for the Safety Evaluation of Irradiated Foods, FDA Memorandum from Krishna Misra, May 12, 1980.

[209] *A Broken Record: How the FDA Legalized—and Continues to Legalize—Food Irradiation Without Testing It for Safety.* Public Citizen, Global Resource Center for the Environment, Cancer Prevention Coalition. Washington, DC, October 2000.

[210] Ibid.

[211] "Evaluation of the Health Aspects of Certain Compounds Found in Irradiated Beef." Life Sciences Research Office, Federation of American Societies for Experimental Biology, Bethesda, Maryland. Prepared for U.S. Army Medical Research and Development

Command, Fort Detrick, Frederick, Maryland, Contract No. DAMD-17-76-C-6055. August 1977. Supplements I and II, March 1979.

[212] *A Broken Record*, op. cit.

[213] "Hearings on H.R. 2496, Department of Energy, National Security and Military Applications of Nuclear Energy Authorization Act of 1984, Before the Procurement and Military Nuclear Systems Subcommittee of the Committee on Armed Services, House of Representatives." March 1-2, 1983. Washington, DC: U.S. Government Printing Office, 1983.

[214] Gutknecht, Dave. *"Hold the Cesium, Please! (It Won't be on the Label)."* Cooperative Grocer, October-November, 1985.

[215] *Federal Register*, Vol. 49, Feb. 14, 1984, p. 5719.

[216] Karr, Albert R. "Call the Pork Anything You Like, Just So It Doesn't Glow in the Dark." *Wall Street Journal*, April 3, 1986.

[217] Lutz, William. *Doublespeak: From Revenue Enhancement to Terminal Living: How Government, Business, Advertisers, and Others Use Language to Deceive You.* New York: HarperCollins, 1990.

[218] Cooke, Robert. "Irradiation of Food: A Safe Alternative to EDB?" *Boston Globe*, Feb. 20, 1984.

[219] "The Status of the Technical Infrastructure to Support Domestic Food Irradiation: Hearing Before the Subcommittee on Energy, Research and Production of the Committee on Science and Technology, House of Representatives." July 26, 1984. Washington, DC: U.S. Government Printing Office, 1984.

[220] Ibid.

[221] Ibid.

[222] Ibid.

[223] "Food Irradiation." Hearing before the Subcommittee on Health and Environment, Committee on Energy and Commerce, House of Representatives, Congress of the United States, on H.R. 956, June 19, 1987. Washington, DC: U.S. Government Printing Office, 1988.

[224] "Recent Safety-Related Incidents at Large Irradiators." U.S. Nuclear Regulatory Commission, Office of Nuclear Material Safety and Safeguards, Information Notice No. 89-92, Dec. 7, 1989.

[225] Grossman, Karl. "Captain Plutonium Aims for Food." *Food & Water Journal*, Spring 1997, pp. 15-19.

[226] Seabrook, Charles. "Feds Waived Tests of Device that Now Has Radiation Leak." *Atlanta Journal-Constitution*, Nov. 6, 1988.

[227] "Some Pros and Cons of Food Irradiation." *Environment Hawai`i*, Vol. 7, No. 8, February 1997.

[228] "The Department of Energy Food Irradiation Demonstration Program." Presented by Richard B. Chitwood, Manager, Advanced Radiation Technology Program, May 1992.

[229] United States of America, Nuclear Regulatory Commission, Atomic Safety and Licensing Board Panel, In the Matter of GRAYSTAR, INC. Docket No. SSD 99-27, ASLBP No. 00-778-06-ML, Feb. 27, 2001. <http://www.hsrd.ornl.gov/nrc/agstates/program/sp01018.pdf>

[230] Letter from Glenn T. Seaborg, Office of the Associate Director-at-Large, Lawrence Berkeley Laboratory to Hazel R. O'Leary, Secretary of Energy, March 22, 1995.

[231] *A Broken Record*, op. cit.

[232] Ibid.

[233] "Nation's Second-Largest District Rejects Irradiated Chow." *Curriculum Review*, Nov. 11, 2003.

[234] Pelisek, Christine. "Francesca De La Rosa: Food for Thought." *LA Weekly*, Sept. 3-9, 2004.

[235] Bruhn, Christine. "Frequently Asked Questions About Food Irradiation." Center for Consumer Research, University of California-Davis, 2002.

[236] "Congresswoman Barbara Lee introduces Right to Know Student Nutrition Act." Capitol Hill Press Releases, September 18, 2003.

[237] Kaufman, Marc. "USDA Proposes to Reverse School Ground Beef Rules." *Washington Post*, April 5, 2001.

[238] Burros, Marian. "Bush Seeks to End Salmonella Tests of School Lunches." *San Diego Union-Tribune*, via New York Times News Service, April 5, 2001.

[239] "USDA Pulls Ground Beef Proposals." *United Press International*, April 5, 2001.

[240] Sack, Joetta L. "USDA Flips on Ground-Meat Rules for School Lunches." *Education Week*, April 11, 2001.

[241] Burros, Marian. "The Question of Irradiated Beef in Lunchrooms." *New York Times*, Jan. 29, 2003.

[242] The Center for Responsive Politics, Washington, DC. (www.opensecrets.org).

[243] *The Plan of Ten Thousand Mistakes: Minnesota's Misguided Food Irradiation 'Education' Program*. Public Citizen, Washington, DC, July 2003.

[244] Press Release. "Food Irradiation Considered Safe." May 16, 2000, Texas A&M University, College Station, TX.

[245] *The Plan of Ten Thousand Mistakes*, op. cit.

[246] Ibid.

[247] Ibid.

[248] Shah, Allie. "Meat Plan Blasted as Marketing Tool." *Minneapolis Star-Tribune*, July 28, 2003.

[249] Phillips, Kathleen. "Murano Urges Food Safety Policies Based on Science." *AgNews*, Texas A&M University System Agriculture Program, News and Public Affairs, Feb. 24, 2005.

[250] "Food Safety and Ionizing Pasteurization." Testimony presented by Michael T. Osterholm, Ph.D., M.P.H. to the Senate Committee on Agriculture, Nutrition and Forestry, Oct. 8, 1997.

[251] Majeski, Tom. "Zapped Beef is Selling Briskly." *Pioneer Press* (Minneapolis-St. Paul), Jan. 2, 2001.

[252] Schmid, Pam. "Minnesota Epidemiologist: The Bug Stops Here." *Grand Forks Herald* (ND), March 12, 1995.

[253] Barton, Jean. "CattleWomen Finish Season in North Carolina." *Red Bluff Daily News* (CA), Oct. 8, 2004.

[254] Carlson, Scott. "Famous Dave's Says It Will Serve Up $2.1 Million Loss." *Pioneer Press* (Minneapolis-St. Paul), Dec. 16, 1997.

[255] Merrill, Ann. "Famous Dave's Says Its President is Departing." *Minneapolis Star Tribune*, Feb 5, 1998.

[256] Johnson, Tim. "Famous Dave's Plans to Scale Back Expansion." *Minneapolis-St. Paul Business Journal*, March 27, 1998.

[257] "Redline Flatlines." *Snow Goer*, Dec 1, 2004.

[258] Carlson, Scott. "National Media Shareholder Suing ValueVision; Edina Firm Blamed for Inflating Stock." *Pioneer Press* (Minneapolis-St. Paul), April 30, 1994.

[259] Geiger, Bob. "Shopping Network Launching at Northeast Minneapolis Studios." *Finance & Commerce* (Minneapolis), Jan. 20, 2005.

[260] Healey, Melissa. "Organic Food Fight." *Newsday*, Oct. 3, 2004.

[261] Application for Funding, Cooperative State Research, Education and Extension Service, U.S. Department of Agriculture, 00-05453, submitted by Christine M. Bruhn, Department of Food Science & Technology, University of California-Davis, June 5, 2000.

[262] "Targeted Data May Combat Irradiation Negativity." *MeatNews.com Newsletter*, Volume 2, Issue 8, Feb. 23, 2000.

[263] Bruhn, Christine M. "Consumer Attitudes and Market Responses to Irradiated Food." *Journal of Food Protection*, 58(2):175-181.

[264] Bruhn, Christine M. "Frequently Asked Questions About Food Irradiation." University of California, Division of Agricultural and Natural Resources, Publication 7255, May 2002.

[265] Snow, Jane. "Is Irradiated Food Good for You?" *Akron Beacon Journal*, April 8, 1992.

[266] "Myths About Food Irradiation." University of California-Davis, Center for Consumer Research. <http://ccr.ucdavis.edu/irr/myth.shtml>

[267] Hopkins, Jim. "Titan Zaps into the Spotlight." *USA Today*, Dec. 4, 2001.

[268] Karp, Jonathan. "Titan Mutates to Meet Needs of Pentagon." *Associated Press*, June 28, 2004.

[269] Rodengen, Jeffrey L. and Richard F. Hubbard. *The Legend of the Titan Corporation.* Fort Lauderdale, FL: The Write Stuff, 2002, p. 60.

[270] "Business Highlights in the News." 1999 Annual Report, Titan Corp.

[271] "Company Unveils Electronic Process that Kills Bacteria in Meat, Fruit." *Futures World News*, Oct. 26, 1999.

[272] Beitelspacher, Kindra. "The OK is on the Way: Beef Irradiation Could Get FDA Approval by the End of the Month." *BEEF*, Vol. 34, No. 4, December 1997.

[273] Rodengen and Hubbard, op cit, p. 127.

[274] Rodengen and Hubbard, op cit, p. 38.

[275] Rodengen and Hubbard, op cit, p. 122.

[276] Center for Responsive Politics <www.opensecrets.org>

[277] Personal communication with Public Citizen.

[278] Brasher, Philip. "Irradiated Ground Beef's Popularity Isn't Sizzling." *Des Moines Register*, June 15, 2004.

[279] Letter from Thomas G. Day, Vice President, Engineering, U.S. Postal Service, to Tony Corbo, Public Citizen, May 18, 2004.

[280] Lubove, Seth. "Green Beams: Controversy over Irradiated Foods Leads to Campaign by Ralph Nader's Public Citizen Against SureBeam Corp." *Forbes*, Nov. 26, 2001.

[281] Press release. "State Orders Food Irradiator to Comply with Air Pollution Laws; Illinois Environmental Officials Require California Firm to Report Ozone Releases." Illinois Food Safety Coalition, Nov. 19, 2001.

[282] "Irradiating Mail: Spreading Radiation and Risk." *Pathfinder*, The Progressive Foundation/Nukewatch, Luck, WI, Winter 2001-2002.

[283] Herzog, Karen. "Zapped Hamburgers Not on Shopping List." *Milwaukee Journal Sentinel*, July 27, 2001.

[284] U.S. Securities and Exchange Commission.

[285] MacDonald, Elizabeth. "Accounting Acrobatics." *Forbes*, April 29,2002.

[286] Multex Investor. <www.multexinvestor.com>

[287] Freeman, Mike. "SureBeam Clears Major Block in Bankruptcy Case." *San Diego Union-Tribune*, April 6, 2004.

[288] Mitchell, Richard. "Meat Irradiation Down...But Not Out." *The National Provisioner*, June 1, 2004.

[289] Merle, Renae. "Titan Admits Bribery in Africa: Contractor Will Pay $28.5 Million to Settle Criminal, SEC Cases." *Washington Post*, March 2, 2005.

[290] "Titan Worker Accused of Iraqi Prisoner Abuse." *Reuters*, May 21, 2004.

[291] Statute of the International Atomic Energy Agency.

[292] "Agreement Between the International Atomic Energy Agency and the World Health Organization." Approved by the Twelfth Health Assembly, Geneva, May 28, 1959. Resolution WHA12.40.

[293] Memorandum from Harold Lubin to Harry N. Peterson, American Medical Association, June 11, 1984.

[294] "Food Irradiation." Journal of the American Dietetic Association, 100:246-253, 2000.

[295] Stevenson, M.H. "Identification of Irradiated Foods." *Food Technology*, 48:141-144, 1994.

[296] Letter from Bruce M. Kelly, Director of Government Relations, Mayo Clinic, to New Jersey Assemblyman John V. Kelly, Oct. 30, 2000.

[297] Letter from Vickie L. Kloeris, Subsystem Manager Shuttle and ISS Food, to New Jersey Assemblyman John V. Kelly, Nov. 9, 2000.

[298] 2000 Annual Report, National Food Processors Association, Washington, DC.

[299] FDA Petition from the Food Irradiation Coalition/National Food Processors Association, Washington, DC, "Approved Sources of Ionizing Radiation," Aug. 23, 1999.

[300] A Passion for Results: 1999 Annual Report of Government Affairs and Communication. National Food Processors Association, Washington, DC.

[301] Skrzycki, Cindy. "Now, You May Never Know Where that Broccoli Came From." *Washington Post*, Feb. 3, 2004.

[302] "Food Irradiation." National Food Processors Association, Washington, DC. <http://www.nfpa-food.org/content/consumers/irradiation.asp>

[303] "Bush Administration Fails to Act on Listeria." *OMB Watch*, May 28, 2003.

[304] Center for Responsive Politics, Washington, DC.

[305] Mattera, Philip. *USDA Inc.: How Agribusiness Has Hijacked Regulatory Policy at the U.S. Department of Agriculture.* Corporate Research Project of Good Jobs First, Washington, DC, July 2004.

[306] Leake, Linda L. "Where's the (Irradiated) Beef? Getting it in Your Grocery Store is Getting to be Big Business." *Agri Marketing*; Feb. 1, 2003.

[307] Hennessy, Terry. "The Good with the Bad." *Progressive Grocer*, March 1, 1999.

[308] Heine, Kurt. "Fight for Judicial Life: Garb Opposed by Pump Foes & Lawyers; He's Flayed in Court." *Philadelphia Daily News*, Nov. 2, 1987.

[309] "Visiting Professor." *Philadelphia Daily News*, July 3, 1987.

[310] American School Food Service Association annual meeting, Indianapolis, Indiana, July 2004.

[311] "Sponsor Profile: Hatfield Quality Meats Adds Education/Trims Fees With AMVES-CAP." *DC Plan Investing*, Institute of Management and Administration, Nov. 9, 2004.

[312] Remarks of Phil Clemens at the American Meat Institute's Annual Convention and Innovation Showcase, New Orleans, Oct. 25, 2002.

[313] Center for Responsive Politics, Washington, DC.

[314] Darden, Richard and Richardson, P.J. *Corporate Giants: Personal Stories of Faith and Finance.* Grand Rapids, MI: Fleming H. Revell, 2002, pp. 108-114.

[315] Naedale, Walter F. "Plan to Irradiate Food Generates Heat in Milford." *Philadelphia Inquirer*, June 18, 2003.

[316] Letter from U.S. Sens. Arlen Specter and Rick Santorum, and U.S. Rep. Robert Wonderling to Dr. Niles J. Diaz, Chairman, U.S. Nuclear Regulatory Commission, July 18, 2003.

[317] Remarks of Phil Clemens at the American Meat Institute's Annual Convention and Innovation Showcase, New Orleans, Oct. 25, 2002.

[318] Wood, Jim. "Irradiation a Safe Process Toward Better Health." *The Intelligencer* (Doylestown, PA), Nov. 3, 2003.

[319] Wartenburg, Steve. "Company Fights Irradiator Restrictions." *The Morning Call* (Allentown, PA), Oct. 14, 2003.

[320] CFC Logistics v. Milford Township, Pennsylvania. Civil Action 03-5655, U.S. District Court for the Eastern District of Pennsylvania.

[321] U.S. Nuclear Regulatory Commission, Order Revoking License, Precision Materials Corporation, Docket No. 30-22063, License No. 29-20777-01, EA 87-156, Feb. 10. 1988.

[322] U.S. Nuclear Regulatory Commission, Report No. 030-22063/87-01, Docket No. 030-22063, License No. 29-20777-01, Oct. 27, 1987.

[323] Associated Press. "Irradiation Company Bows to Pressure, Leaves NJ Town." *Journal of Commerce* (New York City), Sept. 3, 1987.

[324] United States of America, Nuclear Regulatory Commission, Atomic Safety and Licensing Board Panel, In the Matter of GRAYSTAR, INC. Docket No. SSD 99-27, ASLBP No. 00-778-06-ML, Feb. 27, 2001.

[325] Letter from Glenn T. Seaborg, Office of the Associate Director-at-Large, Lawrence Berkeley Laboratory to Hazel R. O'Leary, Secretary of Energy, March 22, 1995.

[326] "Divergent Views on Food Irradiation Expressed as Gray*Star Readies New Equipment." *Food Chemical News*, June 30, 1997.

[327] Naedele, Walter F. "Milford Ordered to Permit Irradiator." *Philadelphia Inquirer*, Oct. 21, 2003.

[328] Wartenberg, Steve, " CFC Logistics Closes Cobalt Irradiator in Bucks County," *The Morning Call,* April 26, 2005.

[329] Sugarman, Carol. "Debate Burns Hotly on Question of Irradiating Our Food." *Washington Post*, Nov. 4, 1997.

[330] Blake, Judith. "FDA Looks into Irradiated Mushrooms in Packaged Products." *Seattle Times*, Jan. 6, 1988.

[331] Leary, Kevin. "Group Simmers over Radiation of Mushrooms." *San Francisco Chronicle*, Dec. 19, 1987.

[332] "Consumer Groups Have Little Appetite for Irradiated Food." *Albany Times Union*, April 8, 1988.

[333] Wheeler, Connie. Letter to the Editor: "Fission Food: Food-Irradiation Plant is New Fruit of N-Industry." *Seattle Times*, Sept. 4, 1986.

[334] Perl, Rebecca. "Zapping Your Dinner: A Gamma-Ray Gamble? Problems Aside, DOE Still Pushing Food Irradiation." *Seattle Times*, Aug. 6, 1987.

[335] "Senator Inouye Announces $6.75 Million Agriculture Loan Awarded to Hawaii Fruit Processor." Press release from U.S. Sen. Daniel Inouye, March 10, 2000.

[336] IBA. <www.iba-worldwide.com>

[337] *Federal Register*, Vol. 68, No. 49, pp. 12087-12088, March 13, 2003.

[338] Brynjolfsson, Ari. "Natural and Induced Radioactivity in Food." Proceedings of the International Conference on Future Nuclear Systems, Global '99: Nuclear Technology—Bridging the Millennia, Jackson Hole, WY, Aug. 29-Sept. 3, 1999.

[339] Associated Press. "Firm Pushes Irradiation as a Way to Make Red Meat Safer." *Columbus Ledger-Enquirer* (GA), April 10, 1994.

[340] *Bringing Technology to Life*. MDS Nordion, Kanata, Ontario, Canada.

[341] MDS Inc. Annual Information Form for the Year Ended October 31, 1999.

342 Epstein, Samuel. Press Release, "Administration Proposal to Serve Irradiated Beef to School Children Poses Cancer, Genetic and Other Risks," April 8, 2001.

343 Wakin, Daniel J. "Irradiation Company Founder Sentenced to Two Years." *Associated Press*, Oct. 11, 1998.

344 "Martin A. Welt." American Men and Women of Science.

345 Knox, Andrea. "Fear of Irradiation Lingers but Food-Preserver Builds on Hopes for Acceptance." *Philadelphia Inquirer*, Dec. 21, 1985.

346 *United States Nuclear Regulatory Commission and United States of America v. Radiation Technology, Inc.*, Civ. A. No. 80-2187, U.S. District Court, New Jersey, Aug. 6, 1981. 519 Federal Supplement 1266.

347 Charlton, Art and Robin Bidgood. "Rockaway Firm Shut Down as Hazard." *North Jersey Advocate*, March 5, 1986.

348 "People: Kudos." *Nuclear News*, April 1986.

349 Katsarelas, Nicholas. "N.J. Firms Cited as Polluters." *Daily Record* (Morris County, NJ), Oct. 23, 1986.

350 Lally, Robin. "NRC Removes Him, DOE Gets Him." *Daily Record* (Morris County, NJ), Sept. 25, 1986.

351 "Jury Told Irradiation Safeguard Bypassed." *Associated Press*, July 13, 1988.

352 Ibid.

353 Letter from Hugh L. Thompson, Acting Executive Director for Operations, U.S. Nuclear Regulatory Commission, to The Commissioners. Subject: Removal of RTI, Inc., from Site Decommissioning Management Plan. SECY-97-019, Jan. 24, 1997.

354 Ibid.

355 "Food Irradiation Pioneer Sentenced for Lying to NRC." *United Press International*, Oct. 12, 1988.

356 "Two Years' Probation in Nuclear Spill Case." *San Jose Mercury News*, Dec. 9, 1986.

357 Pinsley, Elliot. "Firm Dumped Radioactive Water, Grand Jury Says." *Bergen County Record*, June 25, 1986.

358 "Firm and Two on Staff Accused of Hiding Spill." *Associated Press*, June 25, 1986.

[359] Federico, Christine. "Feds: Dover Radiation Spill Concealed." *North Jersey Advance*, June 25, 1986.

[360] "Executive Convicted in Radiation Spill." *United Press International*, Oct. 30, 1986.

[361] Chenoweth, Sue. "Eugene O'Sullivan, Engineer, Deacon." *San Jose Mercury News*, July 23, 2002.

[362] O'Brien, Kathleen. "Nuclear Spill Left No Ghosts in Dover; A $2M Cleanup Resolved Problem." *Bergen County Record*, Aug. 3, 1987.

[363] Dupin, Chris. "Probe Asked at Irradiation Plant." *Daily Record* (Morris County, NJ), May 3, 1981.

[364] Trager, Jr., E.A. *Review of Events at Large Pool-Type Irradiators.* U.S. Nuclear Regulatory Commission, Office for Analysis and Evaluation of Operational Data, NUREG-1345, March 1989.

[365] Strom, Daniel J. and Charles R. Watson. *Food Irradiation: A Potential Unwanted Byproduct of Food Irradiation?* Pacific Northwest National Laboratory, Richland, WA. Presented at Health Physics Society, 32nd Midyear Topical Meeting, Albuquerque, NM, Jan. 27, 1999.

[366] Perl, Rebecca. "Zapping Your Dinner: A Gamma-Ray Gamble?" *Seattle Times*, Aug. 6, 1987.

[367] Seabrook, Charles. "Feds Waived Tests of Device that Now Has Radiation Leak." *Atlanta Journal/Atlanta Constitution*, Nov. 6, 1988.

[368] Kjarmo, H.E. and G.L. Tingey. *Characterization of a WESF Cesium Chloride Capsule After Fifteen Months of Service in a Dry Operation/Wet Storage Commercial Irradiator.* Pacific Northwest Laboratory, Richland, WA, operated by Battelle Memorial Institute for the U.S. Department of Energy. Contract DE-AC06-76RLO 1830, August 1988.

[369] Straus, Hal. "Capsule that Leaked Cesium Not Intended for Commercial Use." *Atlanta Constitution*, Feb. 4, 1989.

[370] Seabrook, Charles. "DeKalb Radiation Cleanup Costly; Sterilization Plant Work: $30 Million." *Atlanta Journal/Atlanta Constitution*, July 11, 1990.

[371] Munger, Frank. "DOE Investigation of Nuclear Leak Turns Into Chilling Horror Story." *Knoxville News-Sentinel*, Jan. 23, 1991.

[372] *WISE News Communiqué.* World Information Service on Energy, Amsterdam, No. 298, Sept. 23, 1988.

373 Seabrook, Charles. "Feds Waived Tests of Device That Now Has Radiation Leak." *Atlanta Journal-Constitution*, Nov. 6, 1988.

374 Seabrook, Charles. "State Report on Radioactive Leak Urges Firm to Stop Using Cesium." *Atlanta Journal-Constitution*, June 27, 1989.

375 Ibid.

376 Emling, Shelley. "DOE Finishes $47 Million Cleanup of Plant Contaminated by Cesium." *Atlanta Journal-Constitution*, Jan. 7, 1993.

377 Ibid.

378 Seabrook, Charles. "French Expected to Get Nuclear Wastes from Decatur Medical Sterilization Plant." *Atlanta Journal-Constitution*, April 22, 1990.

379 "Food Safety and Inspection Service Oversight of Production Process and Recall at ConAgra Plant (Establishment 969)." U.S. Department of Agriculture, Office of Inspector General, Great Plain Region, Report No. 24601-2-KC, Sept. 2003.

380 *Shielding the Giant: USDA's 'Don't Look, Don't Know' Policy for Beef Inspection.* Government Accountability Project, Washington, DC, July 2003.

381 Graham, Judith. "Tainted Meat Warnings Ignored; Inspectors Sought E. coli Investigation." *Chicago Tribune*, July 23, 2002.

382 U.S. Department of Agriculture, op. cit.

383 Migoya, David. "ConAgra Had List of Violations; Tainted Meat Found Dozens of Times at Greeley Facility." *Denver Post*, Sept. 19, 2002.

384 Migoya, David and Allison Sherry. "Critics Urge Reform of Beef-Recall Rules." *Denver Post*, July 21, 2002.

385 Carmen, Diane. "USDA Politics Rile Meatpacker on a Mission." *Denver Post*, Jan. 4, 2004.

386 U.S. Department of Agriculture, op. cit.

387 Government Accountability Project, op. cit.

388 Conason, Joe and Kevin P. Phillips. "Notes on a Native Son." *Harper's*, February 2000.

389 Isikoff, Michael. "9-11 Investigation: 'We'll Go Where the Facts Lead Us'." *Newsweek*, Dec. 9, 2002.

390 Wheat, Andrew. "George W. Bush, Corporate Candidate: How Money Grows on the 'Shrub'." *Multinational Monitor*, March 1, 2000.

391 "The Buying of a President: An Interview with Charles Lewis." *Multinational Monitor*, March 1, 2000.

392 Yung, Katherine and Brooks Egerton. "Dallas-Based Leveraged Buyout Firm Head Succeeds Despite Past Failures." *Knight Ridder/Tribune Business News*, July 12, 1999.

393 Center for Responsive Politics, Washington, DC (www.opensecrets.org).

394 Sinclair, Upton. *The Jungle*. New York: Barnes and Noble Classics, 2003.

395 *Escherichia Coli O157:H7 in Ground Beef*. National Academies, Institute of Medicine, Food and Nutrition Board. Washington, DC: National Academies Press, 2002.

396 Eisnitz, Gail A. *Slaughterhouse: The Shocking Story of Greed, Neglect, and Inhumane Treatment Inside the U.S. Meat Industry*. Amherst, NY: Prometheus Books, 1997.

397 Schlosser, Eric. *Fast Food Nation: The Dark Side of the All-American Meal*. New York: HarperCollins Publishers, 2002.

398 Nestle, Marion. *Safe Food: Bacteria, Biotechnology, and Bioterrorism*. Berkeley, CA: University of California Press, 2003.

399 "America's Looming Food Safety Crisis." *USA Today* (Society for Advancement of Education), Vol. 121, No. 2570, November 1992.

400 Hanson, Christopher. "Roadblocks to Reform: U.S. Inspectors Know Trouble But Action Slow." *Seattle Post-Intelligencer*, Feb. 23, 1993.

401 *Meat and Poultry Inspection: The Scientific Basis of the Nation's Program*. National Research Council, Food and Nutrition Board. Washington, DC: National Academy Press, 1985.

402 *Cattle Inspection*. National Academy of Sciences, Institute of Medicine, Food and Nutrition Board. Washington, DC: National Academy Press, 1990.

403 Eisnitz, op. cit.

404 Rifkin, Jeremy. *Beyond Beef: The Rise and Fall of the Cattle Culture*. New York: Dutton, 1992.

405 Eisnitz, op. cit.

[406] Anderson, Jack and Dale Van Atta. "Inspector Suspended for Doing Job." *The Oregonian*, Aug. 17, 1989.

[407] National Academy Press, 1990, op. cit.

[408] Clorfene-Casten, Liane. "Unhappy Meals." *Mother Jones*, Vol. 17, No. 4, July/August 1992.

[409] Tansey, Ben. "Heads in a Box: The Deadly Results of Foodmaker Inc.'s Corporate Attitude." *Washington Free Press* (Seattle), April 1993.

[410] Clorfene-Casten, op. cit.

[411] Nestor, Felicia and Wenonah Hauter. *The Jungle 2000: Is America's Meat Fit to Eat?* Government Accountability Project and Public Citizen, Washington, DC, September 2000.

[412] "Hamburger Recall Rises to 25 Million Pounds: Burger King, Boston Market Anticipate Shortages." *CNN Interactive*, Aug. 21, 1997.

[413] "Burger King Back in Burger Business: Restaurant Chain Won't Buy Hudson Beef." *CNN Interactive*, Aug. 23, 1997.

[414] "Beef Recall Hits Record 1.2 Million Pounds: USDA Questions Delay in Recall of E. Coli-Tainted Meat." *CNN Interactive*, Aug. 15, 1997.

[415] "Hudson Foods, Managers Charged in Meat Recall." *Meat Industry Insights News Service*, Dec. 16, 1997.

[416] Testimony of Secretary Dan Glickman, U.S. Department of Agriculture, Before the Senate Committee on Agriculture, Nutrition, and Forestry, Oct. 8, 1997.

[417] "Consumer Group Pushes Food Safety Law." *CNN Interactive*, Feb. 4, 1998.

[418] Center for Responsive Politics, Washington, DC (www.opensecrets.org).

[419] Ibid.

[420] Dixon, Jennifer. "Workers: Bil Mar Knew Meat Was Bad." *Detroit Free Press*, August 30, 2001.

[421] Young, Allison, et al. "A Killer in Our Food." *Detroit Free Press*, Special Report.

[422] "Meat Scandal at Sara Lee." *CBSNEWS.com*, August 30, 2001.

[423] Surendran, Aparna. "An Unseen Killer's Toll: Unsafe Meat Ended or Tragically Changed Their Lives." *Philadelphia Inquirer*, May 19, 2003.

[424] "Meat and Poultry: Improved Oversight and Training Will Strengthen New Food Safety System." U.S. General Accounting Office, GAO/RCED-00-16, December 1999.

[425] "Food Safety and Inspection Service: Implementation of the Hazard Analysis and Critical Control Point System." U.S. Department of Agriculture, Office of Inspector General, Food Safety Initiative, Report. No. 24001-3-At, June 2000.

[426] Kilman, Scott. "Listeria Outbreak in Cargill Turkey Poses Problems for Meat Industry." *Wall Street Journal*, Dec. 20, 2000.

[427] "Food Safety: Weaknesses in Meat and Poultry Inspection Pilot Should be Addressed Before Implementation." U.S. General Accounting Office, GAO-02-59, December 2001.

[428] "Meat and Poultry: Better USDA Oversight and Enforcement of Safety Rules Needed to Reduce Risk of Foodborne Illness." U.S. General Accounting Office, GAO-02-902, August 2002.

[429] "Outbreak." *60 Minutes II*, Jan. 23, 2003.

[430] Letter from Rep. Henry Waxman to Ann M. Veneman, Secretary, U.S. Department of Agriculture, Dec. 11, 2002.

[431] Prichard, Oliver. "Inspector: Filth and Vermin Reported, Ignored." *Philadelphia Inquirer*, May 18, 2003.

[432] Press release. "Federal Inspector at Wampler Foods Details USDA Failure to Protect the Public from Deadly *Listeria* Outbreak." House Committee on Government Reform, Dec. 11, 2002.

[433] Surendran, Aparna. "U.S. to Increase Listeria Testing at Meat Plants." *Philadelphia Inquirer*, Nov. 19, 2002.

[434] Weisskopf, Michael. "Can Cold Cuts Kill?" *Time*, March 3, 2003.

[435] Hendrickson, Mary and William Heffernan. "Concentration of Agricultural Markets." Department of Rural Sociology, University of Missouri, February 2002.

[436] Couzin, Jennifer. "Cattle Diet Linked to Bacterial Growth," *Science Magazine*, Volume 281, Number 5383, 11, September 1118, p. 1578.

[437] Nestle, op. cit.

[438] USDA, National Agricultural Statistics Service, "Farms and Land in Farms 2001," Feb. 2002.

439 Mander, Jerry, Debi Barker, and David Korten (Eds.). "Introduction," *Does Globilization Help the Poor? A Special Report by the International Forum on Globalization,* San Francisco, CA, August 2001.

440 Ibid.

441 Rodale Web site: *Gleanings,* The New Farm: Farmer-to-farmer Know-How from the Rodale Press, http://www.newfarm.org/international/gleanings/2003/June/ph_irradiation.shtml.

442 Wallach, Lori and Patrick Woodall. Whose *Trade Organization? A Comprehensive Guide to the WTO,* New York : The New Press, 2004, pg 57-63.

443 Ibid.

444 *Food Irradiation Alert,* Public Citizen, July/August 2003 (http://www.citizen.org/cmep/foodsafety/food_irrad/foodalert/articles.cfm?ID=12722.).

445 *International Standards for Phytosanitary Measures: Guidelines for the Use of Irradiation As a Phytosanitary Measure,* Secretariat of the International Plant Protection Convention, Food and Agriculture Organization of the United Nations, Rome, 2003. Publication No. 18, pgs. 7-8.

446 Public Citizen's Global Trade Watch Web site (http://www.citizen.org/trade/nafta/agriculture/)

447 USDA, Economic Research Service, "Agricultural Outlook: Statistical Indicators 2003," Jan. 2003.

448 Edwards, Katie. "CAFTA: More of NAFTA's Ills," Florida Fair Trade Campaign, May 5, 2005.

449 Ibid.

450 Fact Sheet: "South and Central America." Public Citizen Energy Program, Washington, DC.

451 Press Release, "USDA Under-secretary for Food Safety Elsa Murano to Keynote First World Congress on Food Irradiation." National Food Safety and Toxicology Center, Michigan State University, April 4, 2003.

452 Speech by Arnold Foudin, USDA, at the "Food Irradiation 2001" conference in Washington, DC on Feb. 28, 2001.

453 E-mails from APHIS staffers Andrea C. McNally (2/7/05) and Meghan K. Thomas (2/10/05) to Wenonah Hauter.

454 *"International Trade Statistics 2004,"* World Trade Organization.

455 Sydow, Evanize and Maria Luisa Mendonca (Eds.). *"The Destructive Agrarian Reform Policies of the World Bank,"* Land Research and Action Network and the Social Network for Justice and Human Rights, Sao Paulo, SP, Brazil.

456 "Cargill to buy Brazilian poultry and pork supplier." www.just-food.com, Sept. 2, 2004.

457 "Facts About Food Irradiation." International Consultative Group on Food Irradiation, 1999, p. 3.

458 "A short write-up on ICGFI." International Atomic Energy Agency. <http://www.iaea.org/icgfi/about.htm.

459 "Facts About Irradiation." International Consultative Group on Food Irradiation, 1999, page 35.

460 "Closure of the International Consultative Group on Food Irradiation (ICGFI) and its Website." International Atomic Energy Agency. <www.iaea.org/icgfi>

461 "About iiA." International Irradiation Association. <http://www.doubleia.org>

462 Ibid.

463 Presentation given by Natesan Ramanoorthy, "IAEA's Support to Radiation Processing Technology Practices in Developing Countries." Presentation at the International Meeting on Radiation Processing, February 27, 2006, Hilton Kuala Lumpur, Malaysia.

464 Department of Technical Cooperation, International Atomic Energy Agency. <www-tc.iaea.org>

465 Thematic Planning Presentation, Regulation, Application and Perspect[sic] of Food Irradiation in China, Shizongwei Gaomeixu, www-tc.iaea.org Thematic Planning, Food Irradiation.

466 Meixu, Gao. "Overview of Food Irradiation in China.." Presentation at the International Meeting on Radiation Processing, February 27, 2006, Hilton Kuala Lumpur, Malaysia.

467 Brown, Lester. *Tough Choices: Facing the Challenge of Food Scarcity.* The Worldwatch Environmental Alert Series. New York: W.W. Norton & Company, 1996.

468 *State of the World*, op. cit.

469 Authors' data.

470 Sold at some or all stores.

471 Sold papayas and other tropical fruits irradiated by Hawaii Pride of Hilo, HI.

472 Beef irradiated by Food Technology Service of Mulberry, FL.

473 Beef irradiated by Excel (division of Cargill) of Wichita, KS.

474 Formerly a partnership with SureBeam Corp. of San Diego, CA.

475 An affiliate of the British financial services firm Prudential plc bought IBA/Sterigenics in June 2004 and renamed the company Sterigenics International. In 1999 IBA purchased Sterigenics, which had acquired several facilities operated by Radiation Technology and Process Technology, including Martin Welt's fouled plant in Rockaway, NJ. Sterigenics originally was called Radiation Sterilizers, which operated the cesium-137 facility in Decatur, GA, where a serious radiation leak occurred in 1988. (See "The Machines," Chapter 5.)

476 STERIS purchased Isomedix, of Whippany, NJ, in 1997.

477 Formerly a partnership with SureBeam Corp. of San Diego.

478 KiloGray, or 1,000 Gray, which is equal to 100,000 rads ("radiation absorbed dose").

479 The FDA rescinded this approval on Aug. 23, 1968, when it was revealed that lab animals fed irradiated foods experienced serious health problems.

480 Animal and Plant Health Inspection Service, a division of the U.S. Department of Agriculture charged with protecting the food supply from invasive pests and disease.

481 4.5 kGy for fresh and 7.0 kGy for frozen.

482 Company founder Martin Welt, convicted of lying to the Nuclear Regulatory Commission about accidents at his facility, was released from prison two months before this ruling was issued.

483 Josephson ran the U.S. Army's failed food irradiation research program in Natick, MA, during the 1970s.

484 Now PPM Ventures.

485 National Fisheries Institute and the Louisiana Department of Agriculture and Forestry.

486 Food Safety and Inspection Service, a division of the U.S. Department of Agriculture charged with protecting the safety of the domestic food supply.

[487] Food Products Association of Washington, DC, the main lobbying group for the $500 billion-a-year food processing industry. The FPA filed the petition as the "Food Irradiation Coalition," which exists in name only.

[488] 4.5 kGy for non-frozen and non-dry foods, and 10 kGy for frozen or dry foods.

[489] Hemolytic uremic syndrome—the damage and destruction of red blood cells. Symptoms include bloody stool, anemia, hypertension, swollen feet and hands, kidney failure, and in severe cases, death. Children are particularly at risk.

[490] Estimated cases in the UK. Source: Hilton, David A., et al. "Rapid Communication: Prevalence of Lymphoreticular Prion Protein Accumulation in UK Tissue Samples." *The Journal of Pathology*, 203(3):733-739, July 2004.

[491] As of Dec. 1, 2003: 143 cases in the UK, six in France, and one each in Canada, Ireland, Italy, and the U.S. Source: Fact Sheet: New Variant Creutzfeldt-Jakob Disease. National Center for Infectious Diseases, U.S. Centers for Disease Control.